KU-193-646

AN INSECT BOOK
FOR THE POCKET

By the same Author

A BIRD BOOK FOR THE POCKET
A BEAST BOOK FOR THE POCKET
A BUTTERFLY BOOK FOR THE POCKET

In the same series

A FLOWER BOOK FOR THE POCKET
By M. SKENE

AN INSECT BOOK
FOR THE POCKET

BY

EDMUND SANDARS

GEOFFREY CUMBERLEGE
OXFORD UNIVERSITY PRESS
LONDON NEW YORK TORONTO

Oxford University Press, Amen House, London E.C.4
GLASGOW NEW YORK TORONTO MELBOURNE WELLINGTON
BOMBAY CALCUTTA MADRAS CAPE TOWN
Geoffrey Cumberlege, Publisher to the Unversity

First published 1946
Second Impression 1951

PRINTED IN GREAT BRITAIN

TO THE MEMORY OF

JEAN HENRI FABRE

1823–1915

IN GRATITUDE FOR HIS LIFE'S WORK

AND IN PARTICULAR

FOR THE FOLLOWING REMARK:

'Lorsqu'il me tombe sous les yeux une page hérissée de locutions barbares, dites scientifiques, je me dis: "Prends garde! L'auteur ne possède pas bien ce qu'il dit, sinon il aurait trouvé, dans le vocabulaire qu'ont martelé tant de bons esprits, de quoi formuler nettement sa pensée."'

EDITOR'S PREFACE

EDMUND SANDARS died at Lyme Regis on 19 September 1942 at the age of 65. He had been at work for several years on the *Insect Book for the Pocket*, and only needed a few more months—or even weeks—to put everything in final order for the printer. The colour drawings were finished and the blocks had already been made and proofed. The line drawings were ready for the blockmaker, with a very few exceptions, including the diagrams of the architecture of a spider's web (pp. 311 and 313), and of these he had made rough sketches. The text had been written and worked over, and needed only the checking of various points of detail. All that remained to be done, therefore, was to clear up the outstanding queries, supply the few missing items, and to add a Bibliography and an Index (for which, with characteristic thoroughness, he had already made a detailed scheme). The delay in publication has been due to the preoccupations of war—and peace—rather than to the amount of work that remained to be done.

The aim of the book is explained in the author's Preface, which is printed from his typescript without alteration. In preparing the book for press I have had generous and unstinted help from Dr. B. M. Hobby (to whom the author also acknowledges his debt), especially in the preparation of the Bibliography. The nomenclature has been brought into line with the *Check List of British Insects* by G. S. Kloet and W. D. Hincks (1945), to whose assistance I am also indebted. The section on the Spiders has had the great benefit of Dr. W. S. Bristowe's scrutiny.

A. L. P. N.

July 1946

AUTHOR'S PREFACE

THE Books for the Pocket hitherto issued in this series aim at describing all British species, or at least such species as are of reasonably common occurrence in Britain. This meant about 200 Birds, 50 Beasts, 70 Butterflies, and 850 Flowers.

The Insects present a totally different problem, and nothing of that kind can be attempted. There are probably over 20,000 species of Insects in these islands so that, if the space accorded to each in the Butterfly Book were given here, several hundred volumes would be needed—the pocket would become a pantechnicon van, the author a trades union, and the reader a corpse.

The treatment of British genera would be little better, and even the next larger units—the families—are so numerous that little room would be left after a bare description for any account of the lives and manners of the insects composing them. There are more than 300 families of British Insects, and this number is being increased by the diligence of those whose great knowledge of small differences urges them to subdivide the old established families.

Some further step must therefore be taken to reduce the bulk of the subject. I have chosen the criterion of size. There is no doubt that the interest of the large insects to the ordinary man much exceeds that of the minute creatures, which are usually noticed only when they get into our eyes and which lose that interest as soon as they have been successfully wiped out. By restricting this book to a treatment of those insects which exceed half an inch in length of body, or one inch in wing-span, the number of families in this country to be dealt with is reduced to about 130, and in this number I am able to include all those creatures which are usually called Insects, though the modern scientific use of the word excludes them. The inclusion of the Spiders, Centipedes, Woodlice, &c., has, apart from mere popular usage, a scientific basis. Linnaeus included in his Class of *Insecta* all the animals with hard external coverings and jointed legs, which are now known as

Arthropods. It is true that this included a large number of marine animals, such as the Lobsters, Crabs, and Shrimps which, as no one thinks of them as insects to-day, are not included here.

The units described will be the families into which our Insects, in this wider sense of the word, are divided and which contain large species in this country. The choice of an inch span or half-inch body length is arbitrary, but the method of measurement is imposed by the available data. Span and length are the two measures recorded of different kinds of insects by those who measure them, and as in most insects the span is roughly twice the length, the two measures above mentioned come to much the same thing. Throughout the book 'large' and 'small' will be used with this meaning.

Such is the variety of nature that no two individuals are identical. Even when dealing with species there are exceptions to almost every statement, and this difficulty is much augmented when the unit described is a family. The statement that the Joneses have a taste for cheese and ale is no sooner made than the figure of John Jones, the famous temperance advocate, rises up to confound one. Here I have qualified with 'usually', 'more or less', 'in most cases', and the like until wearied. When I have failed to do so I must beg forgiveness. The only other course is the omission of generalizations, but as generalization makes the main difference between the Beatitudes and a page of the Telephone Book—or between thought and feeling raindrops on one's head—I have preferred to run the risk of occasional inaccuracy.

Apart from the imperative need to reduce the bulk of the subject, there is another reason for excluding the small insects. Those of us who are accustomed to Insect books are guided by pictures such as that which appears on the opposite page. We know that the most important thing in the figure is the tiny cross depicted under the right wing of the alarming creature. This is the size mark, and it means that the insect really looks like this:

In this book I have wished my illustrations to be all of life-size, believing that even a rough sketch of an insect at that scale gives the reader a better idea of its general appearance than an enlargement. As the parts by which the species are differentiated (particularly the mouth-parts, the wing-veining, and the genitals) are often minute, even in large insects, the

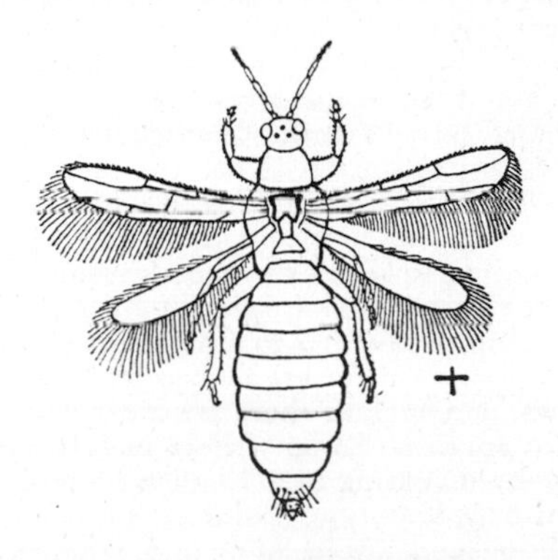

enlargement of figures is essential when the identification of species is desired, but the treatment of families does much to free me from this necessity. With the help of a few enlarged anatomical drawings in the articles upon Insects in general and upon the different Orders, the life-size scale is adhered to throughout the book.

The first object of the book will be to enable the reader to identify the family to which any 'large' insect found in Britain belongs. The 'families' sometimes have been recently sub-divided and are therefore now regarded as super-families. In this case the fact will be indicated. It is a convention of those who name animals that the name of a family should end in '-idae': Apidae, Muscidae, Dytiscidae, Drepanidae, or the like. When a family has been split up its name loses this familiar ending.

The 'small' insects are, in this book, dealt with in three different ways. Some few are, owing to their special interest or (under the ruling in the case of the importunate widow) to their nuisance value, accorded the same treatment as that given to 'large' insects. Where a whole Order, or other big group, consists wholly of 'small' insects it is mentioned by name and its characteristics briefly indicated, so that the reader may get a general idea of the whole Insect world and a knowledge of what insects there are, although for further information about them he must look elsewhere. Other families of 'small' insects are not named, as I think that lists of undescribed animals are tedious.

I have tried to lay stress upon habits and life history rather than upon anatomy and, in the choice of examples for illustration or description, to select common species, though sometimes (as in the case of the Large Blue for the Lycaenidae) other considerations have led to a different choice.

Among the Insects there are all too few genuine common English names, and such as there are mostly apply to groups rather than to species. Some writers have tried to get over this difficulty by inventing new English names. Here I have preferred to use the scientific, Latinized, names, adding, where they can be Englished, a translation and, where a true English name is in general use, this has been added too. In the translations I have altered the order of the Latin, putting the 'trivial' name (often an adjective) before the generic (usually a noun) as we do in our speech, but keeping the capital letter initial for the Genus. I have invented no names of my own.

The scientific names for animals are in an almost incredible confusion owing to recent well-intentioned efforts to apply world-wide rules intended to standardize them. So far the chief result has been to replace many names, long known and universally understood, by others laboriously excavated from obsolete literature or evolved from the fertile minds of systematists. This 'modern' nomenclature I have, reluctantly, adopted, and with much help from kind and learned persons, I have tried to be as much 'up to date' with its ephemeral vagaries as the interval of time between writing and publication will allow.[1] Where those who know old friends among the Insects under well-established names find them here called by some unfamiliar cacophonies, they may feel as they do when a friend is raised to the peerage, but they must not blame me. I have omitted all synonyms and the name of the christening author.

The distinction between large and small species is to some extent complicated by variation in size between insects of the same kind. This gives some latitude, of which I have taken advantage to include or reject at will.

In brief, then, the objects of this little book are to help its reader to identify, and learn something about, any family of British Insects containing large species and, at the same time, to find out what small Insects there are about which he may learn elsewhere.

My thanks are due to all those writers whose works I have consulted and above all to him to whose memory this book is dedicated, to the authorities at the British Museum who have afforded me every facility, and to those of the Hope Department of Entomology at the University Museum, Oxford, and particularly Dr. B. M. Hobby, who have lent me specimens from which to draw and given me invaluable advice.

E. S.

August 1942

[1] Since the author wrote this Preface in 1942, still further changes of nomenclature have had to be made.

CONTENTS

NOTE ON THE COLOUR PLATES

THE following pages contain life-sized coloured illustrations of the chosen examples of each of the Families, or other groups, in which there are 'large' species.

They are intended to form a collection representative of the animals popularly known as Insects.

Each coloured sketch is repeated later in the book in black and white, accompanying the description. References are made in the text, after each creature's name, to the page containing the coloured plate, thus: (*p. 13*).

NOTE

♂ is the symbol of the planet Mars, and means MALE.

♀ is that of the planet Venus, and means FEMALE.

☿ is that of the planet Saturn, and means STERILE FEMALES or 'WORKERS'.

Every insect has a Latin name of two words (*see also p. 8*). The first is the name of the genus, the second of the species. In this book, where the species has the same name as the genus, it is written thus: *Cossus*^{2}, standing for *Cossus cossus*.

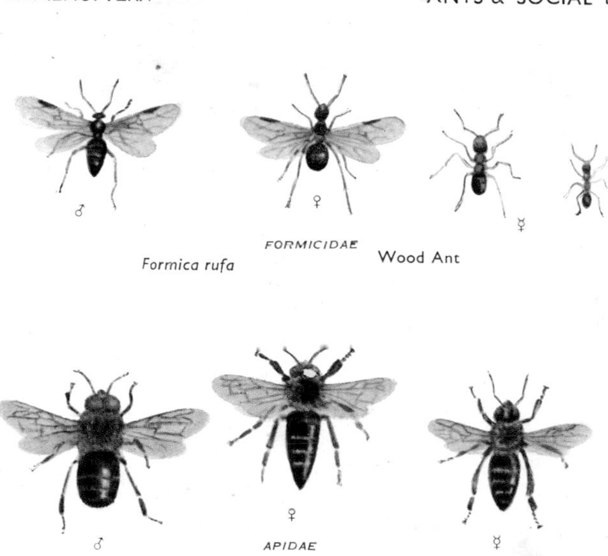

FORMICIDAE

Formica rufa Wood Ant

APIDAE

Apis mellifera Honey Bee

BOMBIDAE Bumble Bees

Bombus terrestris

♂ ♀

ANTHOPHORIDAE
Anthophora acervorum

♀

MEGACHILIDAE
Megachile willughbiella

♀

NOMADIDAE
Nomada lineola

♀

ANDRENIDAE
Dasypoda hirtipes

♀

COLLETIDAE
Colletes cunicularia

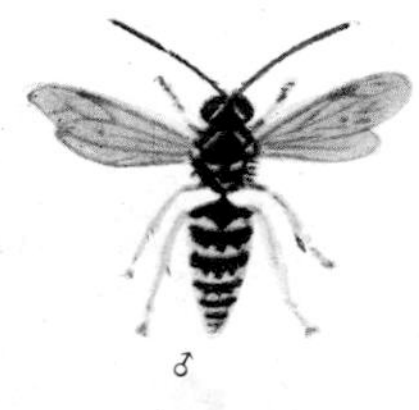

♂

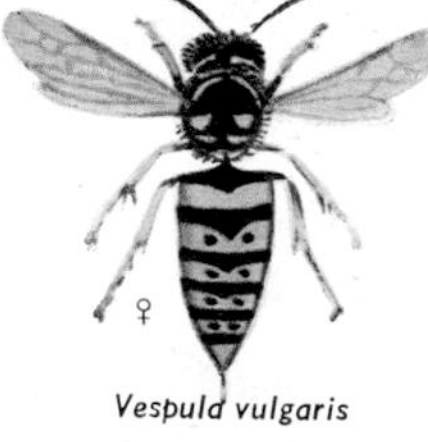

♀

☿

VESPIDAE *Vespula vulgaris* Common Wasp

♀

EUMENIDAE
Eumenes coarctata

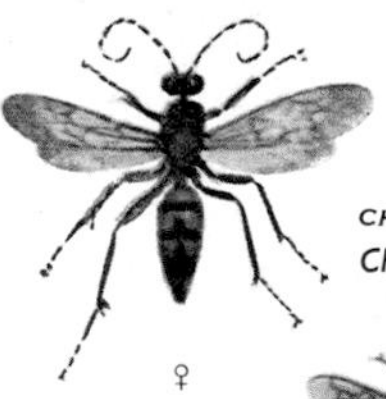

♀

POMPILIDAE
Anoplius fuscus

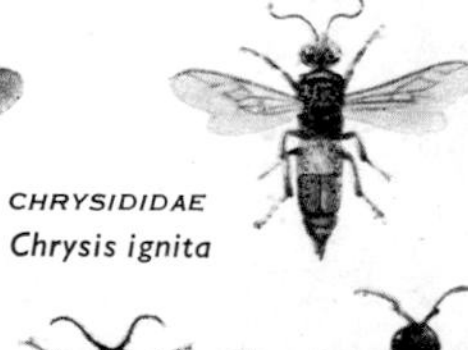

CHRYSIDIDAE
Chrysis ignita

♂ ♀

MUTILLIDAE
Mutilla europaea

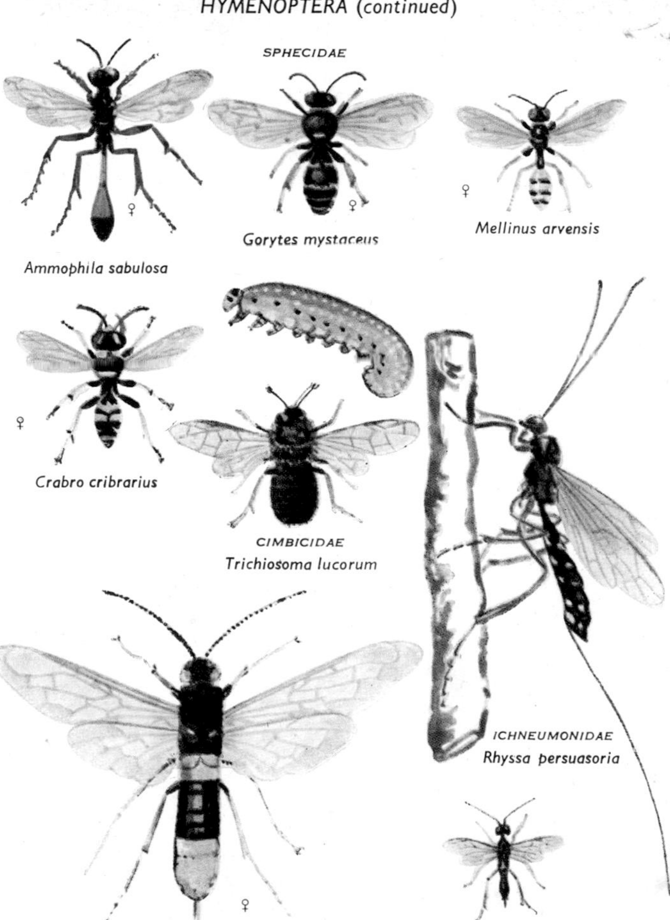

SPHECIDAE

Ammophila sabulosa ♀

Gorytes mystaceus ♀

Mellinus arvensis ♀

Crabro cribrarius ♀

CIMBICIDAE
Trichiosoma lucorum

ICHNEUMONIDAE
Rhyssa persuasoria

CEPHIDAE
Janus femoratus

SIRICIDAE
Urocerus gigas ♀

Calliphora vomitoria

TACHINIDAE
Sarcophaga carnaria

Larvaevora grossa

♀

OESTRIDAE
Hypoderma bovis

SYRPHIDAE
Scaeva pyrastri

♀

BOMBYLIIDAE
Bombylius major

♂

ASILIDAE
Philonicus albiceps

♀

TABANIDAE
Tabanus bovinus

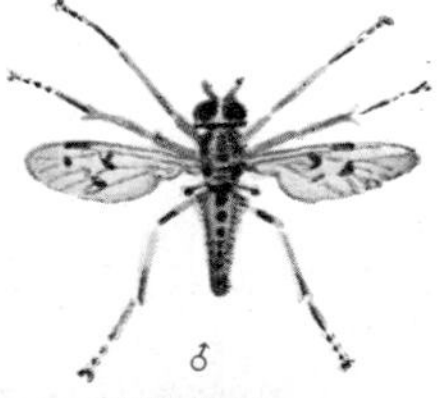

♂

LEPTIDAE
Rhagio scolopacea

♀

STRATIOMYIDAE
Stratiomyis chamaeleon

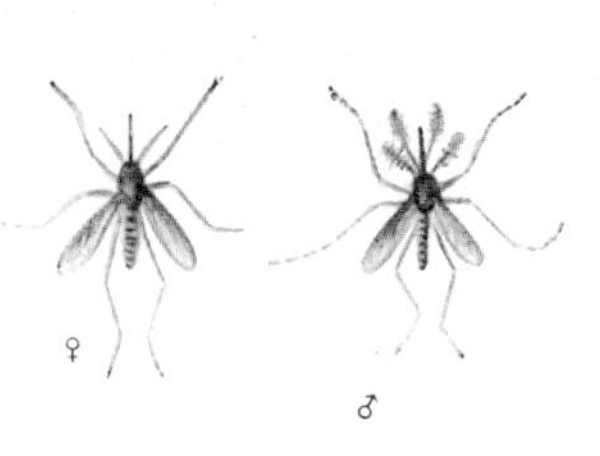

CULICIDAE
Culex pipiens

CHIRONOMIDAE
Chironomus plumosus

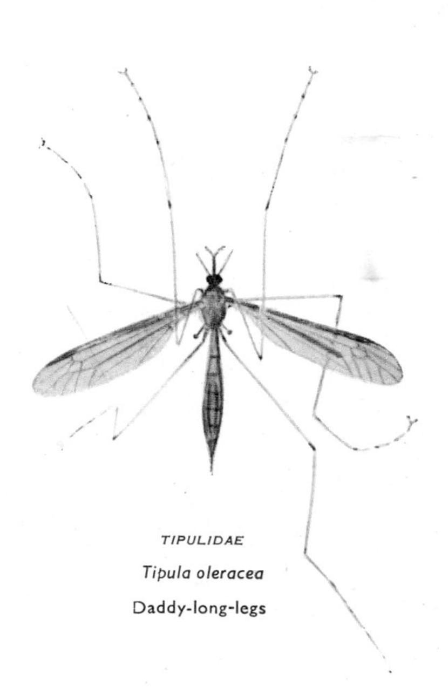

TIPULIDAE
Tipula oleracea
Daddy-long-legs

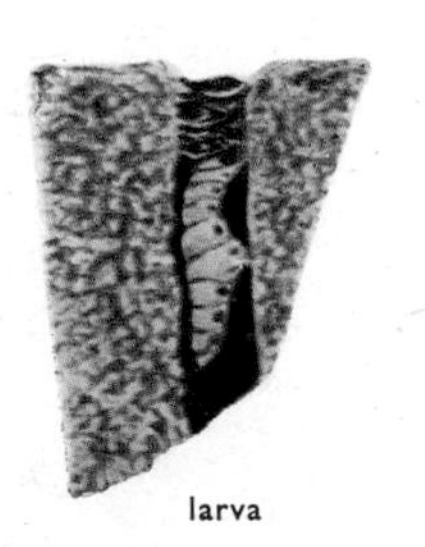

larva

adult

pupa

CICINDELIDAE

Cicindela campestris Tiger Beetle

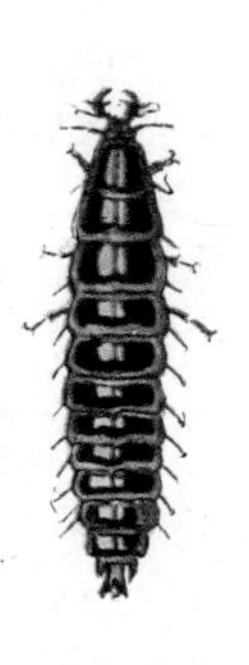

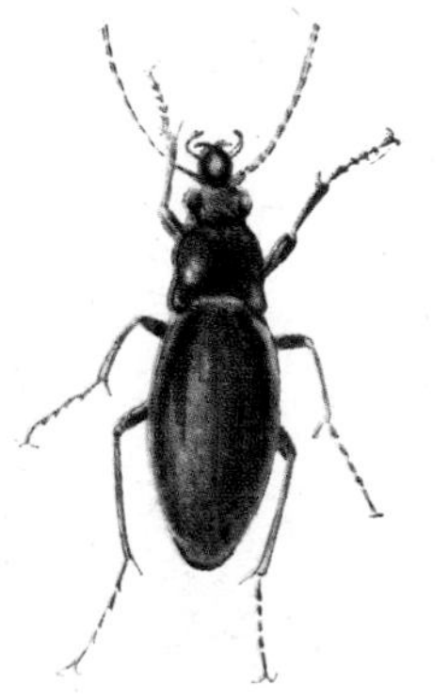

Brachinus crepitans

Bombardier

CARABIDAE

Carabus violaceus

Violet Ground Beetle

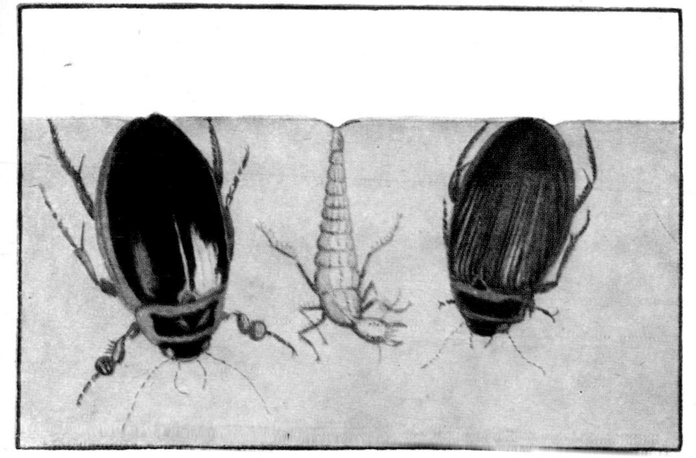

DYTISCIDAE *Dytiscus marginalis*

HYDROPHILIDAE *Hydrophilus piceus*

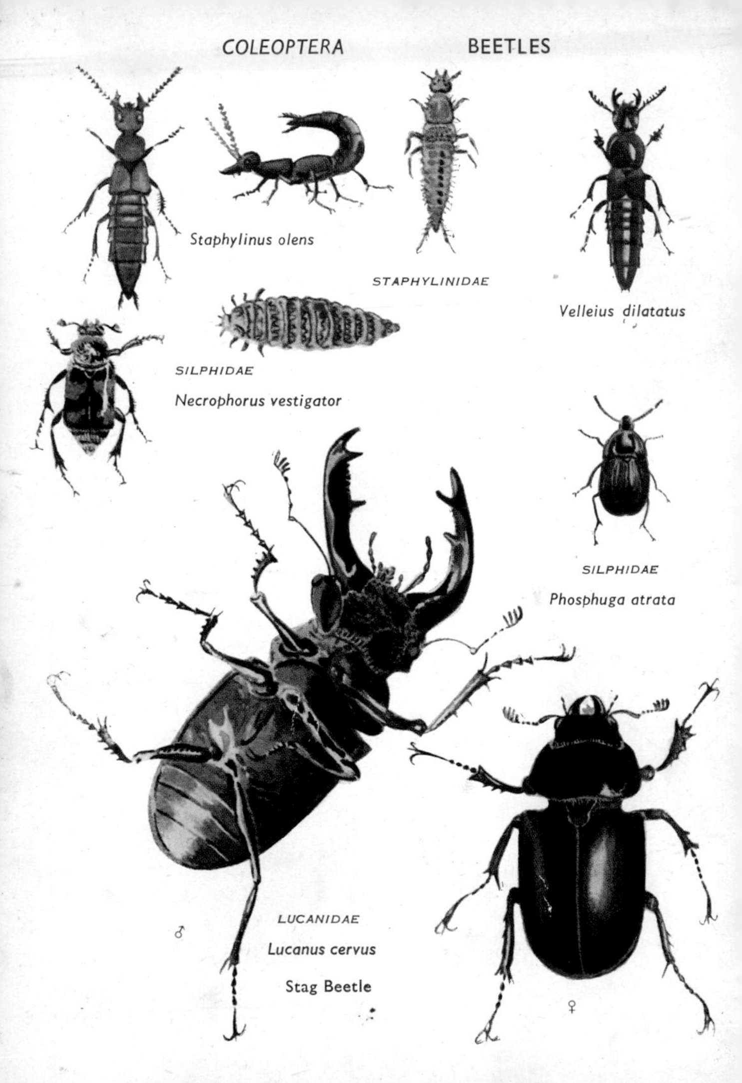

Staphylinus olens
STAPHYLINIDAE
Velleius dilatatus
SILPHIDAE
Necrophorus vestigator
SILPHIDAE
Phosphuga atrata
♂
LUCANIDAE
Lucanus cervus
Stag Beetle
♀

SCARABAEIDAE

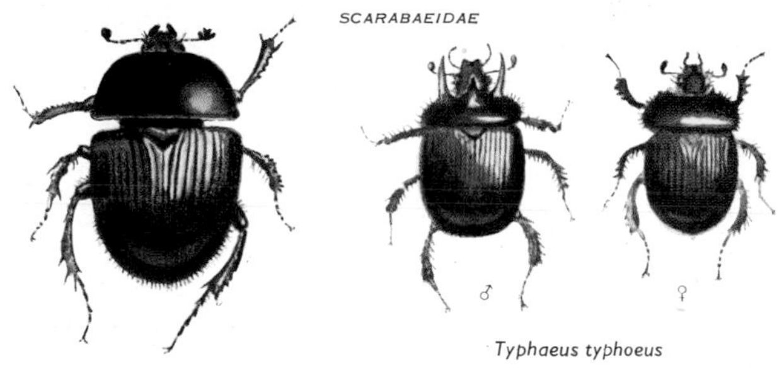

Typhaeus typhoeus

Geotrupes stercorarius

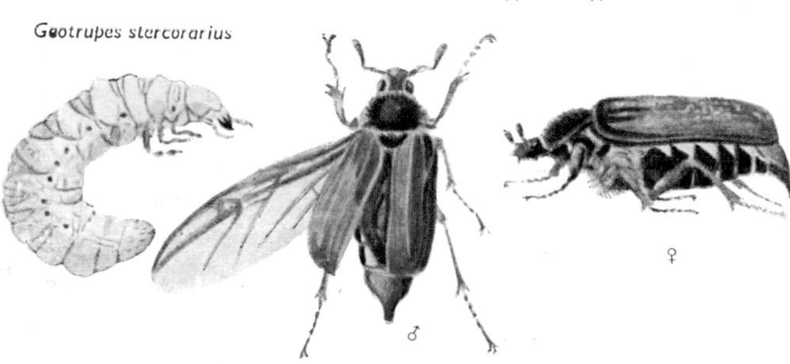

Melolontha[2] Cockchafer

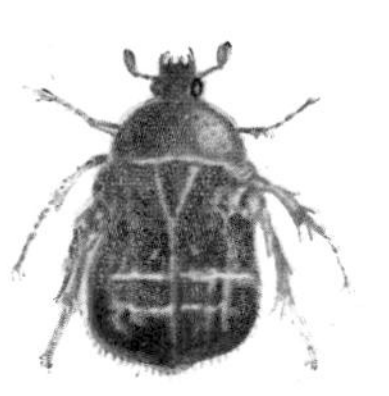

Cetonia aurata Rose Chafer

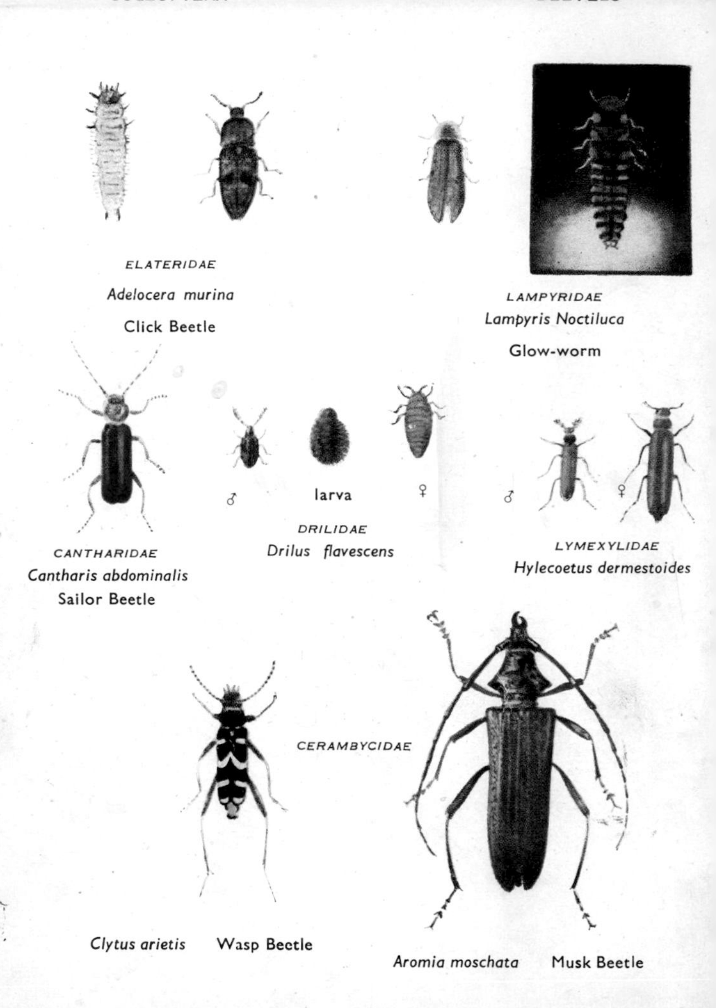

ELATERIDAE
Adelocera murina
Click Beetle

LAMPYRIDAE
Lampyris Noctiluca
Glow-worm

CANTHARIDAE
Cantharis abdominalis
Sailor Beetle

DRILIDAE
Drilus flavescens

LYMEXYLIDAE
Hylecoetus dermestoides

CERAMBYCIDAE

Clytus arietis Wasp Beetle

Aromia moschata Musk Beetle

COLEOPTERA BEETLES

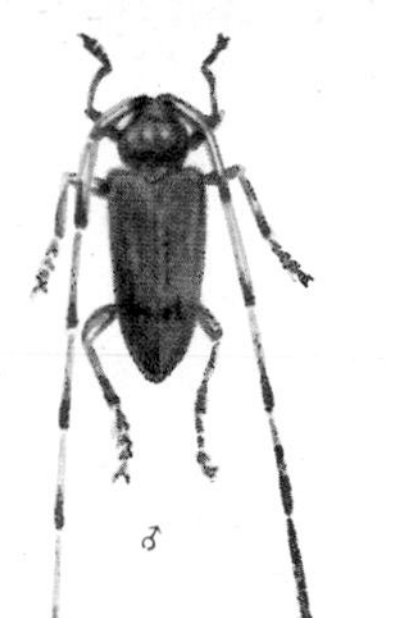

♂

CERAMBYCIDAE
Acanthocinus aedilis
Timberman

Timarcha tenebricosa
Bloody-nosed Beetle

Leptinotarsa decemlineata
Colorado Beetle

larva

pupa

adult

TENEBRIONIDAE
Tenebrio molitor Meal-worm Beetle

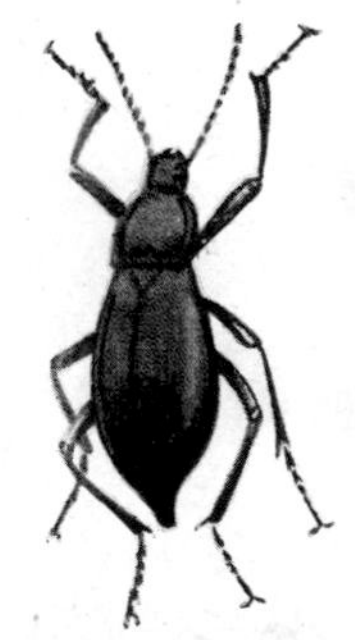

TENEBRIONIDAE
Blaps mucronata Churchyard Beetle

OEDEMERIDAE
Oncomera femorata

PYROCHROIDAE
Pyrochroa coccinea

PYTHIDAE
Pytho depressus

MELOIDAE

Meloë proscarabaeus Oil Beetle

larva I larva 2 pre-pupa larva 3 pupa adult

Apalus muralis

CURCULIONIDAE

Hylobius abietis Pine Weevil

larva

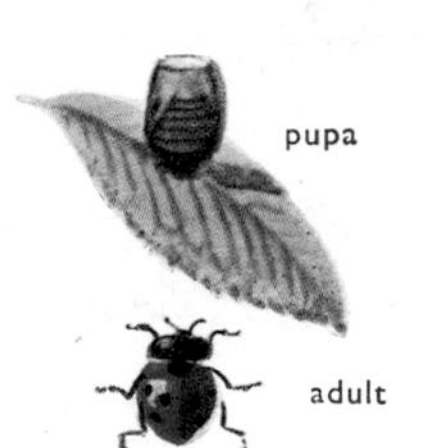

pupa

adult

COCCINELLIDAE Lady-bir

Coccinella septempunctata

LEPIDOPTERA BUTTERFLIES

SPHING DAE *Laothoë populi* Poplar Hawk

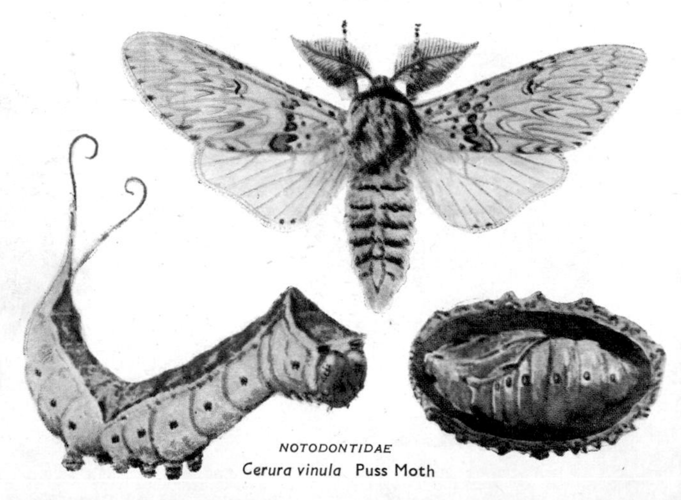

NOTODONTIDAE
Cerura vinula Puss Moth

THYATIRIDAE *Thyatira batis* Peach Blossom

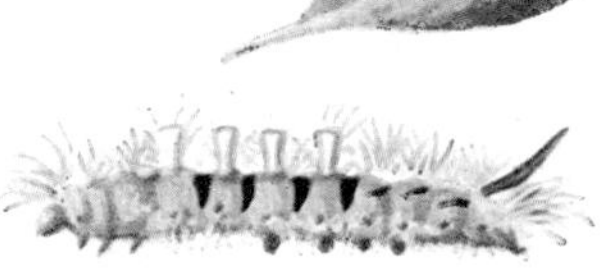

LYMANTRIIDAE *Dasychira pudibunda* Pale Tussock

LASIOCAMPIDAE
Lasiocampa quercus
Oak Eggar

ENDROMIDAE *Endromis versicolora* Kentish Glory

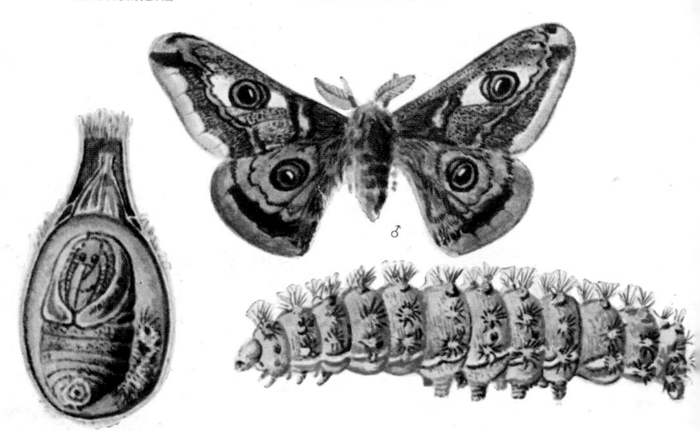

SATURNIIDAE *Saturnia pavonia* Emperor

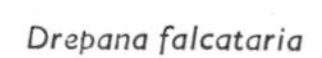

DREPANIDAE *Drepana falcataria* Pebble Hook-tip

ARCTIIDAE *Arctia caia* Garden Tiger

AGROTIDAE *Triphaena pronuba* Large Yellow Underwing

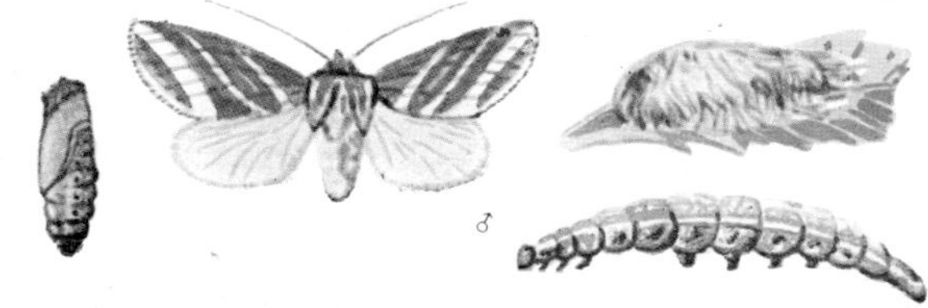

CHLOEPHORIDAE *Bena prasinana* Green Silver Lines

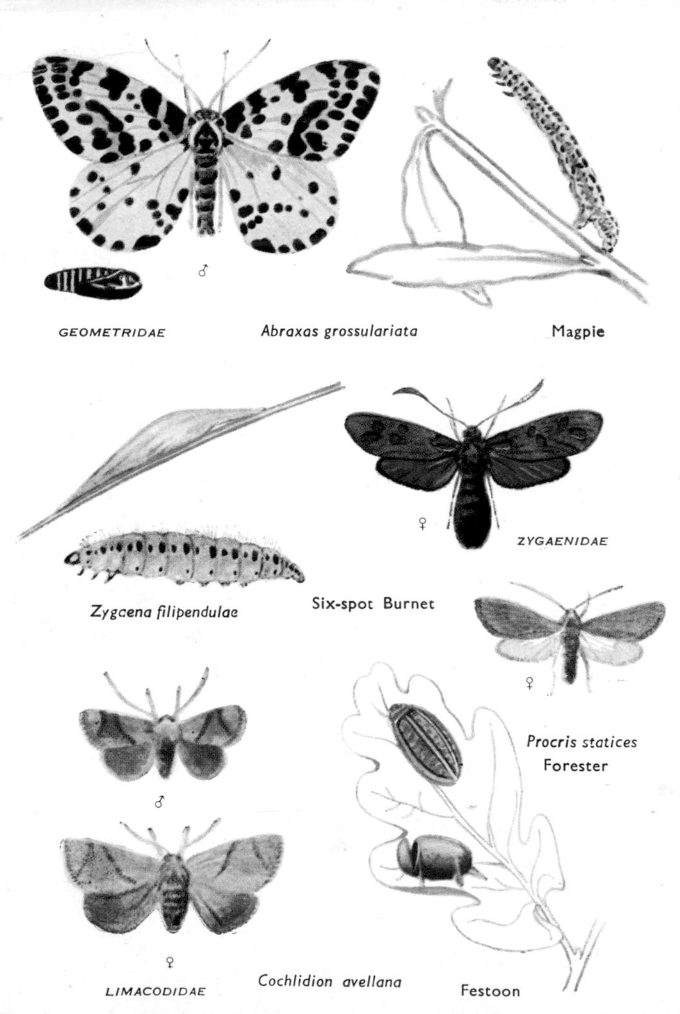
♂
GEOMETRIDAE
Abraxas grossulariata
Magpie
♀
ZYGAENIDAE
Zygaena filipendulae
Six-spot Burnet
♀
Procris statices
Forester
♂
♀
LIMACODIDAE
Cochlidion avellana
Festoon

COSSIDAE *Cossus*[2] Goat Moth

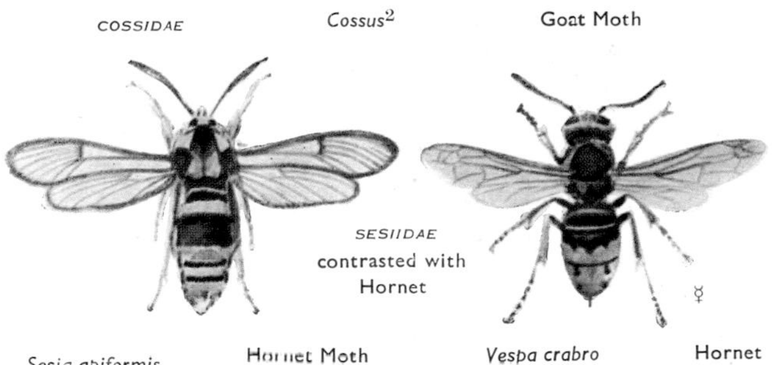

SESIIDAE contrasted with Hornet

Sesia apiformis Hornet Moth *Vespa crabro* Hornet

HEPIALIDAE *Hepialus humuli* Ghost Moth

PSYCHIDAE *Sterrhopteryx fusca*

PYRALIDOIDEA

Pyralis farinalis *Nymphula nymphaeata*

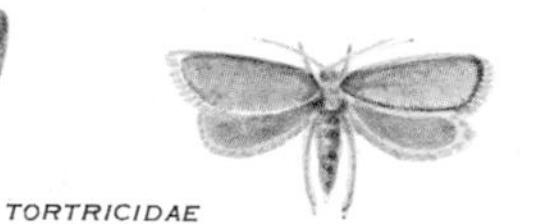

TORTRICIDAE

Tortrix forsterana *Tortrix viridana* and larva

TINAEOIDEA
Ypsolophus mucronellus

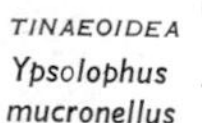

PTEROPHORIDAE
Alucita pentadactyla

ORNEODIDAE
Orneodes hexadactyla

SERICOSTOMATIDAE
Goëra pilosa

LIMNEPHILIDAE
Limnephilus lunatus

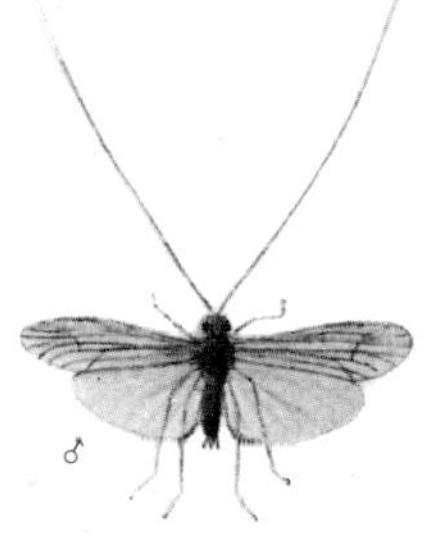

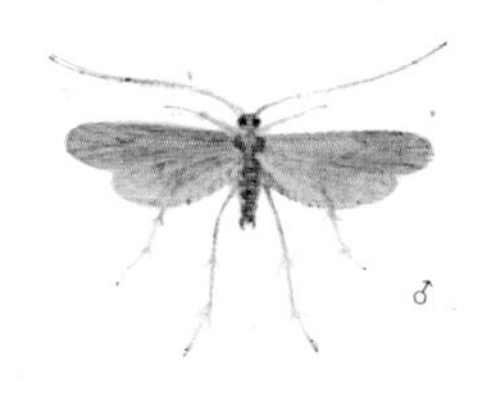

MOLANNIDAE *Molanna angustata*

LEPTOCERIDAE *Leptocerus nigronervosus*

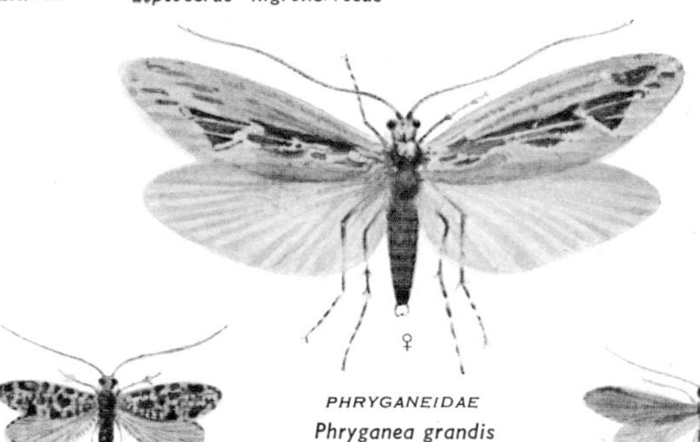

PHRYGANEIDAE
Phryganea grandis

♀

PHILOPOTAMIDAE
Philopotamus montanus

RHYACOPHILIDAE
Rhyacophila dorsalis

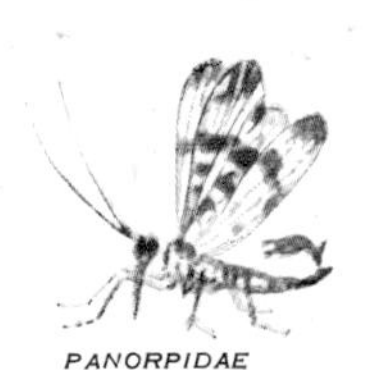

CHRYSOPIDAE

Chrysopa carnea Green Lacewing

PANORPIDAE

Panorpa communis Scorpion Fly

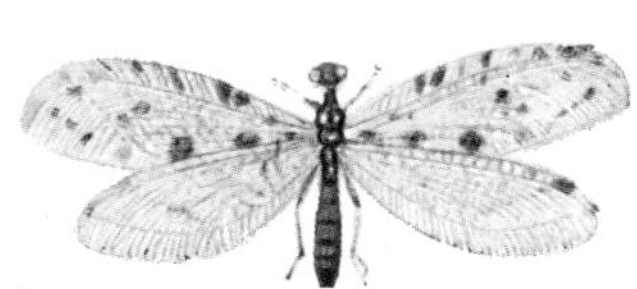

OSMYLIDAE

Osmylus fulvicephalus

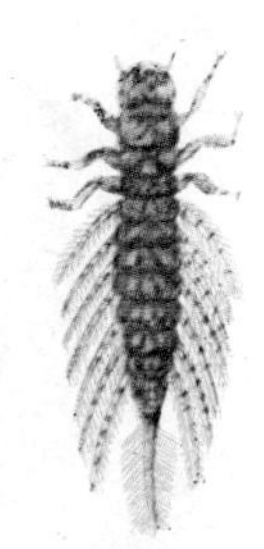

SIALIDAE

Sialis lutaria Alder

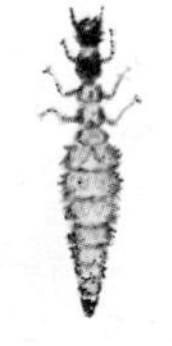

RAPHIDIIDAE *Raphidia notata* Snake Fly

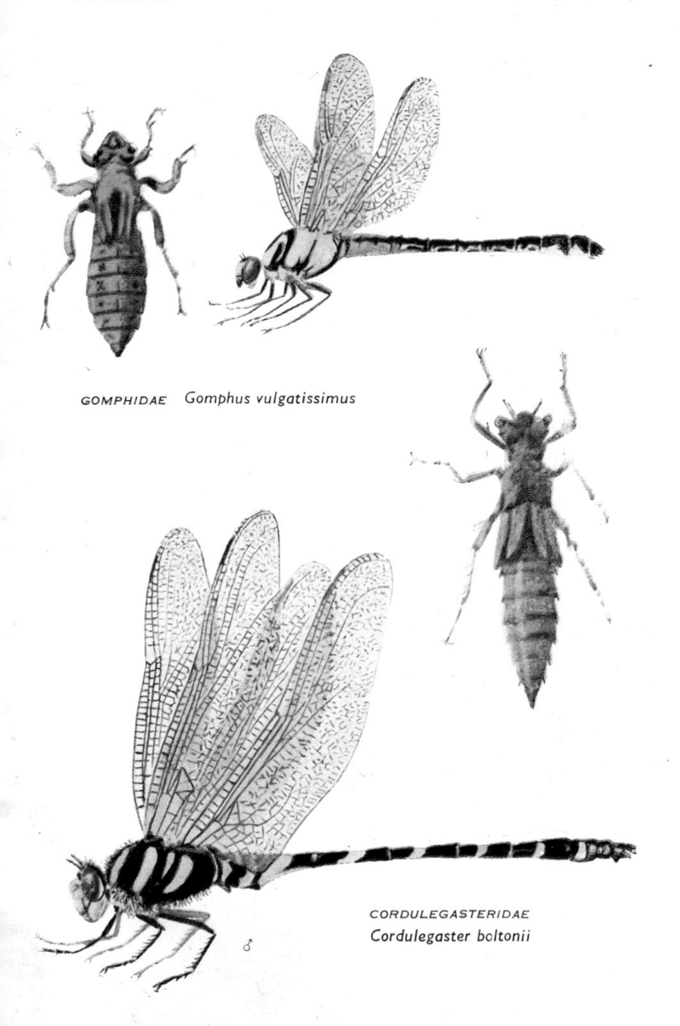

GOMPHIDAE *Gomphus vulgatissimus*

CORDULEGASTERIDAE *Cordulegaster boltonii*

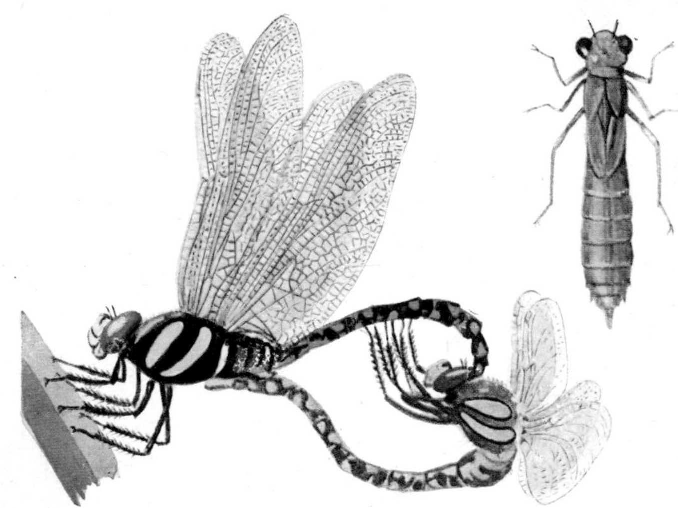

AESHNIDAE *Aeshna juncea*

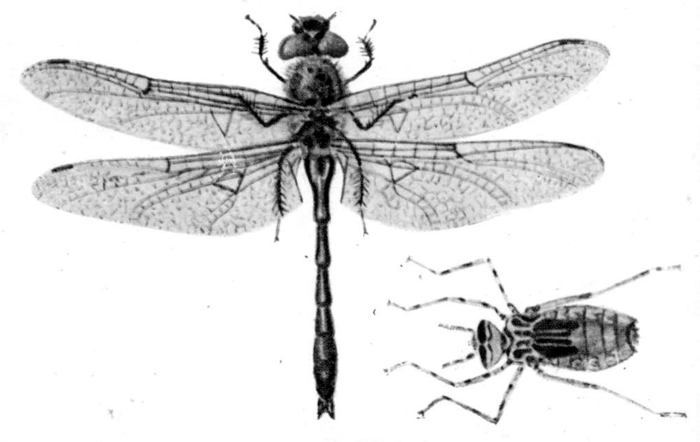

CORDULIIDAE *Cordulia aenea*

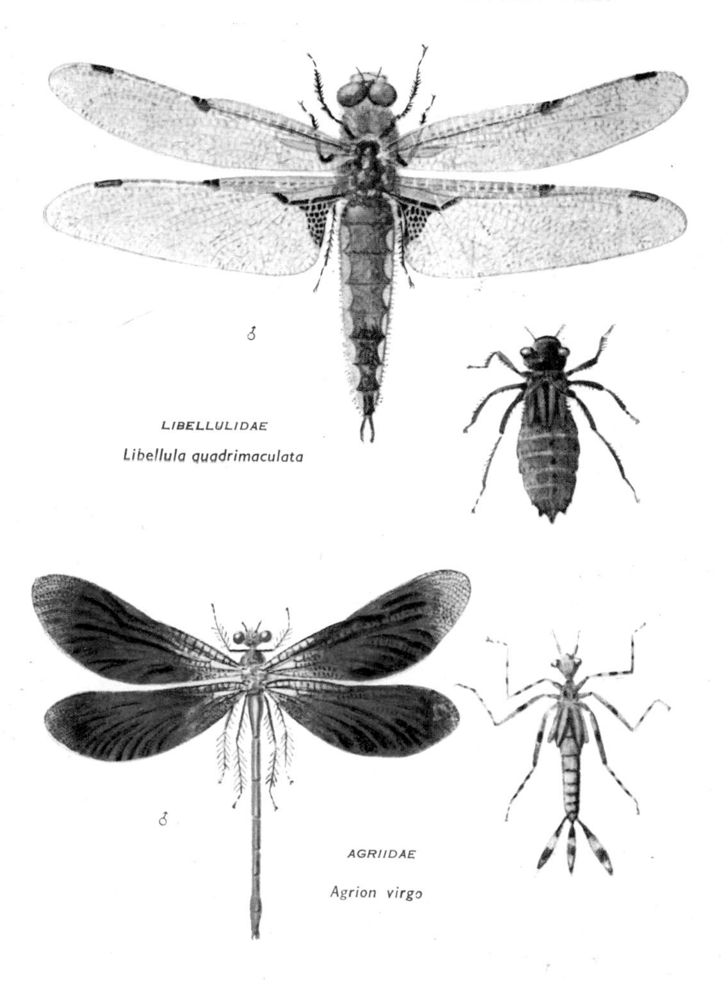

LIBELLULIDAE

Libellula quadrimaculata

AGRIIDAE

Agrion virgo

LESTIDAE *Lestes sponsa*

PLATYCNEMIDIDAE *Platycnemis pennipes*

♂

COENAGRIIDAE
Coenagrion puellum

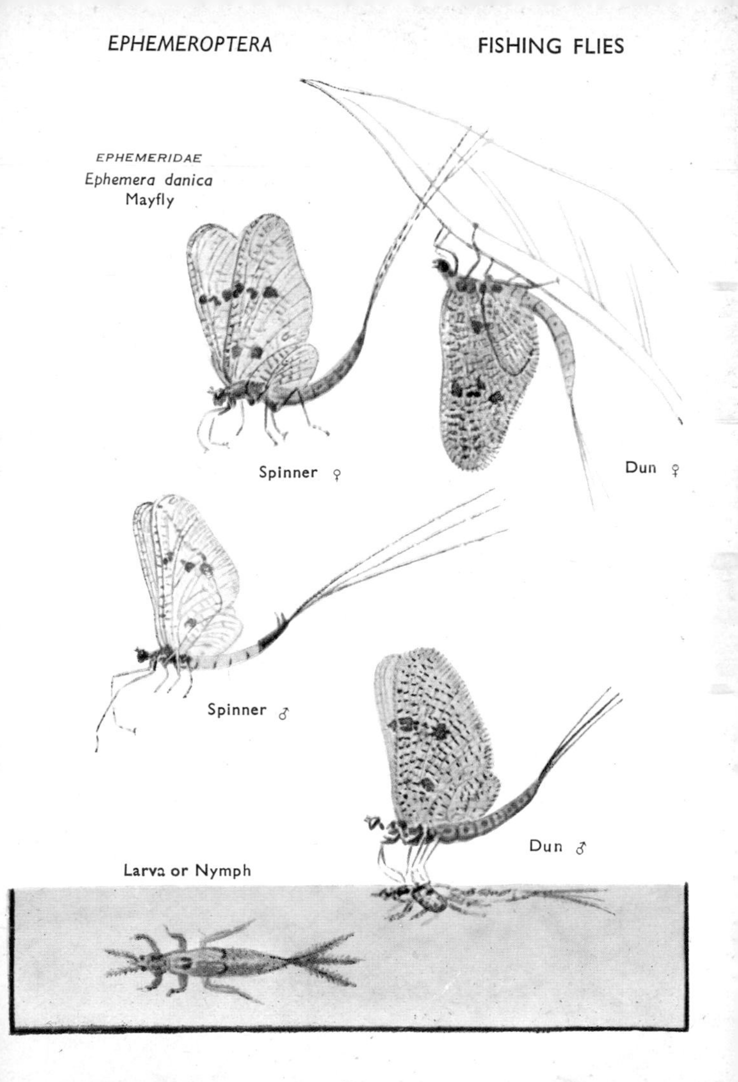
EPHEMERIDAE
Ephemera danica
Mayfly
Spinner ♀
Dun ♀
Spinner ♂
Dun ♂
Larva or Nymph

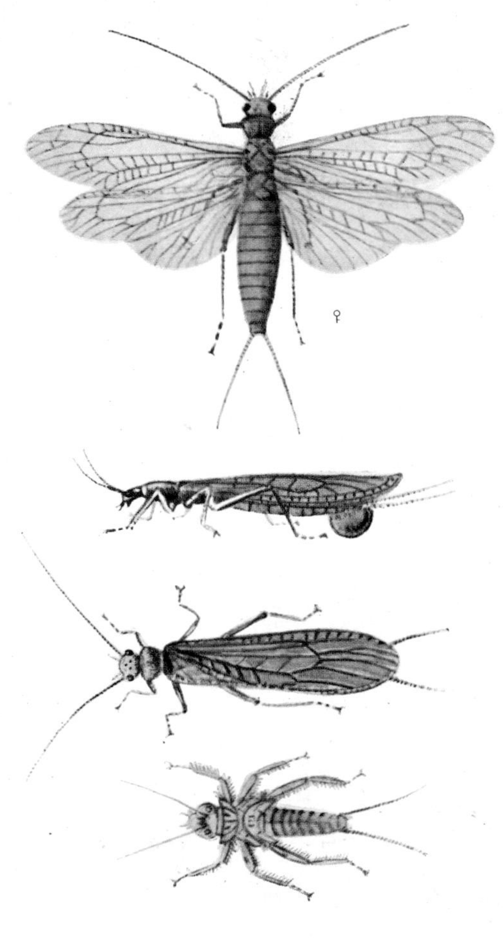

PERLIDAE *Perla carlukiana*

HEMIPTERA
BUGS

PENTATOMIDAE
Acanthosoma haemorrhoidale

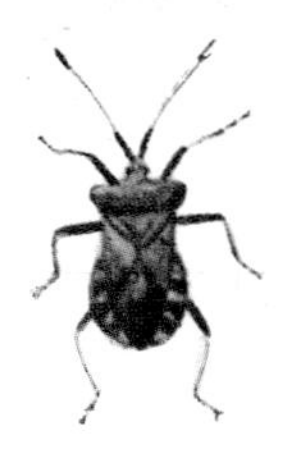

COREIDAE
Coreus marginatus

HYDROMETRIDAE
Hydrometra stagnorum

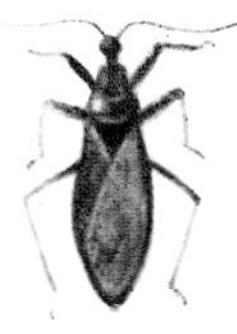

REDUVIIDAE
Reduvius personatus

CIMICIDAE
Cimex lectularius
Bed Bug

NAUCORIDAE
Ilyocoris cimicoides

NOTONECTIDAE
Notonecta glauca

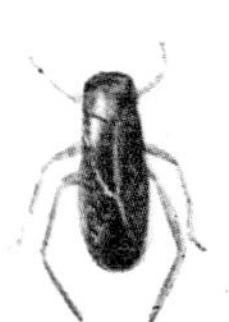

CORIXIDAE
Corixa punctata

CICADIDAE
Cicadetta montana

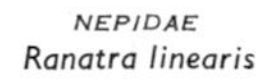

NEPIDAE
Ranatra linearis

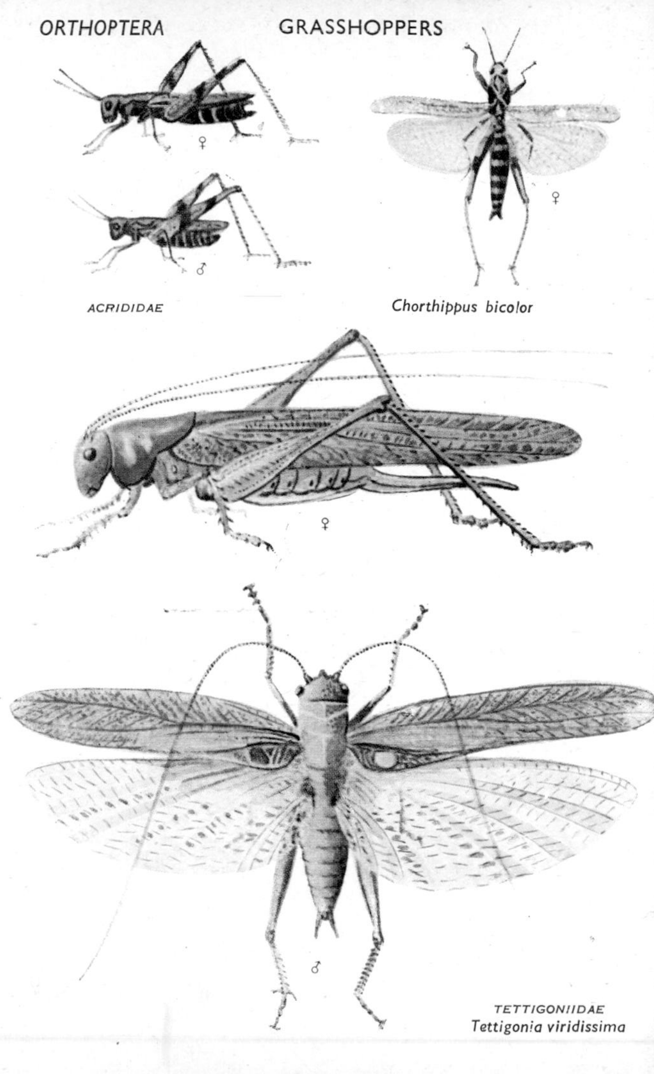

ACRIDIDAE

Chorthippus bicolor

TETTIGONIIDAE
Tettigonia viridissima

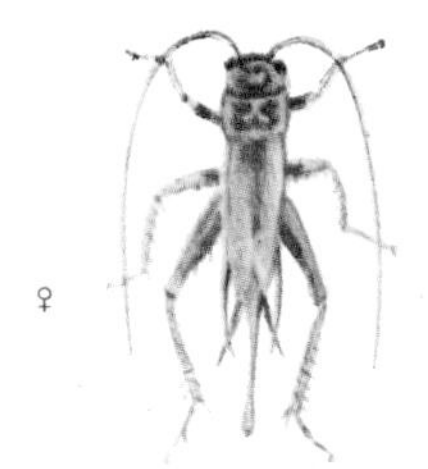

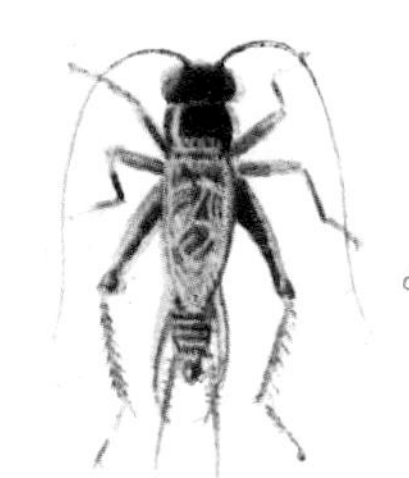

Gryllulus domesticus House Cricket

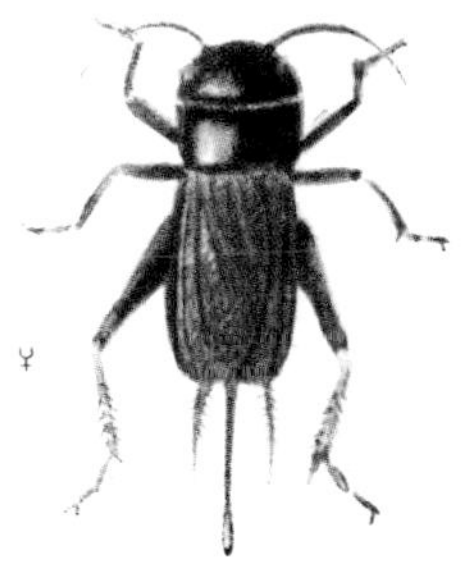

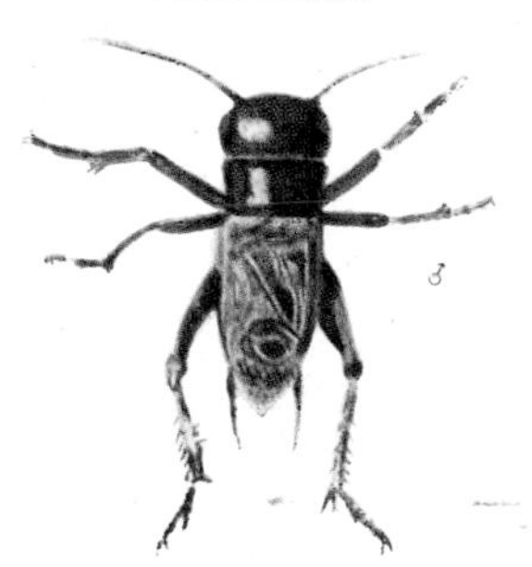

Gryllus campestris Field Cricket

GRYLLIDAE

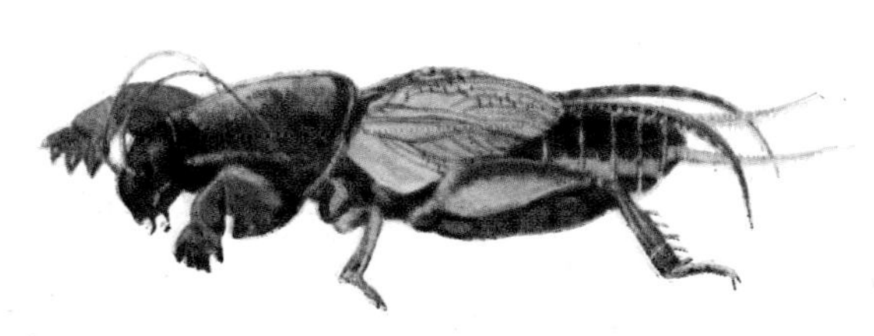

Gryllotalpa[2] Mole Cricket

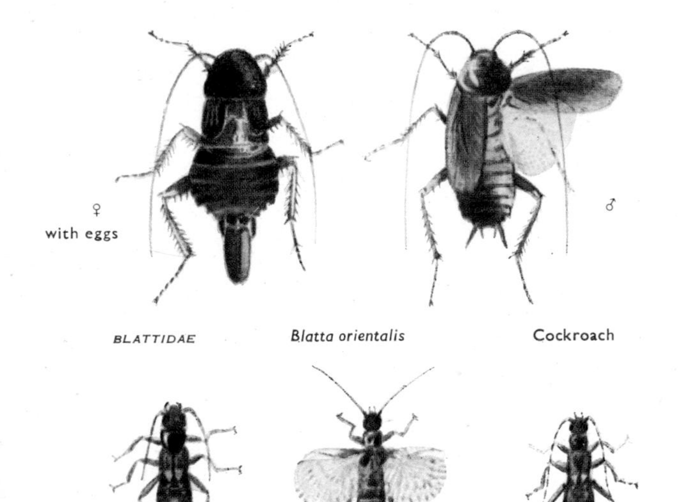

BLATTIDAE *Blatta orientalis* Cockroach

♂ ♀ ♀

FORFICULIDAE *Forficula auricularia* Earwig

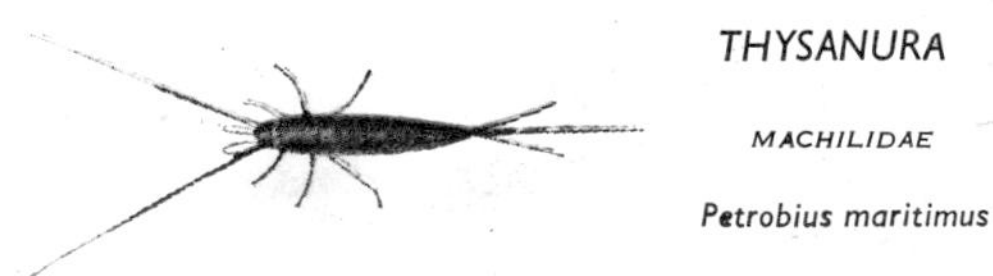

THYSANURA

MACHILIDAE

Petrobius maritimus

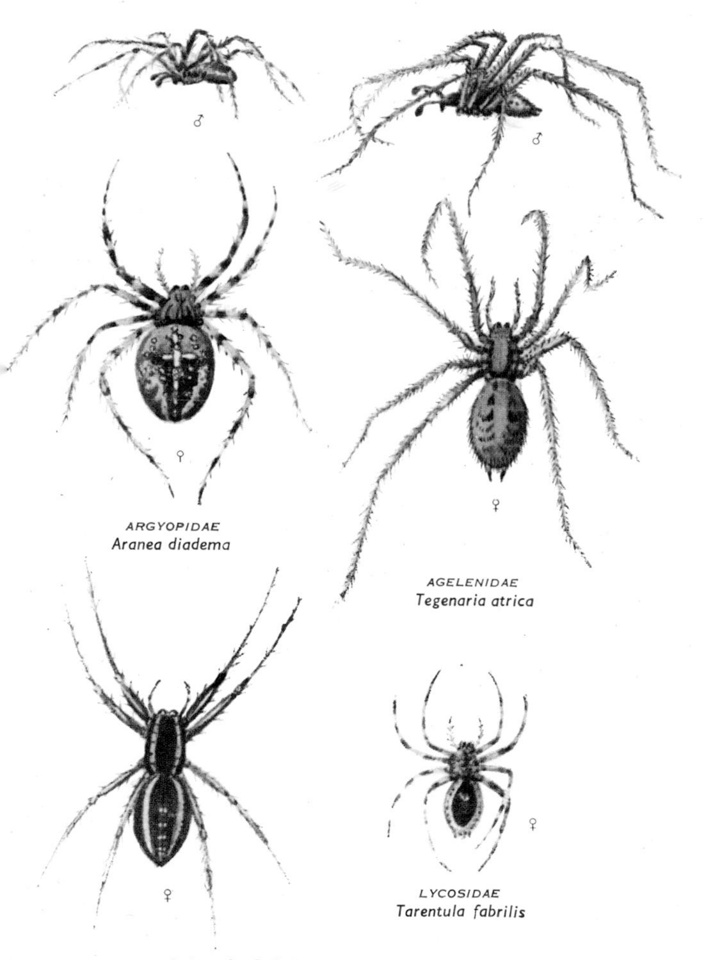

ARGYOPIDAE
Aranea diadema

AGELENIDAE
Tegenaria atrica

LYCOSIDAE
Tarentula fabrilis

PISAURIDAE *Dolomedes fimbriatus*

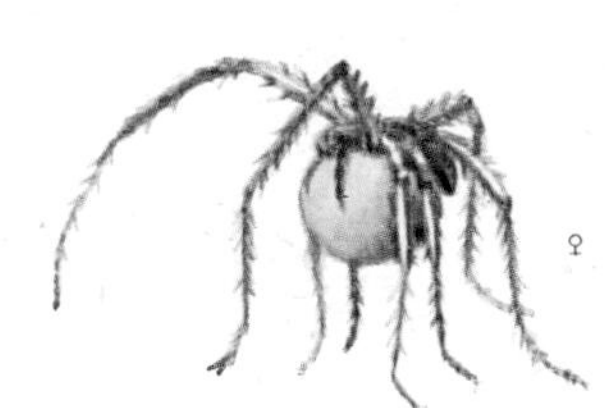

PISAURIDAE *Pisaura listeri* Same bearing eggs

AGELENIDAE
Agelena labyrinthica

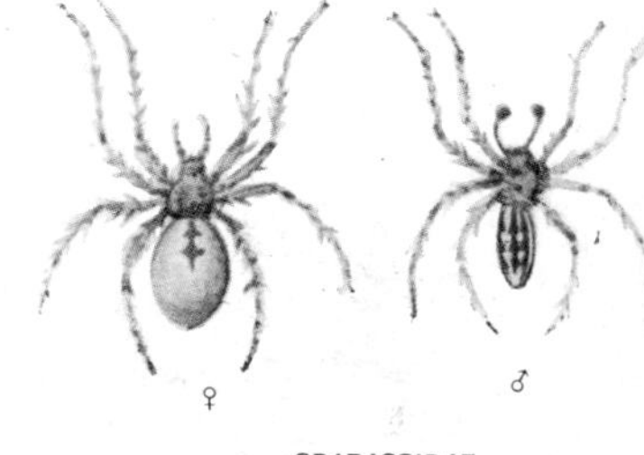

SPARASSIDAE
Micrommata viridissima

DICTYNIDAE *Ciniflo similis*

ATYPIDAE
Atypus affinis

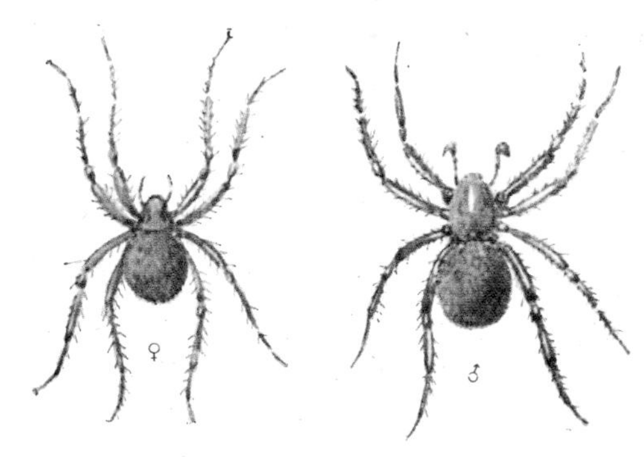

AGELENIDAE *Argyroneta aquatica* and (below) the diving bell

MYRIAPODS

GEOPHILIDAE *Geophilus linearis*

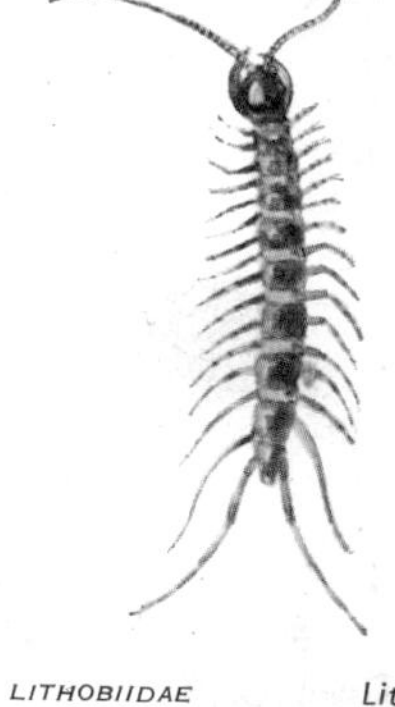

LITHOBIIDAE *Lithobius tricuspis*

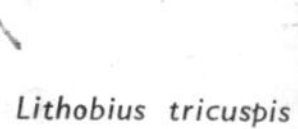

JULIDAE

Julus albipes

CRASPEDOSOMIDAE

Chordeuma silvestre

POLYDESMIDAE

Polydesmus complanatus

GLOMERIDAE

Glomeris marginata

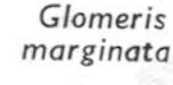

CRUSTACEA

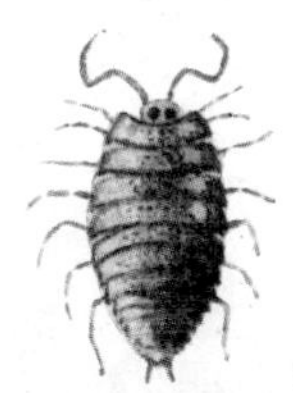

ONISCIDAE

Oniscus asellus Woodlouse

INSECTS

THE Insect Class is far the largest in the animal world. Not only have more than a million different species been described and named, but it is believed that many times that number still await discovery. Also the insects belonging to many of these species are in astronomical numbers. Such phrases as 'clouds darkening the sky' and 'swarms carpeting the ground for miles' are in frequent use by writers who describe them. Light is thrown upon this subject from another angle by a glance at a Hedge Sparrow feeding. You will see him pecking diligently, throughout the daylight hours, at a small patch of ground only a few yards in extent. Some of the things he gathers are plant seeds, but the greater number are minute insects which we can hardly see without the help of a glass. Small as the individual insects are, the total bulk of animal matter in their bodies added together would vastly exceed that of all the other land animals.

In these islands we often rejoice over their comparative scarcity. When complaining of our climate, we add that it has the one merit that we have very few insects. There is some truth in this, at least as regards the flies and gnats which annoy us in more northern or more southern lands. Nevertheless, about 20,000 species of insects have been found in this country and, without doubt, to them many more will be added. This country forms no exception to the general rule that the total bulk of its insects is far greater than that of all other animal life put together.

CHARACTERS

Insects, in the scientific sense of the word, are *Arthropods* (that is, animals with an external skeleton or shell consisting of segments and having jointed appendages), of which the bodies are divided into three parts and of which the adults have six legs and breathe by air tubes (*tracheae*) communicating with the surrounding air by means of openings (*spiracles* or *stigmata*).

ANATOMY

The form of the various insects differs enormously, but a few things can be indicated here which are of general application.

All insects are small. Few of the largest are bigger than the smallest bird or mouse, while many are barely visible to the naked eye.

The outer skeleton or skin of an insect is composed of three layers and forms a complete coating which covers the whole body and all appendages,

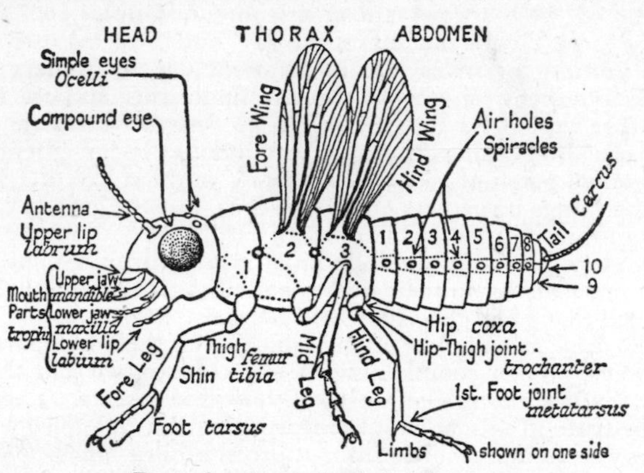

External anatomy of typical adult insect

such as the legs, which project from it, and also extends inwards to line the gut, air channels, and other cavities. This skin contains *chitin*, a substance which is flexible and even elastic, and which is apparently in only the two inner layers. The outer layer contains another substance (*cuticulin*) which, in the living insect, becomes brittle and exceedingly hard after exposure to the air for a short time. Few materials in nature retain their form and resist decay of all kinds better than these two substances. Even the delicate wings of a butterfly and the tiny bags forming each of its coloured scales may survive uninjured by the air in a museum cabinet for over two centuries. In this respect an insect's skin rivals gold or precious stones.

Full advantage is taken of this contrasted hardness and flexibility. The all-enveloping coat is varied all over the creature's body. Where elasticity is needed, no rigid outer layer is formed. Where it is absent there can be movement or distension: where it is present there is immobility and protection. We can think of an insect's body as a pipe-line of steel tubes, not joined together with stiff cement, but connected by a continuous rubber tube inside them, so that the whole line becomes one piece, flexible at the joints. The result is something like a diver's suit or a medieval knight's suit of armour of which the separate pieces (helmet, breast-plate, &c.) are united into a continuous whole by airtight flexible joints.

This complete coat, then, consists of rigid pieces or plates (*sclerites*) separated from each other by bands of flexible material. All insects have two such flexible bands circling them so as to divide them into three parts—the **head,** the **thorax,** and the **abdomen.**[1] The thorax and abdomen are subdivided into a number of rings, or segments, which are themselves broken up into several plates by cross-lines of flexible material, and there are such bands wherever there is an appendage and at each of its joints.

We have, then, three parts (head, thorax, and abdomen), each of which is made up of several pieces, and projecting from these parts a number of jointed appendages, amongst which, in every adult insect, will be found three pairs of legs.

Head. The head, except for its appendages, is not clearly divided into segments but is all in one piece. It is supposed that some ancestor of the earliest insect was a worm-like creature with six segments in the head, each with a pair of appendages, two of which pairs have disappeared. The segments have become one piece by the disappearance of the flexible lines separating them. The surviving appendages of the head are the two horns or **antennae**[2] and the **mouth-parts.** The mouth-parts (*trophi*) are very complicated. Here it will be enough to say that there are two main types of mouth—the chewing or biting, and the sucking. There are various forms of each, and some intermediate between them, and there are also insects in which the mouth is useless and its parts obsolete.

As well as the antennae and mouth-parts, the **eyes** are in the insect's head. These are among their most remarkable organs. Almost all adult insects have two so-called 'compound eyes'. Each of these is made up of a large number (sometimes several thousands) of separate lenses (*ommatidia*) each connected with its own independent nerve, and carrying to the brain an image of what is directly before it. These separate parts of the eye are closely bunched together and, as they taper as they go inwards, they spread out towards the surface of the eye as a whole, pointing each in its own direction, much as do the separate daisies in a child's nosegay. In this way the brain of the insect receives a number of different pictures of what each facet of the compound eye records, and is thus enabled to piece these different records together and see a single picture. This process has been likened to the way in which we can see a picture

[1] I shall use the terms 'thorax' and 'abdomen' throughout this book. Such substitutes as 'fore-body' and 'hind-body', 'chest' and 'tail', are either clumsy or misleading.

[2] 'Antennae' is another technical term which I shall use in this book. The word 'horn' for a flexible, articulated organ with which the insect detects smells and makes signals, suggests a monosyllabic mixed metaphor.

in a mosaic made up of coloured tesserae, each one of which is merely a plain square of coloured glass. Most insects have, as well as these two compound eyes, three single, or simple, eyes (*ocelli*) usually situated on the top of the head, between the large compound eyes.

Thorax. The thorax of the typical insect, unlike the head, is almost always obviously divided into three segments or rings, one behind the other. These segments are also divided horizontally so that each consists of six plates (*sclerites*): one on top, one underneath, and two at each side between them. These plates, and the segments which they make up, have all got names with which we need not be troubled. It is enough to call the segments the 1st, 2nd, and 3rd segments of the thorax, and to note that there is great diversity in their size and in the shapes of the plates which make them up. One rule is, however, constant throughout the insects. The fore pair of legs grow from the 1st thoracic segment, the middle pair from the 2nd, and the hind pair from the 3rd; and, if there are wings, the fore pair of wings grow from the 2nd segment, above the middle legs, and the hind wings from the 3rd segment above the hind legs.

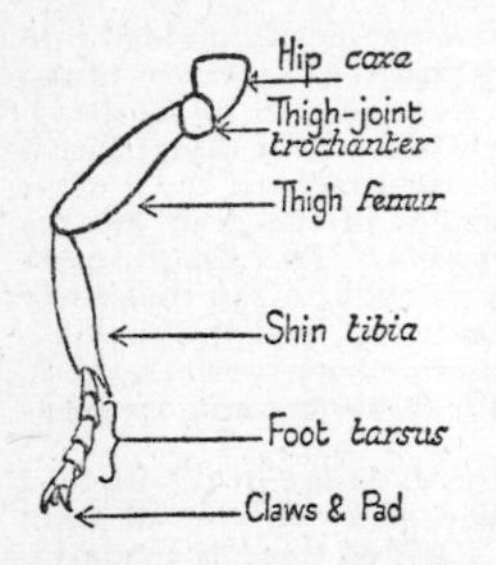

The **six legs** of an insect are usually all much alike, though sometimes they are specially shaped for particular work. Thus some are flattened, or fringed with hairs for swimming, some are enlarged and provided with a pocket for collecting pollen, some are spiked and traplike to grip the insect's prey, and others are specially shaped for digging. They consist of five parts, known, both in their English and scientific names, by somewhat inappropriate terms derived from the parts of the human leg. These are shown in the sketch. The part which varies most is the so-called 'foot' which usually has five joints or segments, the last of which has two claws with either a pad, or hairs, between them. There may be any lesser number, and even a total absence of foot-joints, and the claws, pads, and hairs may also be missing from some or all of the legs.

The **wings** are thin expansions of the general coating which covers the insect. Until the last moult, they are bags containing a number of tubes called veins.[1] After the last moult, the insect forces air into these veins. The result of this is that the veins are lengthened and they spread out into a fan of stiff struts. In so doing they stretch the bags containing them to the utmost, until these bags are flattened. They then have the appearance which we recognize as that of an insect's wing, looking like a single transparent sheet with a network of fine lines.

Abdomen. The abdomen consists of ten to twelve further segments, but all rarely appear as, in the adult, some of the tail-end segments are

[1] Veins, ribs, nerves, or nervures. I shall use the first of these terms, with the warning that none of them is correct. These tubes have in them both nerves and air passages (*tracheae*), but once the wing is formed and hardened, their chief purpose is to strengthen it.

almost always modified to form sexual organs. Except for traces in the most primitive insects, no legs are found on the abdomen of the adults, and the chief projections from it are, in some insects, pincers or tails (*cerci*), stings or egg-laying tubes (*ovipositors*), or male copulatory organs, all at the tail-end. In a few insects only there are some survivals of larval water-breathing filaments or gills. Many more immature insects have gills, and some have soft projections used for walking which are known as pro-legs. These, however, are not articulated or hardened with rigid outer skin layers.

Little need be said of internal anatomy in this book. But we must notice several main differences between the Insects and the Vertebrates (Fishes, Amphibians, Birds, Reptiles and Mammals). The vertebrates have internal skeletons—bones which form solid supports for the muscles. When the muscles contract, they pull upon the bones and so move the body or limbs. In the insect the muscles are fastened to the solid plates of the outer shell or external skeleton, and, by pulling these together, move them and all that is enclosed within them. Although the shell bends inwards in places, the insect has no internal bones. The muscles of insects and vertebrates are much alike, both being bands of elastic tissue which can be shortened and which, when the effort is relaxed, stretch out again to their original length.

The vertebrates grow from within and, as they grow, add to the size of each bone at the same time as they add flesh to flesh and skin to skin. The insect also grows from within, but it cannot increase the size of the hard outer shell which contains it and it must therefore, when its growth has reached a certain point, get out of its shell and procure a larger one. This is done by the formation of a thin flexible coat inside the old one. Then the old one splits and the insect crawls out dressed in its new robe, still moist and flexible. The new coat stretches and soon becomes hard and assumes its colours, and the creature, larger than before, sets out upon the next phase of its life. This process is called 'moulting' (*ecdysis*). Insects when moulting shed only the hard outer layer of the skin, and in so doing they rid themselves of a certain quantity of superfluous nitrogen and carbon which enter into its composition.

These moults sometimes produce merely a larger creature, and sometimes involve a complete change of form. In the latter case the insect, after moulting, is unrecognizable—a total disguise has been effected. Thus the maggot ultimately becomes a bluebottle, or the chrysalis a butterfly. But whether the change is to be great or slight, there will, throughout the period of growth, be periodical and repeated moults.

An insect breathes and supplies its body with oxygen from the air in a way quite different from that of the mammals, such as ourselves. In our bodies the blood is completely canalized in an elaborate network of blood-vessels along which it is driven by a central pump, the heart. It is driven along branching arteries to every part of the body where, in the tiny channels which penetrate every organ, it does its work, supplying food and oxygen and removing waste material. Then, collected again by the convergence of the small channels into larger veins, the blood-stream returns to the heart and is driven to the lungs, where it gives up the waste materials and picks up more oxygen before starting out again on its round. The lungs are cavities filled with air. The blood flows through the lungs in tubes which have such thin walls that the oxygen surrounding them can pass through them into the blood and out again laden with the carbonic acid gas which we then breathe out. In the mechanism of insects much of this is reversed. They also breathe in air and breathe out its nitrogen with carbonic acid gas, which is the result of the burning of the carbon of their tissue, but it is the air which is canalized, and the blood which surrounds and bathes the narrow thin-walled vessels which contain it. The blood fills the whole body of the insect, forming a general bath in which all the organs are bathed. There is no system of blood-vessels. The only approach to arteries, veins, or heart is a single tube which is really little more than a stirrer. It is often called the heart because it has a pump action and a valve action which make the blood flow along it. It lies along the insect's back, and at the hinder end has holes through which the blood enters it to pour out at the forward end by the head. Thus the general blood-bath is stirred up and kept from stagnation, much as is the water of our own baths if we fan it with our hand to retrieve a sunken piece of soap. The air passages (*tracheae*) enter, not at the mouth or near it, but by a number of air-holes (*spiracles*) all along the sides of the body, and all of them are connected by cross-vessels inside. These holes suck in the fresh air and expel the old by the pumping action of the body muscles, though most of the circulation of oxygen through the *tracheae* is by diffusion, and much of the carbonic acid gas passes out through the skin. To prevent evaporation of water there are muscles to close them, and the closing may also serve to cause a circulation of air, which is made to enter at one hole and leave by another.[1]

The **nervous system** of the typical insect consists of a long double cord of nerve, running the whole length of the body along the under side, with branches in each segment which spring from swellings (*ganglia*), each of which forms a sort of brain controlling the muscles of the segment in which it is. Swellings are found controlling the eyes, the mouth-parts, and the throat. The more highly specialized and developed the insect becomes, the larger are these *ganglia* in the head, and the more the others tend to be grouped together. The head *ganglia* are usually spoken of collectively as the 'brain', and upon the size of the brain (other than the parts wholly concerned with the eyes) the instinct or the intelligence of the creature depends. We must, however, note that the subsidiary local brains, dotted along the nerve-cords, have considerable independence, even in the higher insects. Thus the hinder part of a wasp will sting for some time after the head has been removed, and the fore part will go on contentedly eating jam after the abdomen has been cut off.

[1] Although most adult insects breathe by the air-hole and air-passage system, some of them in the younger stages, when their early life is aquatic, have not yet developed this system. In these the air-holes are as yet closed and their bodies are aerated in one or other of two ways. Either their whole outer skin is so thin that the air dissolved in the water reaches the body through it (*cutaneous respiration*), or, alternatively, thin-skinned *lamellae* or threads project from the body and so give the oxygen in the water access to it with the same result. Such structures are called *tracheal gills* and are, in their work, identical with the gills of the fishes. When maturity is attained, however, no insect remains a water-breather, even if it continues to spend most of its time beneath the surface of water, with the exception of a single genus of Bugs, *Aphelochirus*.

HABITS

Insects differ so much that this subject must be discussed mainly under the separate Orders into which they are divided.

Most of them are dwellers on the land and may be found either on the surface, or at a certain depth beneath the soil, or in flight in the air above it. Quite a number spend nearly all their time in fresh water, even as adults; and a great many more live in fresh water until they reach the adult stage. But these aquatic insects are rarely found on very large expanses of fresh water at great distances from the shore.

There are a few species which frequent the sea-shore above low-water mark, but there are only a few tropical insects which are found on the surface of the high seas. Some of the land insects are migrants and, in their journeys, make long flights over land and sea.

As to their **food**, there are insects which eat every vegetable and every animal substance. Some are selective and keep carefully to a very restricted diet, such as the leaves of a single genus (or even a single species) of plant, or the body of a particular mammal; others will eat almost anything, animal or vegetable. While treating this subject, it will be worth while to glance briefly at some of the different groups of insects which eat the different types of food.

Total abstainers. The following adult insects seem to eat nothing at all: Mayflies, some Caddis Flies, some Moths.

Vegetarians. All the adults of the Wasp family, all Bees, adult and young, nearly all Butterflies (larvae and adults) and the great majority of Moths, many Flies, the larvae of the Saw-flies, Wood Wasps, Stem Saw-flies, the great majority of the Bugs, many Orthoptera, a large number of Beetles.

Carnivores. These include all eaters of animal food, alive or dead. The larvae of the Wasp family, those of the Ichneumons or Parasitic Hymenoptera, a number of the Flies both as maggots (Blow-flies) and as adults (Gnats), a large number of Beetles, many Moth larvae, one Butterfly larva, some Bugs. Dragonflies, Lacewings, Long-horned Grasshoppers.

Omnivorous. Many insects can and do eat anything, animal or vegetable, which they can get, particularly those which feed on decaying putrid matter. Many of the Flies, both as larvae and adults. A number of Beetles, both young and adult. Some Crickets and Grasshoppers, and several of the Apterygota.

It will be noticed that while most insects have, in this respect, the same diet as larvae and as adults, the above list gives us a group which change from a carnivorous (larval) to a vegetarian (adult) diet. These include one Butterfly, and many Moths, many Flies, and all the social and solitary Wasps. Some of the Saw-flies alone change from a vegetarian larval diet to a carnivorous adult diet. Upon their food and upon certain other habits depends the answer to the important question of the **utility** or **harmfulness** to man of each species. In estimating this, various things which insects do must be considered, amongst them the following:

One insect (the Honey Bee) has been taken into the service of man and directly supplies us with food. The only other domesticated insect (the Silkworm Moth) does not live here. These may be called the **Servants.**

Many insects make possible the cross-fertilization of flowering plants, by visiting the flowers in search of their nectar and carrying their pollen from one bloom to another. These include nearly all the Lepidoptera, a large number of Diptera, and very many Hymenoptera, and without their help we should have few, if any, flowers or vegetables. In the plant world their role is that of **Stud-grooms,** and they may be so named.

Some insects act as the dustmen of Nature. They cleanse the earth of animal excreta, and of the corpses of all dead creatures, large and small. This is chiefly the work of the larvae of Beetles and Flies, the adults laying their eggs upon the matter to be eaten and sometimes burying it first. Thanks to the work of these **Dustmen** we are spared the spread of much disease and the soil is enriched with fertilizing matter.

Some feed us indirectly by affording food to fish and

therefore also helping us to lure them to our hooks. These may be called the **Angler's Friends.**

Some, which may be called the **Beauties,** are so superbly coloured, patterned, and formed as to afford aesthetic delight to all who see them. This applies mainly to the Butterflies, but there are many others.

Some among the plant-eaters, many of which confine their diet to particular plants, eat only some plant which we regard as a pest because it strangles, or displaces, flowers or other plants which give us or our cattle pleasure or food. Thus, for example, the Small Tortoiseshell Butterfly larva eats only stinging-nettles. These may be called **Weed-eaters.**

The vast majority of insects provide food for poultry and game birds which, in their turn, feed us, and for countless other birds which delight our eyes. These we may call **Chicken-fodder.**

Some, in the larval stage, eat holes in our clothes or other woollen cloths, in leather, paper, and the like. These are Beetles and Moths and may be called **Cloth-eaters.**

Others, also always in the larval stage, destroy our timber or carpentered wood by boring or eating their way through it. These are not very numerous, but belong to three different Orders, the Hymenoptera (the Horntails), the Moths (the Goat Moth), and the Beetles. These are the **Wood-borers.**

A comparatively small number of our insects, all of which are Hymenoptera, have poison stings in their tails with which to attack prey for their young and to defend themselves, and which they use upon us in defence of themselves or their nests. These **Stingers** cause us considerable pain and may even kill, though this is rare, and, at least, they do not convey the germs of illness. The only Stingers are some of the Ants, the Bees, and the Wasps.

A vast number destroy plants upon which we depend for our food, either when growing (for example the Plant-bugs) or when they have already been garnered for storage (for example many Weevils). No part of a plant is without its devouring larval insect, and these **Food-thieves** are found in almost every Order.

A certain number pierce our skins to suck our blood. Most of these belong to the Order of Diptera (a few Flies, some Gnats, and the Midges), some Siphonaptera (Fleas), a few Hemiptera (Bugs), and Lice (Anoplura). Often the bite of these **Blood-suckers** is accompanied with intense irritation caused by liquids of the nature of saliva poured into the wound at the time of biting, and they also not infrequently convey diseases from one victim to another, so that the danger of their bites exceeds the mere unpleasantness.

Some kill, injure, or weaken our domestic animals, either by annoying them and sucking their blood, as the Blood-suckers do ours, or by entering their bodies as larvae and feeding off their flesh as the Oestridae (Bot Flies) do. These **Cattle-pests** among the insects are all Flies.

Just as we started this list with a class to which one single (British) insect alone belongs—the Honey Bee, alone representing the Servants—so it can be ended with a class to which only one, or at any rate only one small group, belongs—the House Fly, representing the **Food-foulers.** These creatures crawl over and feed on all that we eat and, in avid impartiality, over and upon every kind of loathsome putrescence. Added to this they soften their food by spewing up a drop of their last meal on to the next, so that, if a fly gets access to anything we are to eat, we eat filth in our food. This pest-bearer is responsible for more illness in this country than insects which bite, or sting, or otherwise more actively annoy us.

Reviewing these activities (a few only of course) of the insects, we have mentioned the Servants, the Stud-grooms, the Dustmen, the Angler's Friends, the Beauties, the Weed-eaters, the Chicken-fodder, the Cloth-eaters, the Wood-borers, the Stingers, the Food-thieves, the Blood-suckers, the Cattle-pests, and the Food-foulers.

Thus far, the difficulties of determining the merits or demerits of a given insect do not seem serious. It is easy to see that the first seven groups are sheep and the last seven groups goats. The only serious trouble arises from the fact that the same creature is often found in more than one group—is, in fact, both sheep and goat. To give only one example, the young (larval) White Butterflies (*Pieris*) are Food-thieves, and when they become adults they are Stud-grooms to the very same species of plants they destroyed.

There is, however, one most important group which has so far been omitted—the **Insect-eaters.** The insects are engaged in an eternal civil war. The vast majority of those of them that are animal feeders eat other insects. Therefore, before attaining certainty as to the virtues or vices of a particular insect which belongs to this group of Insect-eaters, we must either find out what insects it eats, or make up our minds as to whether the class of insects as a whole is beneficial or harmful to us. It is not often easy to separate the Insect-eaters according to their particular food. Some, it is true, specialize almost as much as the plant-eaters. But the greater number are satisfied with any insect they can catch, and it is therefore upon the merits of the whole class that we must in most cases decide.

This question has been decided by mankind as a whole without hesitancy. Insects are harmful to us, and anything which destroys them or reduces their numbers is meritorious. The swallow and the insect-eating insect are alike our helpers. The most that the entomologist, as *advocatus diaboli*, can do is to plead for exceptional treatment for some groups, and amongst them will be the Insect-eaters. The greater our knowledge, the more wisely shall we discriminate between good and bad, but, until we know, we shall be guided by the instinctive repulsion which leads us to regard all creeping and crawling things as enemies, and to 'swat that fly'.

REPRODUCTION AND GROWTH

With very few exceptions, which among the 'large' insects are negligible, all insects are born from eggs. In all the 'large' insects there are two sexes, male and female, and the eggs are laid by the females after impregnation by the males. Among those insects which are known as 'social' it is usual for the pairing of the sexes to take place once for all, the male then dying and the female thereafter enjoying a comparatively long life throughout which she continues to lay fertilized eggs. These same social species produce a much larger number of imperfect females (known as 'workers'), and some of these workers sometimes produce eggs from which males are developed. So far as the 'large' insects are concerned, this production of eggs from virgin females (*parthenogenesis*) is confined to the Honey Bee and some Saw-flies. In any case, it is so essentially an attribute of the smaller insects that no further reference will be made to it here.

As has already been indicated, the growth of insects necessitates moulting, and moulting often involves, not merely growth, but a dramatic change of form and habit. The usual dramatic changes undergone are as follows: an **egg** is laid and from it hatches a **larva**: the larva feeds and, after several moults and much growth, changes into an inactive, almost immobile, **pupa**: from this, by a final moult, the **adult** emerges. Many different names are in use for the larvae of different kinds of insects and also for the pupae,[1] but in this book I shall use only the words egg, larva, pupa, and adult for any kind of insect.

Where there is no distinct pupal stage, the word 'larva' will be used to describe the insect from the time it hatches from the egg until the last moult from which the adult emerges.

There is one fact which is common to all insects. No insect grows after its last moult and no insect has wings until after its last moult.[2] The common idea that small Flies or Beetles will soon grow up into big ones is a mere mistake. They will not. Once any winged insect has its wings developed and capable of flight, its growth is complete and it will never be any bigger.

Thus the larval stage alone is the stage of growth, the pupal stage (where there is one) is the stage of reorganization, and the adult stage that of reproduction. Therefore the larval

[1] Thus the larvae of Butterflies and Saw-flies are called 'caterpillars', those of many true Flies are called 'maggots' or 'gentles', and those of Dragonflies 'nymphs' or 'naiads'. The name 'nymph' is usually applied to the larvae of all such insects as have no pupal stage. The French word for a pupa is *nymphe* and the English word 'nymph' has often been used as meaning a pupa, particularly in the case of such insects (e.g. the Caddis Flies) as produce comparatively active pupae. The pupae of Butterflies are often called 'chrysalids'.

[2] For something like an exception see the Ephemeroptera (p. 267).

stage is the only stage where the insect's food is of importance to us from the point of view of our own food-supply. As an adult it eats and drinks only what is needed to replace liquid lost by evaporation, to supply fuel for the energy expended in courtship, or material for the eggs. One must, of course, also remember that the adult (particularly of the Wasps) frequently catches, kills, and collects the food for the next generation of larvae.

CLASSIFICATION

The vast myriads of the insect world can hardly yet be said to be ripe for classification. A very large number of the world's species have yet to be described and named, and of those we know, only a very few have been adequately studied. Perhaps the domesticated Honey Bee is the only one of which the habits and instincts are moderately well known, and even about it much remains to be learned. Yet the unripeness of the fruit has not kept out the teeth of the hungry, and many have bitten, though none have fully digested. This little book is no place in which to try to classify the insects, and all that can be done is to explain the way in which they are here divided.

The three main differences upon which classification of insects has been based are in their life-histories, their mouth-parts, and their wings.

As we have already seen, all insects moult repeatedly during their period of growth. Now some, in the course of these moults, do not merely grow larger, but completely alter their appearance, their form, their colouring, their mode of life, and their internal and external organs. For example, the successive stages of egg, larva, pupa, and butterfly look as different from each other as a hen's egg, a snake, a beetroot, and a swallow; yet all are the same individual insect. The insects which go through this series of changes will be described as having the usual three changes. At the opposite end of the scale there are the insects which appear to do little more than to grow bigger through all the series of moults intervening between the tiny larva, which hatches from the egg, and the breeding adult (*imago*). As an example we may take the Grasshoppers. It is true that there are marked differences between the newly hatched larva and the adult. In particular, the adult has wings. But these wings have been slowly forming and growing, as it were from buds on the larva's shoulders, all through the long series of moults, so that at no particular moult do we see a marked change, nor do we feel that the insect has become a different creature. As with ourselves, growth is gradual, there is no inert pupal stage of preparation for a grand pantomime transformation scene, and such insects will be spoken of as having only a slight, or gradual, change.

In addition to the two types of life-history above mentioned, there are intermediate types—insects which change once at least dramatically, but without an inert pupal stage, as, for example, do the Dragonflies. Of these, the winged adult emerges, full grown, from a larva which lives under water. There are also a few insects which go through more than the usual four forms. For an example of this type, see the case of the Meloïd Beetles described on pp. 181–4.[1]

The other chief aids to classification depend upon the form of the adult insects only, and are therefore more conveniently at hand for such as are not well known and whose life histories are as yet undiscovered. The **mouth-parts** of insects are built either to bite or to suck. As has already been seen, there are here again some intermediate forms, in which the main biting jaws (*mandibles*) are well developed, and at the same time the other mouth-parts are formed for sucking or licking. The Bees and Wasps are examples of this. Their biting jaws are often used for building, or other work, rather

[1] There is a whole vocabulary of fine words to describe these facts. The changes between the egg and the adult are called *metamorphoses*. The usual series of three changes is called *complete metamorphosis*. Those insects which undergo more than the usual three changes are said to undergo *hypermetamorphosis*, and the insects which undergo it are called *holometabola*, or said to be *holometabolous*. Those which change less than the usual three times are called *heterometabola* or said to be *heterometabolous*. These *heterometabola* are divided into those which have only the gradual, or slight, change, which are neatly termed *paurometabolous heterometabola*, and those which have some dramatic change, but no inert pupal stage, which are called *hemimetabolous heterometabola*. All these words give great pleasure, but I will try to avoid them in this book.

than for chewing food. Also the sucking tubes are very differently made up, and of different parts.

The **wings** are of such importance that many of the names of the Orders of insects are Greek words descriptive of their wings. The Greek word for a wing (*πτέρον*) appears at the end of all such names. Thus the Butterflies and Moths are called *Lepidoptera*, which means 'Scale-wings'.

The most primitive of insects are completely wingless. None of their ancestors are believed ever to have had wings and no insect closely related to them is winged. These primitive wingless insects form the Orders which are grouped together as *APTERYGOTA*. This situation is, however, complicated by the fact that there are a large number of other wingless insects. These are of two different kinds. Firstly, there are among the 'small' insects one or two groups which are not primitive, but are, on the contrary, highly specialized, usually for life as parasites upon highly developed and comparatively recent animals. Each of these groups is in other ways like some large group of winged insects, and they are believed to be descended from winged ancestors, and to have lost their wings owing to their parasitical life. In the words of a great thinker, 'The bed-bug has no wings at all, but he gets there just the same'. As all these creatures are 'small' we have really no concern with them here and can avoid the difficulty which their classification has created. Only two such groups are mentioned and that because of the annoyance they cause to man, the Fleas and the Lice. Secondly, there are wingless insects which are not only not primitive but are evidently closely related to some winged insects. Almost every Order of winged insects contains some members which are without wings. Sometimes only one sex (usually, but not always, the female) is wingless, sometimes both. It is necessary to mention these facts to make it clear that the Orders of the *APTERYGOTA* do not contain anything like all the adult wingless insects, and of course the young of all insects are without wings.

When we turn to the winged insects, which form the great majority, we find great variety in the wing-structure. Most insects have two pairs of wings. In only one of the great Orders (the *DIPTERA*, or True Flies) is there only one pair, the fore wings. The hind wings have been reduced to a minute pair of stalks ending in knobs, called 'balancers'.

Usually all the four wings are transparent and membranous, but sometimes the foremost pair are thickened into extremely hard cases which close over the hind wings when at rest. This is the mark of the Beetles or *COLEOPTERA*, and their cases (*elytra*) do not beat to propel the insect in flight, but remain open like the wings of an aeroplane and serve much the same purpose, acting as gliders, while the power is given by the beating of the hind wings. Other insects have the fore wings more leathery and thicker than the hind, so that, when laid along the back at rest, they protect and cover the more delicate hind wings. Such are those of the *ORTHOPTERA* (Grasshoppers, &c.) and *DERMAPTERA* (Earwigs), and of some of the *HEMIPTERA* (Bugs). All the wings of the *LEPIDOPTERA* (Butterflies and Moths), as well as their bodies, are covered with tiny flattened scales filled with coloured pigments, which give these creatures their beauty. One further group is labelled with a name which does little to help us. This is the Order of *HYMENOPTERA*, or Membrane-wings (the Ants, Bees, Wasps, &c.). So far as their wings go, the mark of this Order is that the hind wings are smaller than the fore, and all the wings have comparatively few veins.

So far we have Orders the classification of which raises little difficulty. Most recent authors are agreed upon the names of the *HYMENOPTERA*, *DIPTERA*, *COLEOPTERA*, *LEPIDOPTERA*, *HEMIPTERA*, *ORTHOPTERA*, *DERMAPTERA*, and the group of *APTERYGOTA*, and, in substance, upon what insects belong to them. When these are set aside, we are left with a large number of much smaller groups. All these were thrown together by Linnaeus under the name of *NEUROPTERA*, or Veined-wings.[1] The name is not very satisfactory. All insects' wings have veins, and not

[1] Linnaeus even included the *ORTHOPTERA* and *DERMAPTERA* in his Order *NEUROPTERA*.

all these remaining insects have the wings covered with a particularly rich network of veins. A more serious trouble is that there are the greatest differences between the creatures thus classified. This Linnaean Order of *NEUROPTERA* was really only a scrap-heap for the insects rejected from the other Orders. So evident is this that recent writers have broken it up by removing from it one group after another of the insects which it contained. As a result of this process we have five additional Orders of British insects containing 'large' species. These are the *TRICHOPTERA* (Caddis Flies), *MECOPTERA* (Scorpion Flies), *ODONATA* (Dragonflies), *EPHEMEROPTERA* (Mayflies), and *PLECOPTERA* (Stone Flies), in addition to the reduced Order of *NEUROPTERA*, in which remain only the Lacewings, Alder Flies, and Snake Flies. Already the surviving rump of the *NEUROPTERA* shows signs of being subdivided in the near future, but here it will be retained as above described.

This gives us the following classification of our 'large' insects. The wings are four in number and transparent unless otherwise stated. The various groups are subdivided on the pages here cited.

CLASSIFICATION

WINGED INSECTS, WITH PUPAE and the usual three changes:

HYMENOPTERA = Ants, Bees, Wasps, &c.
Chewing and sucking mouths. P. 68.

DIPTERA = Flies. Only 2 wings. Sucking mouths. P. 118.

COLEOPTERA = Beetles.
Fore wings are hard cases. Chewing mouths. P. 150.

LEPIDOPTERA = Butterflies and Moths.
Scaly wings. Sucking mouths. P. 188.

TRICHOPTERA = Caddis Flies.
Hairy wings. Licking or useless mouths.*

MECOPTERA = Scorpion Flies.
Beak-shaped heads. Few wing-veins.*

NEUROPTERA = Alder Flies, Lacewings, and Snake Flies.
Many veins.*

WINGED INSECTS, WITHOUT PUPAE:

ODONATA = Dragonflies.
Chewing mouths. Two changes.*

EPHEMEROPTERA = Mayflies.
Useless mouths. Three changes.*

PLECOPTERA = Stone Flies.
Useless mouths. Two changes.*

HEMIPTERA = Bugs. Sucking mouths. Fore wings often half hardened. Change gradual. P. 274.

ORTHOPTERA = Grasshoppers, Crickets, and Cockroaches. Chewing mouths. Fore wings leathery. Change gradual. P. 285.

DERMAPTERA = Earwigs. Chewing mouths. Fore wings are hard cases and hind wings partly leathery. Change gradual. P. 298.

WINGLESS INSECTS:

APTERYGOTA. Chewing mouths. Slight change. P. 300.

* The six Orders marked with an asterisk were formerly classed as 'Neuroptera'. For the subdivision of these see p. 236.

ORDER *HYMENOPTERA* [Membrane-wings]

ANTS, BEES, WASPS, ETC.

CHARACTERS. The usual three changes, each individual passing through the four stages of egg, larva (or maggot), pupa, and adult. Two pairs of wings, never very large, somewhat sparsely veined, transparent and scaleless, the fore pair being the larger. The head is borne upon a narrow neck, which, however, is sometimes so short, or so drawn back, as not to be seen. The mouth-parts are adapted for biting or for lapping or sucking liquids and, in many species, the main jaws (*mandibles*), which are always well developed, are used for work rather than for feeding. They have usually a waist (often very narrow and thread-like) between the thorax and the abdomen. One family (the Ants) has more than one waist. Some few have no waist at all, the thorax and abdomen being of the same width and directly united. All the females, except some of the Ants, have ovipositors which are often modified for piercing, sawing, or stinging. Alone of our insects, some of this Order (of four distinct families) are social insects. All of these have, as well as the usual two sexes, a caste of sterile female 'workers'.

The larvae are usually legless maggots with only the head well developed.

The pupae are mostly enclosed in a cocoon with the limbs of the future adult free from the body.

ANATOMY. Hymenopterous **larvae** are all tubular in shape and consist of a head and ten or eleven segments. Except for the most primitive types, they are legless maggots only capable of taking food fed to or surrounding them. They have neither eyes nor antennae. The larvae of the three primitive families here treated (the Saw-flies, Horntails, and Stem Saw-flies) are all vegetable eaters and are able to find their food and eat it. They have some legs, eyes, antennae, and hard heads with powerful jaws. Alone in the Order the Saw-flies have larvae which live out in the open, are coloured, and have, as well as the true legs, a number of fleshy prominences along the abdomen, which are called 'false legs'.

The **pupae** are enclosed in a cocoon, which is usually merely a slight silken structure, though some Saw-flies build a tough earthy or parchment-like case enclosing it. The pupae themselves have the limbs and appendages of the adult 'free', that is, separate from the body and surrounded with a thin transparent skin.

The following sketches give examples of the two types of larva, those of the Hive Bees (left), and the Saw-flies (right):

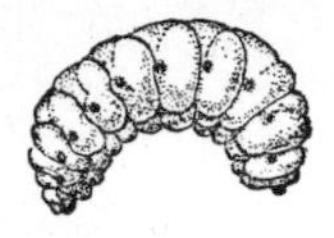

The **adults** have the head free from the thorax upon a narrow neck. The neck is sometimes short and not visible, but allows full mobility to the head. They have compound eyes and, between them, usually three simple eyes (*ocelli*). The eyes of the males are often larger than those of the females. The length and form of the antennae differ much. The mouth-parts are characterized by the persistence of the main jaws (*mandibles*) as powerful biters, even when they are not used for feeding and when the insect feeds wholly by suction. The jaws then serve other uses, enabling the insect to bite its way to freedom after pupation, to build its nest, or to collect materials. The lower mouth-parts are adapted for sucking either animal or vegetable juices by the development of the lower lip (*labium*) into a tube, usually called the tongue. The lower jaws (*maxillae*) only form a short covering sheath. In this the Hymenoptera differ from the Lepidoptera whose sucking tubes are made of the lower jaws alone. Some of the Bees have 'tongues' of great length which enable them to reach the nectaries of the deeper blossoms.

The various parts of the thorax are distinguishable, but usually firmly joined to each other. In the most primitive family of the Order, the Stem Saw-flies (Cephidae), the first segment is loosely articulated with the second, so that it is mobile. A marked character of most of the Hymenoptera is the fact that during and after the pupal stage the 1st segment of the abdomen is fused with the thorax, forming a 4th thoracic ring. When there is a waist it is therefore not strictly speaking between the thorax and the abdomen, but after the 1st abdominal segment, between it and the 2nd.

The two pairs of wings are always present in both sexes among the 'large' species, except in one family (Mutillidae, q.v.) where the females are wingless. In the Ants, however, the worker class are wingless and the females shed their wings immediately after their only flight. The wings are transparent (some slightly clouded) and the veins few in number in comparison with those of most insects. There is a beautiful system of tiny hooks on the top edge of the smaller hind wing which grip a fold along the lower edge of the fore wing and thus make the two into a single wing in action. Many of the 'small' species are wingless. These interlocking hooks are found in all the 'large' Hymenoptera.

The legs of the Bee group are often equipped with special devices for carrying pollen, and the large group of Ichneumons have an extra joint in their legs caused by the thigh-joint or segment (*trochanter*) between the hip (*coxa*) and the thigh (*femur*) being divided into two. The usual five joints of the foot (*tarsi*) are sometimes reduced in number, but there is always a pad between the claws.

The number of abdominal segments which show varies much, and all the Hymenoptera, except some Ants, have an organ at the end of the abdomen which serves either to lay the eggs (*ovipositor*) or else as a sting. When, as in the Bees and Wasps, this organ is purely a sting, the eggs are laid from beneath its root and it is connected with poison glands so that it inflicts a more or less painful wound. People who have allowed themselves to be stung in the interest of science say that the stings of the social insects alone are seriously distressing, and those of the Hive Bees and of the Hornet and other true Wasps are far the worst. Those of the solitary Wasps are used to kill or paralyse the prey which they provide for their young. In structure these stings are hard to tell from the same organ when used as an egg layer by other members of the Order, and these also often have a poison bag. Some of these ovipositors, like those of the Wood Wasp and of the Ichneumon which victimizes it, are very long and strong enough to pierce hard wood. In the Saw-flies it takes the form of the saw from which they get their name and is used to cut slits into which the eggs are laid.

LIFE HISTORY. Most Hymenopterous larvae are unable to seek food for themselves. They must either be fed by their mother or worker sisters, as are all the social insects; or they must be provided by the mother with a supply of food which suffices for their whole larval life. This is the case of all the solitary Bees and Wasps. In a few cases among the Digger Wasps the mother renews supplies during the life of the larvae. The Ichneumons are hatched either in or on living victims and grow by devouring them. The Ants and social Wasps, in return for the food given to the grubs, receive the satisfaction of licking some liquid from them in the form of saliva or other exudation. Their sisterly affection is thus not wholly unselfish.

The larvae of the more primitive types—those of which the adults have no waists—are more active and can feed themselves, either by gnawing their way through wood, or else by eating leaves or stems of plants.

Sometimes when the adults emerge from the pupae they are able to free themselves by the use of their own jaws, and, in the case of the Horntails, this means chewing a passage through solid wood. The social insects cannot even open their delicate cocoons and have to be liberated by the mother or their worker sisters.

The adults of this Order contain species which are noted for the large development of their brains and their astonishing instincts. Among the Hymenoptera alone (for we have no Termites or White Ants in this country) there are social insects (Ants, Bees, and Wasps) which alone produce sterile females or 'workers' (☿), which are incapable of reproducing the species, but are specially equipped to do the work of the community.

Throughout the Hymenoptera the males are short-lived and exist only for the purpose of fertilizing the females, after which they die.

The solitary Hymenoptera, which make up the vast majority of species composing the Order, live wholly for themselves and their families, without help or collaboration from others. The males do nothing towards helping the females to provide for the young. The females work hard throughout the summer, laying their eggs where the larvae will be able to get at food, or providing that food for them. Many of the details of the various ways in which this is done will appear later, but some idea of their variety may be here suggested by a few examples.

Most of the solitary Bees build separate cells for each egg and fill these cells with pollen and honey. This done, they die without ever seeing their young. Most of the solitary Wasps do the same, but they provision the cells with paralysed insects sufficient to last through the larval life. They also die without seeing their young. Some few of the solitary Wasps renew the provisions of insects during the larval life of the young and thus form exceptions to the general rule that the solitary Hymenoptera never see their young. The Ichneumons pursue other insects and lay their eggs in or on their bodies, thus providing the larvae with food and lodging. They also die without seeing their young. The Saw-flies and Horntails lay their eggs in plants upon which the larvae feed, and, like the rest, die without seeing them.

The Hymenoptera are remarkable for the number of species

which resort to various forms of parasitism. There are the Ichneumons which lay in, or on, the bodies of other insects. Their larvae live throughout the larval life upon those bodies. These are far the most numerous of the entire Order. Then there are many solitary Bees and Wasps which, instead of providing food for their own young, lay in the cells of other Hymenoptera and thus get them nourished at the expense of those others. These are called Cuckoo Bees or Cuckoo Wasps.

CLASSIFICATION. The main distinction is between those which have waists (*Petiolata*) and those which have none (*Sessiliventres*). The former include all the most highly developed members of the Order and are divided into the Ants, which have two or more waists, the Bees, which have pollen-collecting feathery hairs, the Wasps, which have no feathery hairs, and the Ichneumons and 'small' parasites. Except the Ichneumons and other parasites, all the above have poisonous stings. The Ichneumons, as already stated, are the most numerous group containing 'large' species in the Order. They have ovipositors and are also distinguished by having two joints instead of one in the joint between the hip and the thigh (*trochanter*). Two other groups, the *Cynipoidea* (Gall Wasps) and *Chalcidoidea* (Chalcid Flies), are very numerous, but consist wholly of 'small' insects.

The waistless Hymenoptera have also ovipositors, which they use only for the purpose of egg laying, they have single thigh-joints, and their larvae are plant-eaters. Except for a few of these, almost all the adult Hymenoptera are vegetarian feeders, feeding themselves (as distinct from their larvae) on the nectar gathered from flowers.

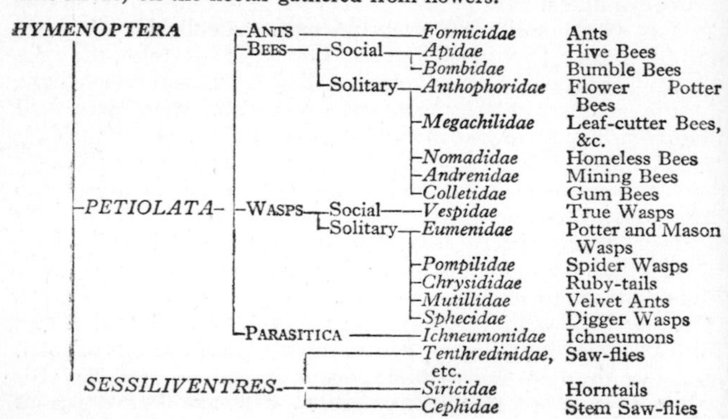

FAMILY *FORMICIDAE* ANTS

Thirty-six British species, all of which are 'small'

Although these insects are all 'small', they are included here for two reasons. In the first place they are in many ways the most highly developed of all the insects—models held up to mankind by the wisest of men. Secondly, although the individual ant is small, it forms an inseparable part of a community (the nest) which is exceedingly large.

CHARACTERS. Social insects, having two or more 'waists'. They have elbowed antennae and, always, in addition to the males and females (which differ in form), a third form, known as 'workers'. The workers (indicated by the sign of the planet Saturn—☿) may themselves differ in form according to their functions, so that there may be more than three forms of a single species.

ANATOMY. The **eggs** are minute and the **larvae** which hatch from them are quite incapable of maintaining their own life without the constant attention of the adult ants. The only food they can take is that which is pumped into their mouths from the crops of the adults. If, as is the case with several species, the larvae form cocoons in which to pupate, it usually happens that the emerging ants are incapable of biting their way out of the cocoons, so that the adults have to open the cocoons to free them.

The **adult ants** differ from all other insects in having at least one enlargement (or *scale*) in the narrow waist-like part (or *petiole*) of the body. This produces two waists, one before and one behind the scale, and gives great mobility to the hinder part of the abdomen. Sometimes there are two such enlargements and therefore three waists, and the sub-families, of which we have three, are classified according to the diversity of this character.

The mouth-parts of ants are unusual in the separation between the functions of the main jaws (*mandibles*) and those of the rest of the mouth. In most insects the mandibles spring from between the upper lip (*labrum*) and the lower (*labium*) in such a way that when the jaws are used the mouth is necessarily open. Such is not the case with the ants. Their lower lips can be closed over the upper, completely shutting the mouth, and yet leaving the jaws free, at each side, to open or close without interfering with the mouth. The result of this is that ants' jaws are not mere eating tools, but can be used much as we use our hands, independently of the mouth.

Their heads are also remarkable for the relatively large size of the brain, which greatly exceeds all other nerve-ganglia throughout the body. Their wings, which are usually lacking altogether in the workers, and which are present in the male and female, are much like those of the other Hymenoptera. Their legs are remarkable for a device combining brush and comb at the junction between the shin and foot of the fore legs. In the abdomen are at least three notable organs. Some ants have stings (♀ and ☿) together with a gland which makes poison to be injected by them. In others the poison is there, but the sting is replaced by a squirt with which it is discharged towards the enemy. Almost all the British ants are of this type. All ants have two stomachs, the first of which is the 'crop', the second the stomach proper. Between them is a valve which, if opened, allows some of the food in the crop to pass to the stomach and be digested for the benefit of the ant itself. The contents of the crop, however, belong not only to the ant but to the State—to the nest—and must be administered for its good, pumped up for the needs of the queens, of the young, or of the hungry.

Queen ants, the fully sexed females (♀), have an organ (called the *receptaculum seminis*) in which are stored all the sperms of the male, passed to her in the single act of pairing, and over which she has a valve control which enables her to fertilize her eggs for the rest of her life.

Generally speaking, the males and the females are of about the same size while the workers vary greatly in size, though they are usually smaller than the males or females. The workers, in addition to being always without wings, have much larger heads and much smaller eyes. The males, always winged, have smaller heads, but much larger eyes, than those of the queens. The queens, winged until after their single flight and then wingless, have eyes larger than those of the workers, but smaller than those of the males. Some of the forms taken by our largest ant—***Formica rufa***[red Ant], the Wood Ant (*p. 13*)—are here shown.

This is the species which is perhaps the most conspicuous in those places where it is found, because it often builds in pine woods and a considerable part of its nest consists of the large mound, or dome, built of pine-needles, which forms its upper part.

LIFE HISTORY. Here, at what is in many ways the highest point reached by insect life, we come across the social community. All the ants live together, in more or less large numbers, in nests. The inhabitants of the nest are mutually dependent members of a State, and the State, or nest, may last for ever. The building of the home is the result of the common labour of certain of its inhabitants, and each of the individual ants does its allotted part of the duties which must be performed to enable the nest to survive. Only when we ask ourselves who does the allotting—who is the leader?—do we find ourselves taking cover behind the word 'instinct'. It is true that we have grown used to speaking of the mothers of the nest as 'queens', but there is nothing to suggest that they exercise any government.

Before mentioning any of the details of the lives of ants it is advisable to take a general view of the founding and operation of a new nest.

Some heavy, hot, midsummer day, a winged female ant leaves the old nest and, for the first and last time, takes to the air in flight. She is not alone. All the other maiden queens of the nest have risen with her, and also all those of neighbouring communities. At the same time all the males have taken flight. This cloud of flying ants is known as the 'nuptial flight'. It is believed that it is organized and directed by the wingless workers, who prevent any premature flights by either males or females, and finally drive them all out of the nest when the appointed zero hour arrives.

The pairing of the sexes takes place either in the air during the flight or else immediately afterwards on landing. In any case, it seems that to have flown is essential to mating. The flight may be ever so short. The female may only rise a few feet into the air and come back at once to the nest from which she started. In this case she will always be hospitably received and join the breeding-staff of her old home. On the other hand, the flight may be a long one and she may meet her mate when already far away from home. These flights (as the numbers of the two sexes in any nest at a given moment are rarely equal) give an opportunity of introducing new blood. The structure of the queen ant above mentioned enables her to take, at this one union, all the fertilizing sperms of the male, to store them in the special reserve store in her body, and to release them, one by one, for the fertilization of her eggs as she lays them during the rest of her life. Thus, when she has once flown and met her mate, she can abjure the other sex for life and yet, in cloistral seclusion, become the mother of many thousands. The male, having shot his bolt, dies.

The first act of the expectant mother is to get rid of her once-used wings. They (like her husband) have served their purpose and would be a mere encumbrance, and she can shed them the more readily, rubbing and twisting them off, owing to a hinge-like weakness at their bases. Her next move is to find a place where she can bring up her brood. If she finds her way back home, she has no further problem. Her working sisters will look after her. The same is true if she gets to any other nest of her own species. There, where a worker or a male from a 'foreign' nest would be instantly driven off or killed, she will be welcomed and cared for for the rest of her life. Neither of these courses leads to the foundation of a new nest. For that she must find a suitable hole in the ground, or make one, and then enlarge it into a small chamber where she can remain in seclusion until her eggs are matured. These she lays around her and watches until the larvae hatch, and these larvae she feeds with liquid from her own mouth until they pupate. All this time, perhaps several months, since she left the nest she has taken no food, but is both living, and feeding her young, off her own fat. These pupae (erroneously called 'ants' eggs' and sold for feeding pheasants) she will, at the proper time, tear open so that the ants may be able to emerge. All these first larvae will be of the third sex, the incomplete females called 'workers'. In this way she will have brought up adult young and founded a nest of her own.

From this moment the life of the queen is completely changed. Instead of an independent insect building a home and feeding an increasing brood from her own body, she becomes a mere specialist, turning food, brought and pumped into her by her worker-daughters, into a steady stream of eggs, laid at the rate of one every ten minutes, for the rest of her life, which may last six or seven years. Indeed, there is a case on record of a queen living over sixteen years.

Her worker-daughters now take complete control of the entire business of feeding, housing, nursing, and defending her, the eggs, and themselves—in short the nest. They forage outside the nest for food for the queen, for the larvae, for themselves, and for those of their own number who are employed upon other than foraging duties. They pass the food from mouth to mouth, as the hungry beg of the replete, and thus ensure equality of rations. Other workers are detailed to build the nest, or to repair it if it is injured. The form of building used varies in different species. Generally speaking it may be by digging in soil or sand—miner's or mason's work—or building with sticks, pine-needles, or leaves—carpenter's work. Again, it may be a combination of the two and it may need mortar provided from glands opening in the ants' jaws. However the work is done, it is done by the workers, and those that do it are fed from the mouths of those of their sisters who bring in food from without. Other workers feed the queen, and others again carry the endless stream of her eggs to the special chambers built for them, where they will have the required warmth and dampness. When the maggot is hatched it is they, its sterile sisters, cousins, or aunts, who feed it from their mouths. They move the larvae from one chamber to another as cold and hot, dry and wet, days succeed each other, so that they may have exactly the right temperature and atmosphere. After the larvae have pupated they open the pupae at the right time for those larvae which could not do this for themselves and would die if this duty were neglected. For the proper 'air-conditioning' of the nest, quite apart from its defence, a staff of porters has to be set at the doors, which must be closed at night, or in rain or severe cold, opened in hot weather and, normally, by day. In the winter the nest must go deeper underground, and some species even keep two different nests, one for the winter and the other for the summer.

The above is a brief account of the founding of a new nest and of its development into a young self-supporting community. Once the nest is in full swing as a going concern, its permanence must be assured by the production of males and females. As the summer approaches the eggs taken from the queen begin to produce winged ants—males and females—and these will all be sent forth on a wedding flight like that of their parents, the males to die, the females to shed their wings and to renounce the world, returning to the old nest, or finding hospitality in another, or founding new nests of their own.

The problem of who, or what, decides between the sexes to be born from the eggs, and how the decision is made effective, is still nowhere near solution. We have to be content with guesses. Is it the nature of the food given to the maggot? Or of the food given to the queen? Can the queen fertilize her eggs at will (making females)? Or not fertilize them (producing males)? Can the workers ensure the birth of such sexes as they wish? Possibly, but who or what issues the orders? Does the ever-fertile mother add to her remarkable sexual attainments those of a national leader? As well as turning food into eggs, does she turn information into orders? Does she from her bed issue directions to the whole nest? And, if so, how does she keep informed, and in perfect harmony with her fellow mothers? (For, remember, there is not one queen. In any but a small nest there may be many.) Let us say at once 'We do not know'.

Between the queens in an ants' nest there is no sign of jealousy. The arrival of a newly fertilized queen is regarded by all as a welcome addition to the staff of the breeding department, and nothing more.

There are several other sides of ant life which must be mentioned even in so brief an account as this.

LONGEVITY. The nest is without a period of life. Theoretically it might go on for ever. Nests have been known to exist for over eighty years. The larger the nest the more likely it is to gather in new queens and thus secure perpetuity. This power of self-enlargement by the nest is fostered by the habit of creating satellite nests. When the population grows too big for a home which can no longer be enlarged with ease, a migration takes place. (Again, ordered by whom?) Out march all the surplus population, with one or more queens, and establish themselves in a new site where they set to at once to build a nest. If the new nest is near enough to the old for their ants to remain in constant touch with each other the new colony will become a mere satellite town and citizenship will be enjoyed in common between the two. The colony becomes really a mere enlargement of the original nest and shares its fortunes. If, however, the migration goes farther, so that the new nest, when established, is out of touch with the mother country, its ants will very soon become 'foreigners', they will lose the community smell by which friends are recognized, and (as between the fiercer species) will become enemies to be repelled and killed. The antennae are the organs through which friend and foe are known.

The individual ant may live as long as sixteen years or more and therefore has opportunities of learning, and teaching its successors, which are denied to most insects. It is, however, not easy to attribute any particular result to this opportunity.

GUESTS, ETC. One remarkable fact about ants' nests is that there are usually other creatures besides ants to be found in them, and these not merely as casual interlopers but as permanent residents. As many as 300 species have been found living in the nests of our thirty-six British species of ants. Some of these are minute parasites, living on, or in, the ants. Others are mere hated intruders who for some reason are able to retain their place in the nest. These are mainly Staphylinid beetles (see p. 162) and some of them are useful scavengers. Others again, the greater number, are tolerated in the nest. They include beetles, fly larvae, spring-tails, and others. Lastly (a smaller number) come those which are true guests, being welcomed, and even sometimes carried, into the nest, by the ants. As to these see the story of the Lycaenid butterfly *Maculinea arion*, on p. 198. Most of these welcome guests pay for their keep by exuding a sweet liquid which it is the ants' delight to lick from their backs, and to this indulgence is due the impoverishment, and final death, of many ants' nests. The guest (usually a beetle) takes payment for his tipple, not only in lodging but also in board, eating the larvae of his hosts. There is an odd interplay of motives and results in this business. The ant feeds the beetle (e.g. a small Staphylinid of the genus *Lomechusa*) from her own mouth and treats it as one of the family. So much so that she takes its eggs and gives them and the beetle-grubs the same care and attention as is given to the young of the nest. When they have pupated, and at the proper time for an ant's pupal case to be opened, the ants kindly open the pupae of the beetle. This kills the beetles, so that it is only those pupae which are negligently forgotten which become beetles. Meanwhile the beetle grubs eat the ants' larvae and thereby reduce the working staff of the nest so much that more and more beetle pupae are neglected, and therefore hatched alive. The whole story would serve as a text for a temperance reformer.

It is remarkable that where a migration occurs the guests and other lodgers are to be seen as a procession of camp-followers accompanying the ants on their march.

Various species of ants may be found in the same nest. These may be simply cases of two kinds of ant, quite apart, in the same nest. Thus a small species may build its tunnels and chambers in the walls separating the much wider passages of a larger species. Such is the case of nests dwelt in in common by *Formica fusca* [dark Ant] or the Negro Ant and the tiny *Solenopsis fugax* [fleeing Furrow-face]. These two seem to fight fiercely if ever they meet.

There are other cases of living together in which one species is said to be the slave of the other. One kind of ant feels its talents to lie in the field of battle rather than in the arts of peace. In some foreign species so much is this the case that there are ants which cannot feed themselves or build a nest. We have no such extreme examples of totalitarianism here, but we have one species (*Formica sanguinea*, the Blood-red Ant) which, though it can live a normal and peaceful life, greatly prefers to fight. This career it attains by stealing the worker pupae of another kind of ant (*Formica fusca* above mentioned) and then, when they grow up, letting them do all the housework and foraging for the nest, while they, the *sanguineae*, mobilize their strength twice or thrice a year and issue forth to repeat their slave-raids. The queens of their race remain at home laying eggs of the undefiled Blood-red breed to be brought up by the slave Negroes. There is another type of nest inhabited by two kinds of ant in common. In this case an expectant mother belongs to a race which cannot or, more often, prefers not to look after her own family. She may then start a new nest by a single-jawed attack upon a nest of a smaller 'slave' species and the capture of pupae to serve her, the 'slave' queen having been killed in the fight. Or she may join company with a 'slave' queen and found a nest jointly with her. In this case the partner queen will probably be short lived.

FOOD. The most primitive members of the family appear to be wholly carnivorous, but all the British ants are mainly vegetarian. They do not disdain the blood of another insect, but their main resources are the nectar from flowers, the juices of seeds, fruit, fungi, and, above all, the honey-dew exuded from the bodies of Green-fly or Aphids. These Aphids the ants cherish and protect from enemies, filling their own crops with the honey-dew milked from them, while sentries are posted to defend from all invaders the aphid-cattle which belong to the nest. The various nests (e.g. of *Formica rufa*) have defined territories with their own paths leading to such trees or shrubs as form their pastures. Sometimes a large tree may be divided between two nests and each will jealously defend its own side. In this country the food carried back to the nest is wholly in liquid form in the forager's crop. If an ant is seen to take a grain of corn to the nest it is not as a provision against night-starvation in the winter, but as a convenient cornerstone with which to build.

GROUP *APOIDEA*

THE BEE GROUP

The following six families make up the Bees, social and solitary, and are distinguished from all the other Hymenoptera by the following characters:

Every bee as an adult feeds upon the nectar of flowers, and its young, in the larval stage, are fed upon the pollen of flowers mixed with honey, the latter being a substance made in the body of the bee out of the nectar gathered from the blooms. To this rule there is no exception, but it must be noted that, in the case of certain species, known as cuckoo-bees, the larvae, before beginning to eat the stored honey, devour the egg or larva of another species of bee in whose nest they have been placed.

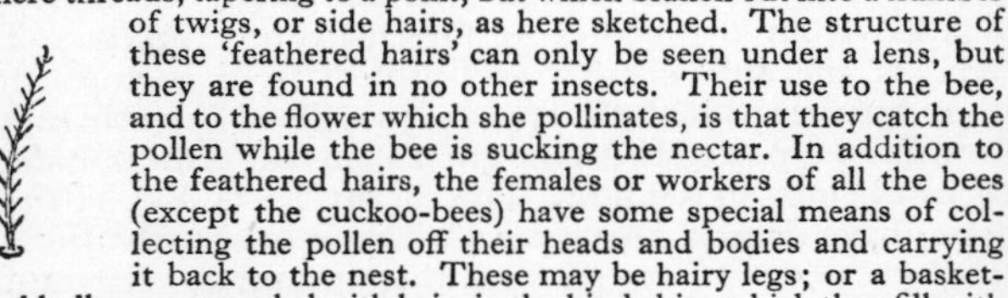

Every bee has, upon its head or thorax, a number of hairs which are not mere threads, tapering to a point, but which branch out into a number of twigs, or side hairs, as here sketched. The structure of these 'feathered hairs' can only be seen under a lens, but they are found in no other insects. Their use to the bee, and to the flower which she pollinates, is that they catch the pollen while the bee is sucking the nectar. In addition to the feathered hairs, the females or workers of all the bees (except the cuckoo-bees) have some special means of collecting the pollen off their heads and bodies and carrying it back to the nest. These may be hairy legs; or a basket-shaped hollow surrounded with hairs in the hind shins which they fill with pollen moistened with honey at their mouths to make it sticky; or again there may be a brush of long hairs under the belly.

No bee folds its wings in any way, thus differing from the wasps.

No bee is wingless, or has more than one waist, thus differing from the ants.

Most of the bees have long, sometimes very long, 'tongues' (see that of *Apis* here sketched). These enable them to reach the nectaries of deep-cupped flowers and to suck the nectar from them. The tongues are made out of the parts of the lower lip (*labium*) and protected by sheaths made of the lower jaws (*maxillae*), and the word 'tongue' is objected to by the anatomists, but it is convenient and must serve here.

One British species, which is 'large'

This species, ***Apis mellifera*** [honey-bearing Bee] (*p. 13*), is rarely found wild, and, when it is, has doubtless escaped in a swarm which the owner has failed to follow. It is the only domesticated insect kept by man in this country.

CHARACTERS. Social insects, forming permanent communities. They have a marked waist and the hairs upon the head and thorax are not

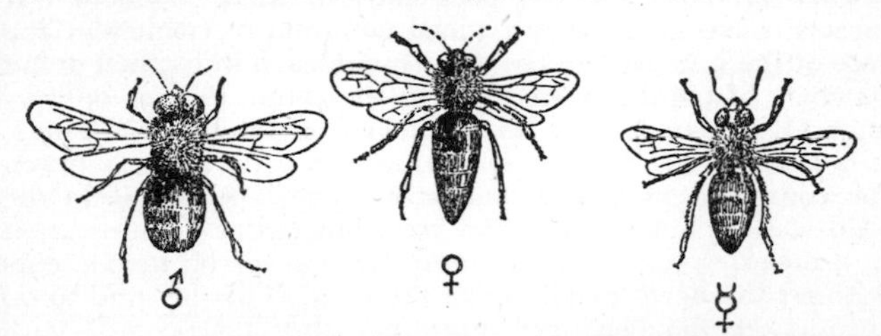

simple threads, but branch out into feathery projections as described on p. 82. This is of value to the insect in collecting pollen from flowers, and although it is too small to be seen by the naked eye, it is the mark of all bees and distinguishes them from the wasps or other Hymenoptera. The Honey Bees have males (drones), females (queens), and sterile females (workers), and there is more difference between them than is found in any other bee.

The eggs are male or female, but the distinction between the queens and the workers is caused by the different food accorded to the larvae. For the first four days after hatching all the brood are fed alike, but those destined to be queens are given the richer 'royal food' throughout their growth and are provided with cells which are larger and better ventilated.

The drones are large, stingless, and big-eyed. The queen, as recorded in the case of the ants, takes from the male, when paired, all his store of sperms and retains these in a special receptacle in her body for use in fertilizing her eggs for the rest of her life, which may last for three or four years. We believe that the female eggs (which produce queens or workers) are fertilized with male sperms, while the eggs producing males are not, and that the duly mated queen can fertilize the egg she is about to lay or abstain from so doing. The power of laying female eggs is lost by ageing queens, if this store of sperms becomes exhausted. But they, and even unmated females, can produce drones.

The workers are much smaller and have larger brains. They alone have basket-shaped hind thighs for gathering pollen, and honey-making and wax-secreting organs. The egg-laying organ (*ovipositor*) is absent in the drone and is used by the queen for laying her eggs and as a sting only when she kills a rival queen. In the workers it is developed and used as a sting, a weapon connected with a poison sac. It is so shaped that after use it can only be withdrawn if the bee carefully cork-screws it out. If the bee is hastily shaken off, the sting and other organs are torn from her and she dies. A keen bee-man may be recognized by his patiently waiting for the bee to extricate her sting!

LIFE HISTORY. These bees and the ants, alone of our insects, have a permanent social community (which in the case of the bees we call the 'hive') with each individual doing its share of the duties involved in the community's continuance. Before giving the briefest review of the life of the hive, it is perhaps helpful to record the main differences between the communities of bees and ants. The bees' home in the wild state is built in a hollow tree, but under domestication in a hive designed by man to enable him to rob its contents without the need for killing all the bees. This he used to do throughout the ages until quite recently. The 'comb', with which the hive is furnished, is built of wax prepared in the bodies of the worker-bees, and has an architectural symmetry to which nothing in the ants' nest is comparable. Each young bee is reared from the egg to the adult stage in its own separate hexagonal tubular cell: the young ants are moved from communal ward to communal ward. Except for very brief periods, there is only one queen-bee in a hive at a time. The hive is stored with garnered foods: the ants' nest (of British ants at least) contains no stored food. Lastly, the bees fly out to gather food: the ants have to walk.

The founding of a new hive is, briefly, as follows. In this case, as in that of the ants, we know nothing of the government of the community. We are reduced to the use of impersonal phrases—'it is felt', 'it is decided', 'it is ordered', 'duties are allotted'. By whom we do not know.

Some time about the month of May it is felt that the hive is becoming overcrowded and that a new queen will be needed. Queen-cells, much larger than those built as nurseries for the worker-bees or drones, are built. These are few in number, perhaps half a dozen. The queen is led round them by her attendant workers and, after looking in (as she does in the case of every cell), she turns round and lays an egg in each. These cells are, throughout the life of the larva, victualled with the special food (royal jelly). In about sixteen days the first of the bees developed in them will emerge from her cell, a maiden queen, or princess. Usually before the princess has emerged, her mother—the old queen—will have left the hive and flown off, accompanied by a 'swarm' consisting of perhaps 30,000 bees, or almost a half of the number in the hive, those which are surplus to the needs of the hive. They will be mainly workers, though drones will be among them.

Wherever the queen alights, she will be wrapped in a protecting clot of bees as big as a football and, if the beekeeper is lucky, or his neighbours honest, he will collect them in a 'skep' and bring them home to a new man-made hive prepared for their reception.

There, on arrival, the workers will set about the business of building comb, plucking the flakes of wax from between the segments of their bellies, moulding it in their jaws, and building the exact cells which are the admiration of mankind. There will be the standard-sized cells, of which those in the centre are to serve as nursery cells for the young workers, and those around them as storage cells for honey and pollen. There will be larger cells for drones, and, when needed, the still larger royal cells for future queens. As soon as cells are ready, the queen will be led to them to begin afresh, in the new hive, her routine of egg laying, which, with brief intervals for rest, and for taking food from the tongues of her attendants, forms her life work. Her output is strictly regulated by her attendants and can be increased or diminished by the amount of food given her. In winter she does not lay and feeds herself at the storage cells.

The swarming workers take, in their crops, from the old hive a few days' rations of honey from which the wax for the new hive will be made and life supported, but new stores must be gathered at once and put into the new comb as it is built. No substitute for pollen and honey will support the larvae of the brood, though old bees may be kept alive on sugar and water. Each cell containing a larva must be victualled by the workers, and the nature of the food is varied as the larva grows. Before the larva pupates, the workers seal up its cell with a lid of pollen and wax which the emerging bee can eat so as to get out.

Ventilation is of prime importance in the hive, and it is assured by a body of workers (usually youngsters who have not yet flown) steadily fanning with their wings so as to make a current of fresh inflowing air, while another party fans outward to remove the vitiated air. This fanning serves not only to ventilate and cool the hive, but also to evaporate the surplus water from the honey. A staff of guardians are appointed at the entrance to stop intruders, and particularly robbers from other hives. Some intruders which cannot be stung (such as ants) are fanned away from the entrance. The queen and the drones must be fed and cleaned; dead bees must be removed from the hive (outgoing workers carry their bodies and drop them at a distance); repairs of the comb must be effected with a special glue (called *propolis*) which is obtained from resinous buds and twigs and secreted by workers; overloaded foragers must be relieved of their burdens on regaining the hive; and many other tasks undertaken. All these duties are in addition to the collecting of nectar and pollen. Incoming bees report to their fellows the discovery of any rich source of food by a dance of triumph. This is well known to bee-keepers. The smell of the dancing bee tells the others what kind of flower they must seek, and once a bee has found nectar the colour of the flower helps to guide her back to it.

The new hive is a going concern. We must now consider the state of the old hive from which the swarm came. Shortly after the departure of the swarm, the first of the princesses emerges from her cell. She knows her duty. Her first act is to make straight for the cells in which her sister princesses are still in the pupal stage, tear open their cells, and end their careers at once by stinging them to death. Sometimes she will be prevented from doing this by the workers. It may have been decided that a second princess is needed to allow of another swarm, and in that case she will be physically restrained until the second princess has emerged, and then the two will be kept apart until one of them has left the hive. Thus the second swarm will be led by a virgin princess.

In any case where a princess is the only female in the hive, her duty is to mate and return to the hive as a fertile queen. Until she does so, the workers pay her little or no regard. She has no attached attendants and must feed herself at the comb. Further, until she goes forth on her wedding flight, no male shows any interest in her. Before the nuptial flight she must, like every other bee, fly round and about the entrance to learn her way home. This homing instinct is odd. The bee learns the spot where the entrance is, not the look of the hive. If a hive be moved a few yards while bees are out, they will never find their way home again. When the princess has learned her way home, she flies off to get a mate. Then, by the sound of her wings, or by the sight of her purposeful and determined flight, all the drones in the neighbourhood are stirred to excitement and follow. One of them reaches her in the air and they pair. She receives from him all his sperms and in separating tears away part of his body, and he dies. The queen, crowned at last, comes back to the hive, and thereafter will be fed and escorted by a posse of attendants, as she walks untiringly over the brood-comb laying her eggs. She may live for three or four years, and during the summers the only breaks in her routine of fertility will be when she goes out with a swarm.

Her end is an ordered tragedy. When it is noticed that her powers are failing, her escort will ruthlessly crush (not sting) her to death, or, if a daughter-princess has been reared, no effort will be made to keep them apart. In either case there will be what the lawyers call a 'demise of the Crown'.

Once the new queen has begun to lay and no further queens are needed for swarms, when there is a shortage of food in the hive, or when, at the approach of winter, it is realized that no idle mouths are wanted, there comes the yearly tragedy of the drones. Those returning to the hive, hungry after their usual short unhurried flight in the sunlight, are denied admittance, and all drones in the hive are attacked, maimed by the amputation of a wing, and thrown out. The succession is assured. The drones have served their purpose. Those which were out at the time of the massacre, after crawling helplessly about for a day or two, die of cold and starvation. (Sometimes a hive which has lost its queen will keep its drones through the winter.)

The life of a worker bee is not a long one. Those born in the early spring die in summer, while the summer brood (sleeping much in the winter) just lives to rear the new spring brood.

FAMILY *BOMBIDAE* BUMBLE BEES

Twenty-five species, all of which are 'large'

Six of our species belong to the genus *Psithyrus*, which differs in its habits so materially from the other genus (*Bombus*) in the family that it will here be treated separately.

CHARACTERS. Of the genus *Bombus* many of the attributes are those of the Honey Bee (*Apis*) already described. They are social insects, forming communities consisting of one female, numerous sterile workers and, later in the year, a number of males and females. Their communities are, however, not permanent. All their members except the fertilized females die off at the approach of winter. They have the feathery pollen-collecting hairs of all the bees, and their females and workers have hind shins shaped like hollow scoops or baskets, flanked with hairs, in which to collect the pollen and carry it home. The chief difference in appearance between the *Bombi* and the Honey Bees lies in the fact that the former are much fatter and hairier, and that there is less difference between the sexes than in the slimmer insect. One of the commonest is ***Bombus terrestris*** [earth Bumble] (*p. 13*) shown on the opposite page.

LIFE HISTORY. The *Bombi* (of which we have nineteen species) differ much in colour, and even those of the same species are very variable, so that it is far from easy to differentiate between them. They differ in their habits. Some are underground dwellers and some build their nests on the surface. These last are sometimes called 'carder-bees'.

All begin the year in the same way. None but the females survive the winter. They hibernate asleep in some retired place, a mouse-hole or behind the loose bark of a tree. When the first flowers bloom (those of the sallows) the queen bumble bee wakes up and gathers some nectar, and, when there is a true outburst of spring flowers, she sets about the lonely business of founding a family. Diligently and noisily, she seeks for a home. If she belongs to the underground

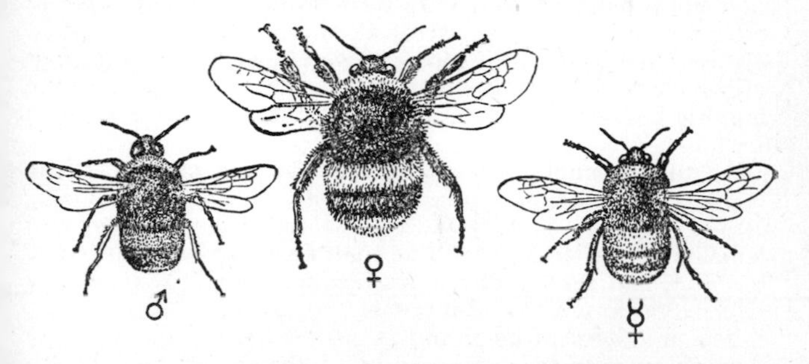

bumbles she must find a hole, for she does not belong to a race who dig their own holes. She has enough other work to do. Like the hive bee, she will, if possible, find a cavity prepared by someone else, the nest of a field mouse or the like. Here, or in ivy or matted grass, if she belongs to the species which nest in the open, she will bring a quantity of stems, blades of grass, or moss which she plaits together into a nest, not unlike that of a small bird.

When she has the nest ready she builds, of wax and pollen, small spherical pots, the size of hazel nuts, into the first of which she lays a dozen eggs and then seals it up. Later, when the larvae have hatched and eaten some of their pollen, she will open the pot and revictual it. Meanwhile she builds similar storage pots for honey and many more nursery pots for further eggs. The first bees to emerge from their pupae will do so about three weeks after the laying of the first eggs, and until then the mother bee will be the only labourer in the nest. After that, the first-born, which are always workers, will gradually relieve her of her tasks, until she is able to devote all her time to the duty of laying eggs. The cells used for nurseries for the workers, for honey and, later, for females and males, are of different sizes and the brood cells become deformed by the larvae as they grow. They are not cleaned out to be used again when the young bees leave them, and they are often torn, or partly torn, to pieces for the sake of their materials. The result of all this gives the nest, when exposed to our view, the look of several handfuls of nuts, half of which have been opened and eaten. This exposes the bumble bee to odious comparisons with the hive bee as an architect.

As the summer goes on females (at first small like the workers) and males are born, and just before the end of their season (as early as July with some species) the males and females fly out and pair. The males are not re-admitted to the nest, and the females, once fertilized, seek the quiet of a safe retreat in which to hibernate.

The numbers to be found in a nest at the height of the season vary with the species and with the general good health of the community. As many as 300 or 400 may be in the nests of the ground species.

The other genus of bumble bee—*Psithyrus*—to which six of our species belong, though so similar in some things, is so different in others, that it needs separate treatment.

CHARACTERS. Structurally they are much like the *Bombi*, but scientists have managed to make up a list of forty-two differences. The males are hardly distinguishable: the females are somewhat less hairy, and have their abdomens and stings more bent under them, their jaws pointed (as for killing) rather than toothed (as for moulding wax), and they have the outer surface of the hind shins smooth and rounded instead of being hollowed out to gather pollen.

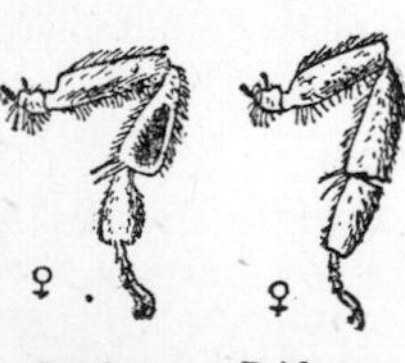

Bombus *Psithyrus*

In colour they follow very closely the various *Bombi* species, with which, and at the cost of which, they live.

LIFE HISTORY. But in their life histories they differ greatly. Like the *Bombi*, only their females survive the winters, and it seems that they usually face the spring climate later than do the *Bombi*. It is not until the nests of the *Bombi* are equipped with workers that the Cuckoo-bee (as the *Psithyrus* is called) puts in an appearance. Then she seeks out the nest of her destined hostess and enters it. At first she seems to create a certain amount of commotion among the inmates, and there are records of her failing to get in, or rather of her selling her life dearly after getting in. Usually, however, she seems to be admitted in peace, and thereafter can come and go unmolested. Thenceforward she entrusts the entire care of her family to the workers of her hostess. She, and later her male and female children (for she produces no workers), will fly out to sip nectar from the flowers on fine days, and it is probable that she may even make a specially large pot or so for the upbringing of her young. But apart from this she does nothing. She collects no pollen and she makes no honey. The workers of the *Bombus* feed her young, and from their honey-pots she and her brood take toll when the weather prevents her from enjoying a stroll among the flowers. When she does go out, her unhurried and leisurely demeanour distinguishes her from a busy *Bombus* better even than does her un-hollowed shin. There is also ugly evidence against her on a charge of murdering her hostess. There is little doubt that, after a harmonious life in the small nest for several weeks, she feels that her progeny would be the better for the unshared attentions of the workers and, to secure that result, stings the builder of the nest to death.

To her credit be it said that she does to some extent share the work of plant fertilization which is the main function of all the bees. But her character is nasty.

FAMILY *ANTHOPHORIDAE* [Honey-gatherers]
FLOWER POTTER-BEES

Five British species, of which two are 'large'

CHARACTERS. Solitary bees, in appearance resembling bumble bees. They have pollen-collecting apparatus like that of other bees and, like them, live wholly upon nectar, feeding their young upon honey and pollen. Unlike the social species, they produce no workers and, although they are often found in large communities, living and digging their burrows side by side, there is no interdependence between them. Each bee works for herself and her children, and for them alone. None helps another, and no work is undertaken in common.

Structurally our two 'large' species can only be distinguished from bumble bees by such minor characters as the details of the mouth-parts and the fact that their eyes reach the base of the jaws, from which those of the Bombidae are always well separated. The sexes differ markedly in colour and (being solitary) only one bee will be seen to enter any particular hole.

LIFE HISTORY. The fertilized female bee alone survives the winter. In the spring she comes out and begins the work of founding her family. The species here depicted, ***Anthophora acervorum*** [mound Honey-gatherer] (*p. 14*), is one of the earliest bees to be seen in the spring in this country. It differs from the other 'large' species in the male's mid-foot, which is hairy. The female, then, working wholly alone, digs herself a burrow in sandy soil or in loose earth, which consists of a shaft from the sides of which she excavates a small chamber. Into this she brings clay and with it builds a small pot, which she carefully lines with a paper-like substance and then fills it with a mixture of honey and pollen. On to the surface of this honey she lays a single egg, closes up the mouth of the pot, and then sets about the digging and furnishing of other nurseries. When she has completed her work and laid her last egg, she dies without ever seeing her children.

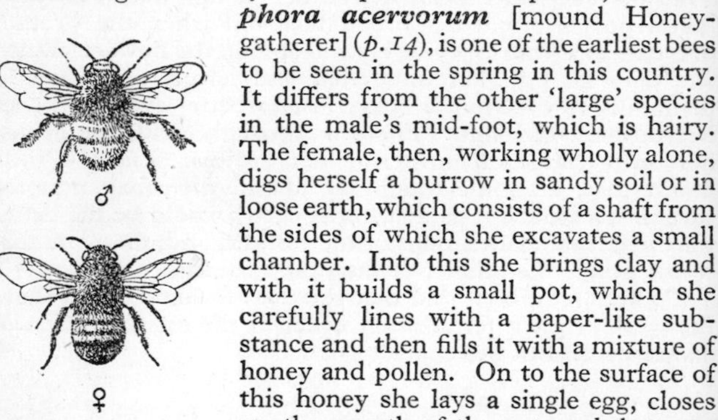

The chief enemies of these Potter-bees are parasites who take advantage of the careful preparations which they make for their young. Among them are the Oil Beetles (Meloidae) whose larvae cling to the bee's hairs and, at the final moment, while the egg is being laid, jump on to it and are closed up with it by the unsuspecting bee. Other parasites are other bees which will be mentioned later. (See p. 95.)

FAMILY *MEGACHILIDAE* [Big-jaws]
LEAF-CUTTER BEES, ETC.

(Here taken to include the genera *Megachile*, *Osmia*, *Anthidium*, and *Coelioxys*.)

Twenty-eight British species, of which ten are 'large'

CHARACTERS. This family consists wholly of solitary bees which in their general appearance resemble the hive bee. *Coelioxys* is parasitical and must be treated separately.

LIFE HISTORY. Except for *Coelioxys*, all the Leaf-cutter Bees provision the cells in which their eggs are laid with a mixture of pollen and honey, and their life history is generally the same as that of the Anthophoridae. Their cells differ in structure and in sites. Some species bore their way into wood, though, even of these, the greater number prefer to find borings already made for them by man (a nail-hole), or by beetle, or moth larvae, and most of the wood-boring species will resort to a convenient hole in the ground, if they can find one, rather than undertake the labour of boring wood. Other species will resort for preference to a boring in the soil and are rarely found in wood. Thus such names as 'carpenters' or 'miners' are confusing, owing to the overlapping of these trades.

When once the site for the nest has been found (and we must remember that although some species show decided preferences, others may choose either a nail-hole in a post, a boring in decayed wood, the deserted shell of a snail, or the hollow twig of a bramble), the next problem is that of the actual cell to hold the food and the egg.

The typical Leaf-Cutters, of which ***Megachile willughbiella*** [Willughby's Big-jaw] (*p. 14*), usually found boring in decayed willows, will serve as an example, make their cells out of pieces of leaf cut from the leaves of particular plants. After cutting a number of long-shaped pieces which she rolls together with the natural edge of the leaf outwards until she has built a short hollow cylinder, the bee adds to this a circular piece as a bottom to what thus becomes a small leaf-thimble. This tiny bucket she fills with pollen and honey, lays an egg on the surface of the food, and then puts a similar circular lid on the top to close the cell. After this she adds another cell on to the top of the first and continues so to do until her whole clutch of eggs, first the females, and later the males, has been housed and provisioned. The work accomplished, she goes away from the burrow and dies, leaving the next generation, whom she has never seen, to their own devices. It is noticeable that when the adult bees have to eat their way out of their thimble-cells they must do so in strict succession, the last placed leading the file. Each waits until the bee ahead of it has gone, so that the exit to the open air is barred by nothing but the lid of its own cell. If the first bee to develop (which might well be the first placed in its cell) began to eat its way through its brethren, the whole brood would be destroyed. As it is, the males first reach the open air and wait for their earlier established sisters upon the flowers which are the food providers of all alike.

The cells of other members of the family are made up of earth plastered with the bee's saliva. Those of others again are made of the woolly coating of certain stems and leaves of plants, which the bee shaves off and rolls into a pellet. This she carries under her chin to her burrow and uses it to make a warm woolly cell, inside which a watertight lining of a transparent glue-like substance is plastered on with the bee's tongue, and duly filled with food and egg.

The genus *Coelioxys* is included in the family because of

its very close structural likeness to the other members. It is presumed that it is a relative that has 'gone wrong'. Anyhow, its seven British species (of which three are 'large') are cuckoo-bees which lay their eggs in the cells of other members of the family, themselves doing no work.

FAMILY *NOMADIDAE* [Nomads] HOMELESS BEES

(Here taken to include the genera *Nomada* and *Melecta*)

Twenty-nine British species, of which seven are 'large'

CHARACTERS. These are all cuckoo-bees, having the branched hairs of all the bees, but no specialization of the legs, or hairs upon the abdomen for the collection of pollen, nor do they make or store any honey. The typical *Nomada* are in appearance more wasp-like than any other bees, having the yellow and black colouring usually associated with the wasps.

Nomada lineola [lined Nomad] (*p. 14*) will serve as an example. It preys upon various species of *Andrena* which breed during the spring. The females may be seen hanging about the nests of the *Andrena* bees, into which they enter and lay their eggs in their cells. Their grubs, when hatched, eat the food provided for the young of the maker of the cell and, sooner or later, the eggs or larvae also. The other genus, *Melecta*, which is classed with them, preys in a similar way upon the family of Anthophoridae, and is quite different in appearance, as its two British species look like their victims, though they do not possess pollen-gathering organs.

FAMILY *ANDRENIDAE* [Waspish] MINING BEES

(Here taken to include the genera *Halictus*, *Andrena*, *Melitta* and *Dasypoda*.)

101 *British species, of which seventeen are 'large'*

CHARACTERS. Solitary bees, having, for the most part, the general appearance of hive bees, though the greater number are much smaller. Their tongues are shorter than those of any of the families hitherto described and are flattened as shown in the accompanying sketches.

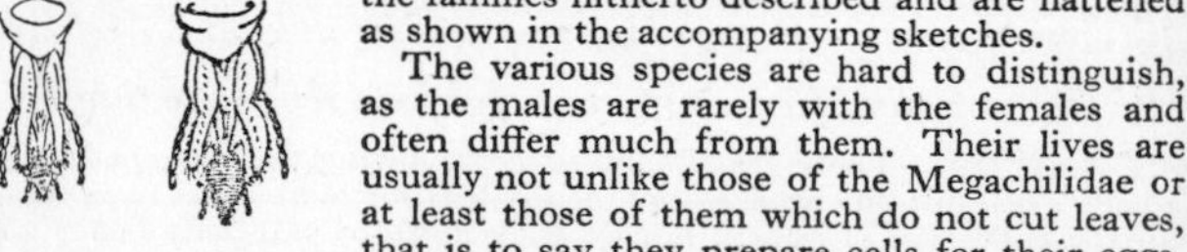

The various species are hard to distinguish, as the males are rarely with the females and often differ much from them. Their lives are usually not unlike those of the Megachilidae or at least those of them which do not cut leaves, that is to say they prepare cells for their eggs, provision them with honey and pollen, and then die, leaving the next generation to emerge and get through the winter. These Mining Bees are almost always miners in sand, gravel, or earth.

Dasypoda hirtipes [hairy-footed Shaggy-foot] (*p. 14*) will serve as an example of the family, as its habits have been studied and described at length. The female digs a deep burrow (down to two feet below the surface) and, as she does so, carefully scatters the excavated soil around the entrance so as not to attract attention to the opening. This she does with her feet, using the fore feet to pull the earth backwards, the mid feet to support herself, and the hind feet to brush the earth to the sides. When the shaft reaches the bottom, she digs a cell and sets out to provision it with an almost solid ball of honey-moistened pollen. To make such a ball takes six or seven journeys to the flowers, although, with her amply haired hind legs, she can carry half her own weight of pollen at a time. The ball is shaped with three knobs, or feet, so that it will not roll over but stand firmly, and then the egg is laid on its summit. She then begins to dig the next cell, slightly higher up the shaft, and uses the earth dug from this to close the first cell. In all from three to six cells will be dug,

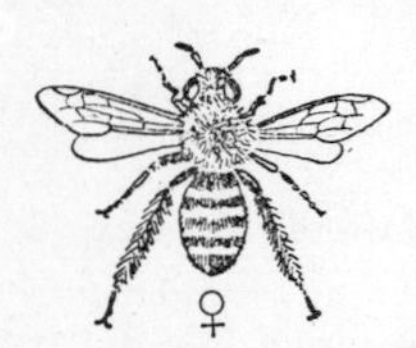

provisioned, and equipped with eggs, and then the bee comes to the surface and dies.

There is a remarkable fact in connexion with the larvae of these bees. They do not excrete, but retain all refuse inside their skins until the food is exhausted. This species delays the last stages of metamorphosis until the following year. Then the adults emerge and pair at once so that the females can begin their digging operations almost immediately. Some members of the family have two generations a year, and the difficulty of recognizing the species is increased by the fact that the spring and summer broods sometimes differ in appearance.

One noticeable fact about the Andrenidae is that many of them return to the same patch of ground where they were born, so that large 'villages' (sometimes as many as 2,000 nests) may be found together. In these cases, when the spring opening of the nests occurs, they can easily be mistaken for a colony of hive bees.

FAMILY *COLLETIDAE* [Gummies] GUM BEES

(One genus, *Colletes*)

Seven British species, of which one only is 'large'

CHARACTERS. This genus, the last of the bees to be mentioned here, is classified in a separate family because of the distinctive form of its tongue. This is not only short, but also ends in a broad, flat, forked shape, of which the sketch gives a rough idea. For comparison with the short pointed tongues of the Andrenidae, and the long tongues of the other bees, see pp. 82 and 96.

Our only 'large' species is ***Colletes cunicularia*** [burrowing Gummy] (*p. 14*), the habits and form of which are typical of the genus as a whole. It digs to a depth of some 8–10 inches in hard sandy soils and in large colonies together. No side cells are dug, but the tunnels are used more in the manner of the Megachilidae,

the cells being strung out in a row along the tunnel. The tunnel is lined by the mother with a parchment-like membrane which is the result of the drying of a gluey substance secreted by her and laid on to the sand with her flat tongue. Partitions of the same material are made between the cells, which are provisioned with a liquid mixture of pollen and honey before the eggs are laid in them. It is believed that the mother bee makes more than one such tunnel.

In addition to the hairy shins and feet, the female *Colletes* has a brush of pollen-gathering hairs on the under side of the abdomen.

GROUPS *VESPOIDEA* and *SPHECOIDEA*

THE WASP GROUPS

The next six families are made up of insects usually called Wasps, social and solitary. Like the bees they are all, as adults, feeders upon vegetable substances, fruit juices, or flower nectar. Their young, however, in the larval stage feed upon the bodies of other animals, chiefly those of other insects or spiders. None of them gather pollen or make honey, and therefore they have neither branching feathery hairs nor special pollen-collecting organs.

One family only—that of the *Vespidae* or True Wasps—is composed of social insects and has sterile workers. These True Wasps and one other family—the *Eumenidae* or Potter and Mason Wasps, which are solitary—fold their wings lengthwise when at rest. The others lay them flat along the body, unfolded.

The *Pompilidae* are the spider hunters, and there are two families of cuckoo-wasps (the *Chrysididae* and *Mutillidae*) which lay their eggs in the cells of other wasps or bees. In their case, however, it is upon the bodies of the insects provided by the builder of the cell for her own young, or, when bees are the victims, upon the bodies of the bee larvae themselves, that the carnivorous cuckoo-wasp grub feeds.

The last of these families of wasps which have 'large' species are the *Sphecidae* or Digger Wasps and Sand-wasps. These, and a number of families of 'small' wasps, differ from the others in the make-up of the thorax and are therefore placed in a separate group (*Sphecoidea*) by the classifiers, but are here considered with the large group of the other wasps, from which they do not differ greatly in habits.

FAMILY *VESPIDAE* [Wasps] TRUE WASPS

(Two genera, *Vespa* and *Vespula*)

Seven British species, all 'large'

CHARACTERS. Social insects living in large colonies and producing, in addition to males and females, a large number of sterile females or workers. Their colonies are seasonal only, the sole survivors which live through the winter being young fertilized females (queens), each of whom

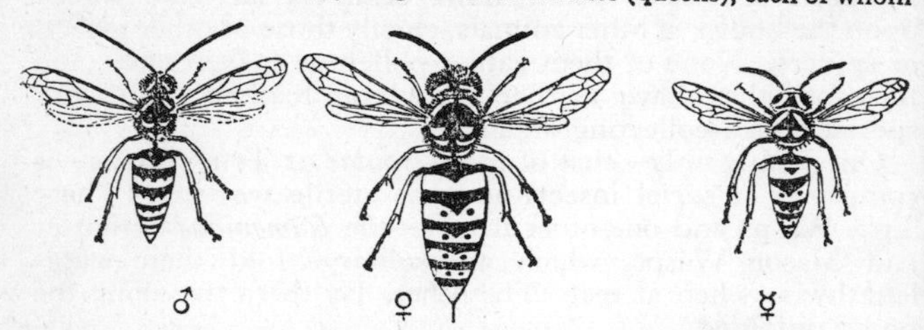

begins the building of a new nest in the spring. In this respect their life resembles that of the bumble bees and not the hive bee.

Vespula vulgaris, the common Wasp (*p. 14*), is typical of the others and will serve as an example. Throughout the family the sexes differ little in general appearance except that the queens are markedly larger than the males or workers. The males have thirteen segments in their antennae and seven visible segments in the abdomen, which is relatively narrower, while the queens and workers have twelve and six segments respectively. The tongues are short and forked. There is no thickening of the first joint of the feet, nor any pollen-gathering apparatus such as is found in the bees. They carry the wings folded lengthwise when at rest. The fore legs have a brush and notch between the shin (*tibia*) and the foot (*tarsus*) for cleaning the antennae. The queens and workers have a sting and poison bag and can inflict a painful wound which, however, conveys no germs of disease. There seems to be fair evidence that the sterility of the workers is not complete. In a queenless nest at least, the workers sometimes produce male eggs without being impregnated.

The adults are vegetarian, drinking nectar from flowers and other forms of sweet liquids, and especially delighting in ripe fruits and jams. The young brood, however, is fed, after perhaps a few meals of nectar, upon insects captured by the adults and chewed up by them before being fed to the larvae.

Life History. The following is a brief account of the life history of the common Wasp to which that of our other species is very similar.

The paired females (queens) have, like all the other Hymenoptera, in the act of pairing taken all the sperms of the male, so that they are able to fertilize their eggs for the rest of their lives without further intercourse with a male. As soon as the cold weather sets in they settle down to hibernate. This they do by hanging by the jaws to a curtain, or other rough surface, in some secluded spot, often in our houses or barns, or in some hole in a wooden fence or cranny in a tree. Fairly late in the spring each of these dormant queens awakes and, after refreshing herself upon the nectar of some favourite plant, begins her solitary construction of a nest.

(For those who wish to kill wasps—a wish which is only excusable where they are near to a house and will, therefore, make breakfast a penance later in the year—now is the time. Take a small bottle of petrol and a camel's hair brush. Dip the brush and with it touch the queen wasps as they feed on some flowering bush. When touched, the wasp will instantly curl up dead and there will be one wasp's nest the fewer.)

The queen's first duty is to find a hole, in a bank or under the roots of a tree or shrub, and there laboriously to excavate a cavity large enough to build the first comb of her nest.

This differs wholly from that of the hive bee in its materials. The wasps have no wax. They build with wood-pulp paper, filings of wood shaved from any wooden surface with their jaws and made into paper with the wasp's own saliva. The shape of the comb is bee-like in one respect only: the cells are hexagonal tubes, set one beside the other, and each destined for one egg and its development into an adult wasp. The plates or layers of comb are (unlike the bees') horizontal, with only one set of cells hanging downwards from the flat sheet of paper. The top layer, which is first built by the queen, hangs as does a chandelier by a solid rod of wood-paper, and consists at first of only a very few cells. This solid rod hangs from a root strong enough to sustain the whole nest when completed. Later layers or stages will be built below the first, each hanging from the one above it by similar rods and forming a platform upon which the wasps can walk with access to the open ends of the cells above their heads. The whole is surrounded and enclosed in a paper envelope of several thicknesses which can be, and is, constantly enlarged by tearing down, re-pulping, and using again the paper of which it is built. When the nest is finished in about August, it may have from seven to ten stages and be the size of a football, while the excavation made to enclose it will be larger still. Every piece of sand or soil dug out will have been carried out of the nest and dropped a foot or two outside, and only stones more than three times the weight of a wasp will be left at the bottom of the hole.

To return to our lonely queen. Having built parts, at least, of a few cells, she lays an egg in each and when the larvae hatch out (each hanging on to its paper wall so as not to fall out of the cell) she must forage for them all, bring in countless caterpillars, flies, and other insects which she chews up and deals out from her own tongue to her hungry brood. As the larvae grow, she has to complete their cells, which, when they are ready to pupate, they will themselves close with a lid, through which, as adult wasps, they eat their way on emergence. All the first eggs develop workers and, after they have had a short time in which to harden their skins and get their full colour, the queen can at last rest from foraging and building and, like the queen bee, give herself up to egg-laying. From the laying of the eggs to the appearance out of doors of the first wasps will take about a month.

Thenceforward, until about August, the nest increases and prospers and then a final comb will be built, with larger cells, for the production of male and female wasps. Soon after their emergence insect food for the brood begins to run short, the workers find it hard to get nectar for themselves, and, perhaps above all, feel that their own life is drawing to a close. They go to the comb and tear out the unhatched larvae from their cells and throw them to the bottom of the nest hole, where also all excrement and wasp corpses have been cast. There the young are left to die and shortly afterwards the whole population of the nest dies of cold, starvation, and old age, leaving the few fertilized queens alone to survive and start fresh nests in the following year.

PARASITES. As in the nests of other social insects, others than the true owners are found in wasps' nests. One such guest is *Velleius dilatatus* (a large Staphylinid beetle, see p. 163), and there are several other beetles and flies, some of which help to clean the nests.

FAMILY *EUMENIDAE* [Furies]
POTTER AND MASON WASPS

(Four genera: *Eumenes*, *Odynerus*, *Pseudepipona*, and *Ancistrocerus*.)

Fifteen British species, of which seven are 'large'

CHARACTERS. The wings, like those of the social wasps, are carried folded lengthwise when at rest. They differ from the social wasps in having their claws double-pointed, and in having only one spur on the shin of the mid legs. Their waists are either short (*Odynerus*) or much elongated into a stalk (*Eumenes*). They are purely solitary, each mother working for her own family. The males do nothing to help, after or before pairing. There are no communities, and no worker caste is produced.

LIFE HISTORY. The males appear to hatch and scatter before the females emerge, thereby avoiding inbreeding. ***Eumenes coarctata*** [compressed Fury] (*p. 14*) is our only species of the typical genus and is known as the Potter Wasp owing to the form of its nest. This takes the shape of a small pot, as here illustrated, made of clay and small pebbles fastened together with the saliva of the wasp and built either upon the stems of heather or some other small plant, or with a flat bottom upon a wooden post. Here, for the first time in this book, we come across a very surprising fact. The provisions laid up in the nursery cell for the young consist of caterpillars, hunted and stung by the mother wasp. But, and this is the strange fact discovered by Fabre, they are not dead, but merely paralysed. The provisions must be kept fresh for the whole time (nearly a year) that the young wasps are in the larval stage. If they were dead, they would rot and dry up within a few days. The required result is obtained by the wasp's sting. This gives a partial paralysis which preserves life, and so prevents decay, and also preserves the tender egg and young larva of the wasp from injury due to any movement which the living caterpillar might make. In the case of the Eumenidae a further precaution is taken against the latter danger. The egg, when laid, is hung up in the cell by a fine thread of silk fastened to the roof, so that the egg hangs just short of the store of caterpillars. When the larva hatches, and until it attains sufficient strength to be out of danger from any power of movement which may remain in the caterpillars, it stays in the egg-shell, suspended by its cable from the roof, and eats the provided larvae. The egg-shell lengthens out so as to give the little larva a longer reach. When it is strong enough it leaves its cable and, dropping to the bottom of its pot, continues its meal until all the caterpillars provided are eaten. Then it pupates and the adult wasp eats its way out of the pot. If male, he goes to the flowers to wait for a mate; if female, she will first pair and then begin the long task of pot-making, food-storing, and egg-laying. When the last pot is closed she will die, without ever having seen the young for whom (she herself a sucker of nectar) she has supplied so great a number of victims, so carefully selected and so skilfully paralysed.

The other Eumenidae differ in their methods of cell-building. They mostly build a mass of cells upon the surface of some wall of stone or brick instead of making the separate cells of the Potter. Others make a boring in hard soil, and, while the boring is in progress, make a chimney with a kink in it out of the excavated earth. Afterwards they pull this down again so as to close, and conceal, their cells. These have been called Mason Wasps.

The whole family are valuable to man as destroyers of Lepidopterous larvae which are so injurious to vegetation.

FAMILY *POMPILIDAE* [Escorts] SPIDER WASPS

(Genera of 'large' insects: *Anoplius*, *Priocnemis*, and *Cryptocheilus*.)

Thirty-eight British species, of which four are 'large'

CHARACTERS. Solitary wasps, which provide paralysed spiders for their young. Their wings are never folded but, when at rest, carried flat along their backs. They have narrow waists, not, however, forming a long stalk. Their legs are unusually long.

♀

LIFE HISTORY. They are amongst the most active and nimble of all the Hymenoptera. They rarely fly any distance, but run quickly, with brief flights between the runs. They work only in bright sunlight, crouching, hidden, when a cloud passes. Our largest and commonest species is ***Anoplius fuscus*** [dark Unarmed] (*p. 14*) which may be seen from April to August. After pairing, the females of most species hunt, capture, and paralyse a spider as food for their young. The spiders taken are of almost all kinds, though the various wasps seem usually to keep either to web-spinning or to vagrant spiders. The spider appears unable or unwilling to bite the wasp and it takes refuge in attempts to escape or in shamming death—a device which does not always succeed. The wasp paralyses the spider by stinging it, usually in or near the mouth, thus disarming it. Then she drags it off and hides it, usually on a grass-blade or shrub, to keep it safe from ants or other thieves while she digs a hole of the size needed to receive it in a sandy bank. During the digging she visits her victim several times and, to memorize its position and that of the hole, has been seen to fly around repeatedly. When the hole is ready, she drags the spider to it and, after a last inspection of the cell, pulls the spider in, lays an egg on its abdomen, and carefully closes the entrance, patting down the sand with her abdomen. The whole of this process is repeated with, perhaps, twenty spiders. If the spider is removed from its hiding-place, the wasp is said to hunt first just below where it was, as if aware of the habit of spiders of taking evasive action by dropping.

FAMILY *CHRYSIDIDAE* [Golden ones] RUBY-TAILED WASPS

(One genus containing 'large' species, *Chrysis*)

Twenty-one British species, of which two are often 'large'. The size is very variable, depending upon the amount of food available to the larva.

CHARACTERS. Solitary, without workers, and parasitical upon other Hymenoptera which store insects for their young. Our commonest species, ***Chrysis ignita*** [fiery Golden one] (*p. 14*), is typical of the family. It preys upon *Odynerus*, laying its eggs upon the caterpillars stored by the host. The Ruby-Tails are all of brilliant metallic colours and have short abdomens which are often bent up under the thorax. The ovipositors of the females are long and thick and most of them do not act as stings.

FAMILY *MUTILLIDAE* [Mutilated] VELVET ANTS

Two British species, of which one is 'large'

CHARACTERS. Solitary, without workers, parasitical upon the Bombidae, in and about the nests of which the females are found. The females are completely wingless. They are not ants, having only one waist and totally different habits.

Our large species, ***Mutilla europaea*** [European Mutilated] (*p. 14*), lays her eggs in bodies of the larvae in the cells of the bumble bees and herself feeds off their store of honey. The males, as soon as they are developed, go out of the nest and will be found feeding upon flowers.

FAMILY *SPHECIDAE* [Wasps] DIGGER WASPS

(Genera containing 'large' British species: *Ammophila*, *Mellinus*, *Gorytes*, *Cerceris*, and *Crabro*.)

103 *British species, of which twelve are 'large'*

CHARACTERS. Solitary wasps, with no worker class. They have the 1st segment of the thorax (*pronotum*) small and like a narrow collar, not reaching to the base of the wings. Their wings are not folded when at rest. They have active stings (♀) with which they paralyse various forms of insect prey as food for their young. Their hairs are simple threads—not branched as are those of the bees. They have two undivided claws on each foot. They all have narrow waists, which, in some, are drawn out into a long stalk.

LIFE HISTORY. In so large a family there are marked variations of habits, but usually their lives are much like those of the Pompilidae and Eumenidae, already described. The adults are wholly vegetarian, taking nectar from the flowers. The males do nothing else, except pair, and take no share in the laborious lives of the females. The latter provide some form of chamber to hold their eggs (one in each) and a supply of paralysed insect food sufficient to sustain the larva until fully grown. Although the great majority are diggers in sand, some species extract the pith from plant stems and make their cells in the tubes so obtained, and others dig in decaying wood. In the case of the more common sand-diggers this chamber is usually at, or branching from, the end of a boring in sand or loose soil. The boring may even be as much as a yard in depth. When it and the first cell are dug the wasp goes off in search of prey. Of our 'large' species those of *Ammophila* prey upon lepidopterous larvae, those of *Mellinus* and *Crabro* upon true flies, and of *Gorytes* upon Frog-hoppers (Cercopidae), and that of our large *Cerceris* upon weevils. Other 'small' species of *Cerceris* prey upon solitary bees.

The process of paralysing varies with the anatomy of the victim, caterpillars being stung repeatedly along their under side, beetles and flies usually only once beneath the thorax. Fabre thought the behaviour was just as if the wasps were gifted with an instinctive knowledge of the anatomy of their prey. His description of the habits of these wasps forms one of the most intensely interesting records of animal life.

In several cases the sting is not the only means used to make the prey suitably inert. Without breaking its outer skeleton, the wasp sometimes chews and bruises the captured insect with the same result. This is seen in the case of the few species which capture the adults of some of the bees. It seems that this chewing serves three distinct ends: it completes the inertia of the victim; it softens its substance for the good of the wasp-larva; and it squeezes out the honey which gives the mother-wasp a meal and removes what might be poison to her larva.

The Sphecidae usually take the precaution of carefully closing their nest-holes with sand or stones while absent on their hunting trips, and sometimes a pine-needle or a leaf seems to be laid by the nest as if to mark its site. They show an astonishing homing instinct, returning to their nests from long distances (to which they have been carried in the dark) and finding them even after various devices have been adopted to conceal them from their sight or smell.

The moment when parasites (chiefly Diptera) defeat the wasps is when the wasp lays down her capture near the hole while she opens the entrance. Then the fly lays her egg on the caterpillar, and the maggot which hatches from it will eventually eat both the young of the wasp and the provisions prepared for it.

There are some species in which the provision of food for the young takes a different course. These species, which usually find a hole rather than dig one for themselves, kill their prey and so, to supply fresh food, must bring newly killed victims throughout the life of their larvae. This is a departure from the general rule that the adults of the solitary bees and wasps never see the young for whom they toil.

Where the insect provided is so large that the young larva cannot eat it quickly enough to prevent decay, it begins by eating such organs as are not vital and thus its victim is kept alive until it can be finished before it deçays. As the larva and its appetite grow, such precautions are laid aside. It, like its mother, behaves as though it had a knowledge of caterpillar anatomy.

The following four examples of Sphecidae (*p. 15*) will be enough to give an idea of the variety of their forms. They each belong to a group which is by some writers accorded family

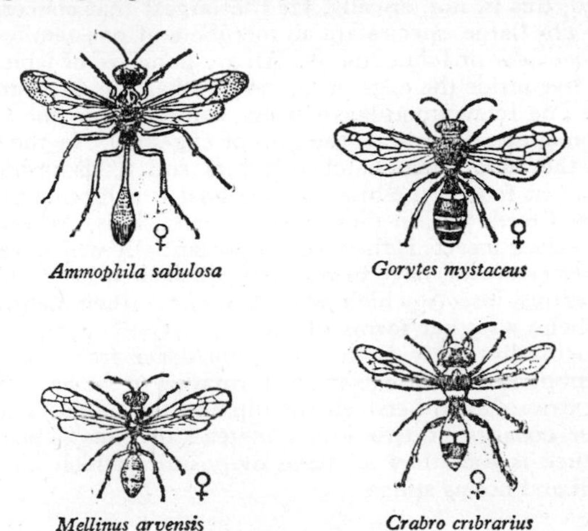

Ammophila sabulosa ♀ *Gorytes mystaceus* ♀

Mellinus arvensis ♀ *Crabro cribrarius* ♀

rank, though here the system of treating the Sphecidae as a single family is adopted.

Ammophila sabulosa [sandy Sand-lover] feeds her young on caterpillars. ***Gorytes mystaceus*** [moustached Quiver] hunts for the Frog-hoppers (Cercopidae). Plunging her legs and sting into the 'Cuckoo-spit', she pulls out the nymph. ***Mellinus arvensis*** [field Honey] and also ***Crabro cribrarius*** [sievelike Hornet] are both collectors of Diptera. The latter has gained its name of 'sievelike' from an odd outgrowth upon the fore legs of the males used to grasp the females. All the four species illustrated are burrowers in sand or loose soil.

GROUP *ICHNEUMONOIDEA*

ICHNEUMON GROUP

Of the groups into which the Hymenoptera with waists are divided, this is, numerically, far the largest that concerns us here. The 'large' species are all members of one family—the *Ichneumonidae* or Ichneumons. All are parasites of which the larvae live inside the eggs or larvae of other insects or arthropods. The Ichneumon lays her egg sometimes in the victim and sometimes outside on the skin or egg-shell. In the latter cases, the larva when hatched enters and feeds inside the victim. Its food is the blood of the host which remains alive and itself feeds until it dies of starvation. This vast army of insect-eating insects is the most important ally which we, and all other creatures, have in the struggle against the hordes of plant-eating insects which would, without their help, soon overwhelm all other forms of life.

Structurally, these Ichneumonoids differ from the other Hymenoptera-with-waists in the formation of the legs. There is an extra segment between the hip and the thigh. The trochanter consists of two joints instead of one. The other difference is that they all have ovipositors which are used as such and not as stings.

FAMILY *ICHNEUMONIDAE* ICHNEUMONS

Over 2,000 British species, of which a third are 'large'

CHARACTERS. Parasites until the adult stage, their eggs being laid on or in other insects. They have an extra joint in their legs, the segment between the hip (*coxa*) and the thigh (*femur*), which is called the *trochanter*, is double and consists of two joints as here sketched. Their antennae are long, composed of many joints, and not elbowed or sharply bent at any point. The 1st segment of the thorax is rigidly fastened to the 2nd (*mesonotum*) which is large and makes up almost the whole thorax, as the last segment is very small. The 1st segment extends backwards to the bases of the wings. There is a narrow waist, two segments of which

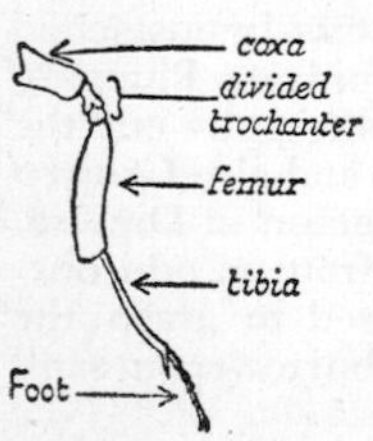

are flexible, from which the abdomen gradually becomes thicker. The segments of the abdomen are distinct. The females have ovipositors, which in some species are of great length, in others are short or even barely visible. These organs are made up of three parts, the actual egg-laying tube (which consists of three rods, and arises from the abdomen at some distance from its tip), and two hard protecting sheaths, one on each side of it. When the bodies of their victims, or any other matter is to be bored, the piercing is done by the egg-laying tube alone. The sheaths are mere guards, acting as a scabbard when the tube is not in use. The wings are fairly well veined and have a black spot in them called a *stigma*. Wingless forms are found only among the 'small' species.

LIFE HISTORY. The earlier stages in the life of the Ichneumons have not been very amply studied. It is not easy to do so, as all their immature life is spent inside some other insect, to kill which kills the Ichneumon. Such observations as have been made seem to show that several of them have various successive forms of larva before the final pupation. The great majority attack the caterpillars of the Lepidoptera (against the depredations of which they form our main defence), though the Tenthredinidae (Saw-flies) are also largely attacked. A few prey on beetles; fewer on Diptera; and still fewer on Aphididae and spiders. Some lay where their larvae will compete with and destroy other parasites. The egg is laid on, or into, the victim, sometimes through leaves or even hard wood. Some Ichneumon larvae suck their victims from the outside, others suck their blood and fat from within, only completing their destruction when about to pupate. In the case of the larger Ichneumons, only one parasite can get enough food from a single caterpillar.

The small Ichneumons (and the family of *Braconidae*, which are similar and all small) sometimes lay many eggs in a single victim and sometimes while the victim is still an egg. Some insects, which do not strictly concern us owing to their minute size, have extraordinary methods of larval reproduction which enable a single parasite egg to produce several hundreds of parasites within a single host caterpillar or pupa.

The largest of our Ichneumons is ***Rhyssa persuasoria*** [persuasive Burglar] (*p. 15*) which preys upon another Hymenopter [*Urocerus gigas*, the Wood Wasp] described on p. 116.

The Wood Wasp's larva spends its life boring through pine wood and, to reach it, the *Rhyssa* has an ovipositor of great length. She thrusts this tube into the solid wood where, by the sense of smell in her antennae, she detects the presence of the tunnelling Wood Wasp larva. She actually places her egg in the victim's body and the young *Rhyssa* feeds on its body, pupates, and becomes an adult which is capable of eating its way out of the pine-trunk. For various reasons there are many failures. The young Ichneumon may fail to reach the outer air: its power of endurance is said to be limited to three days' chewing. The larva in which it is planted may be too young and therefore incapable of supporting the parasite, or, again, the Ichneumons may make the mistake of laying in a larva already infested by another Ichneumon. In this case, all three larvae will die, but, and to us this is the important point, the destruction of the timber will be stopped. Speaking generally, this family must be regarded as of the utmost benefit to man.

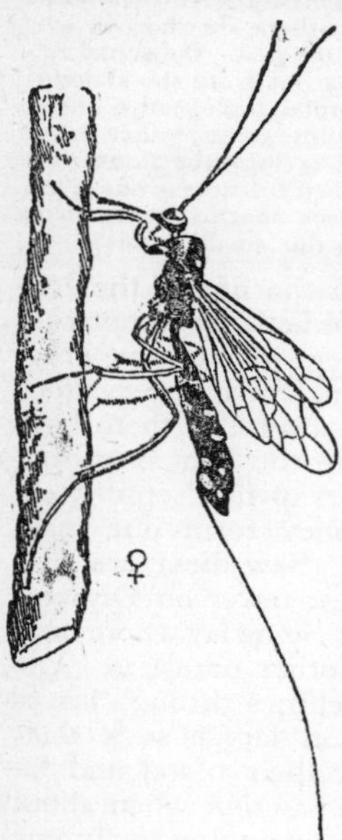

In addition to the above families or groups of Hymenoptera-with-waists containing 'large' species, there are two other groups, the *Cynipoidea* (Gall Wasps) and *Chalcidoidea* (Chalcid Flies), consisting wholly of 'small' insects, among them the species whose larvae produce galls on trees and plants.

SUB-ORDER *SESSILIVENTRES*
WAISTLESS *HYMENOPTERA*

FAMILIES *TENTHREDINIDAE*, *CIMBICIDAE*, *PAMPHILIIDAE* SAW-FLIES

(The genera with large species are: *Tenthredo*, *Macrophya*, *Dolerus*, *Allantus*, *Nematus*, *Cimbex*, *Trichiosoma*, and *Pamphilius*.)

388 *British species, of which twenty-nine are 'large'*

CHARACTERS. No waist, head and thorax broad, body of soft texture, abdomen equipped with a saw-like ovipositor. The larvae are unlike all others in the Order and generally resemble those of moths. All the larvae are vegetarians, while the adults mostly suck flowers, though some are carnivorous and eat other insects.

ANATOMY. As shown by their English name, the distinctive mark of these families is their possession of the saw ovipositor. It is not possible to give a full description of this organ (which, of course, appears only in the females), but the following diagram and account will be sufficient to give an idea of its form and operation. There are two saw-edged blades which project backwards on the under side of the abdomen side by side, with the saw-teeth on their lower edges. Their upper edges are thickened, their sides cross-ribbed and studded with minute teeth, and the zigzags of the teeth of the saws are themselves finely toothed. The saws work in opposite directions, one being thrust out backwards as the other is drawn in forwards. This is done by flexible wire-like attachments, the other ends of which are fastened to plates on the under side of the abdomen. Thus they pierce with their points; cut with their lower edges; and file with their rough sides, making a slit in the leaf or stem of the plant in which the egg is to be laid. On each side of the blades is a cover, the two together forming a sheath which protects the saws when they are withdrawn and not in use. The eggs pass out between the saw-blades, and

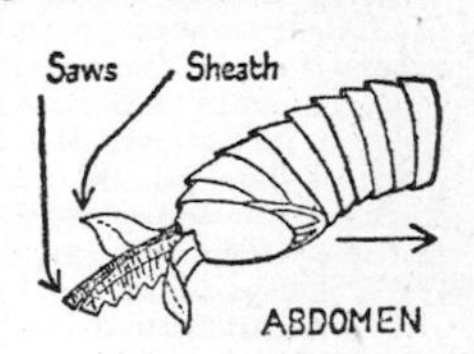

there is also a poison gland which extrudes a drop of liquid with the egg. It is possibly this liquid which affects the tissue of the plant and, in some cases, provokes the growth of a gall. Other species gnaw the bark surrounding the twig and thus prevent the flow of sap which might injure the egg.

Thus the **eggs** are laid in slits cut by the saws of the mother in the leaves, twigs, buds, or fruit, of various plants, mainly trees or shrubs, more rarely in herbaceous plants. The eggs, after being laid, have the unusual attribute of becoming slightly larger either by growth or by the absorption of liquid from the plant.

The **larvae** are quite unlike any others of the Order, being, as a rule, formed and coloured much as are those of the Lepidoptera. All have the three pairs of legs on the first three segments, and, although a few have no others, most species have from six to eight other pairs of 'false legs' on the segments of their abdomens. A few have such legs on every segment of the body, making twenty-six legs in all. The false legs of the Saw-fly larvae (which are often called caterpillars) have no gripping claws but only a hair or two at their ends and they are not much used in crawling. Wherever false legs are present, a pair will be found on the 5th (= 2nd abdominal) segment, which is never the case among the Lepidoptera. The larvae have only two simple eyes. Their colouring may be bright, black and yellow (supposed to serve as a warning), or green (for camouflage), and there is often a marked change of colour at some moult during the larval life. They are often provided with stink-glands from which a protective liquid is sprayed or squirted. They are all plant-eaters, the greater number living in the open and eating the leaves. Others remain inside the stems and fruit, or in galls provoked by the egg-laying process, while a few are leaf-miners. Some are solitary and others gregarious, and it is not unusual for the latter to mass together, so attracting attention to their warning colours.

The positions assumed by the larvae are peculiar to the family. Some hold their tails up in the air, and others curl them round sideways, or otherwise keep them away from their food.

When about to pupate a **cocoon** is formed, which is sometimes double (hard in its outer shell and softly lined within), and built either upon the plant or, less usually, underground. The greater number of species get through the winter in the cocoons, but, in this case, the larva remains in the cocoon for a long time before pupating, as the period of the pupal life is always short.

The **adult Saw-flies** have the head broad (but less so than the thorax) and held close to the thorax, though there is a longish neck which can be extended. They have three simple eyes and two larger compound eyes and their antennae vary greatly in form, in length, and in the number of segments composing them. This number (usually nine) may be from five to twenty-two or more.

LIFE HISTORY. The greater number have only one generation in the year and spend the winter as pupae, or rather, as larvae in the pupal cocoons before pupating: some, however, produce two generations. The adults are short-lived, the males dying within a few hours of pairing and the females after laying their eggs, a process which takes only a few days. They are sluggish fliers, not usually flying more than three or four yards, and mostly only in the sunshine. The males appear to be the first to emerge and fights between them have been recorded, conducted by bumping into each other in flight.

Trichiosoma lucorum [woodland Hairy-body] (*p. 15*) or Hawthorn Saw-fly, family *Cimbicidae*, is among the commonest of our 'large' Saw-flies. Its larvae feed during July and August on the hawthorns and make upon the branches of the trees large cocoons in which they spend the winter, the adults emerging in summer by biting round the side of the cocoon so as to make a hinged lid. The larvae have, in all, twenty-two legs. The hairy body of this species is unusual in the family, in which the outer covering is generally smooth and often shiny. There is much variety of coloration, but a black shade with yellowish abdomen is perhaps the commonest among our Saw-flies.

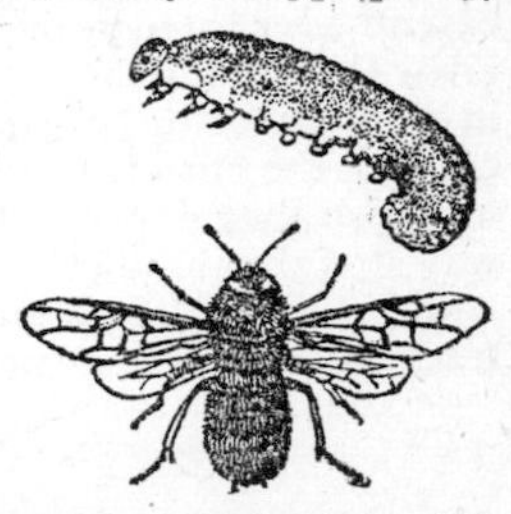

FAMILY *SIRICIDAE* [Sirens]
HORNTAILS OR WOOD WASPS

(Here taken to include *Sirex*, *Urocerus*, and *Xiphydria*)

Six British species, all 'large'

Characters. Large, brilliantly coloured insects, without waists and differing from the Saw-flies in having hard bodies and the (♀) ovipositor long and formed for boring into wood (not for sawing or cutting).

The larvae live by boring and feeding in the wood.

Anatomy. The larvae have only six small, stumpy projections which replace the true legs, and have powerful jaws (*mandibles*). The adults have broad heads, not, however, as broad as their bodies, with narrow necks (long or short), and long parallel-sided bodies without any narrowing at the waist. The ovipositors have the appearance of formidable stings, though they are not used as such, and the Horntails are, in that respect, quite harmless.

LIFE HISTORY. The eggs are thrust, by means of the ovipositor, through the bark of timber trees into the soft wood. The mothers seem to choose dead or sickly trees rather than those in which the sap is running freely, and will attack a tree as soon as it has been felled. The larvae, when they are hatched, begin to bore through the wood, and in small logs go deep into the heart wood, causing much injury to the timber. They continue to bore throughout the larval life, which may extend over three years, and then, behaving exactly as if they knew (how?) the shortest way to the open air, turn their heads in that direction (still in the wood) and form a softly lined cocoon, the outside of which is made of digested wood-filings, in which they pupate. When the adults emerge they eat their way straight ahead of them through the wood to the air, light, and freedom. They are known to have chewed through a lead casing covering carpentered timber.

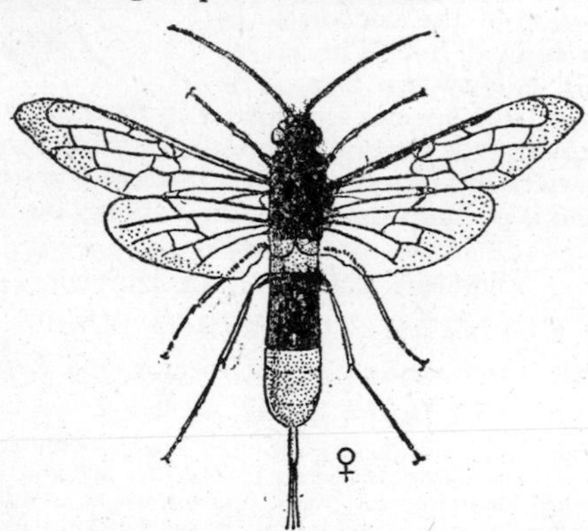

Urocerus gĭgas [giant Horntail] (*p. 15*) is a fir-tree borer often imported in foreign timber and now well established in this country. It is said to lay 100 eggs, each separately in a distinct boring in the tree, and its life in the wood appears usually to be of 2½ or 3 years' duration.

FAMILY *CEPHIDAE* [Drones] STEM SAW-FLIES

(Four genera, *Hartigia, Janus, Calameuta, Cephus*)

Ten British species, of which four are 'large'

CHARACTERS. No waist. Head wider than the thorax, on a longish neck. Slender bodies of soft delicate texture. The 1st segment of the thorax is large and jointed to the 2nd so as to be movable. There are only vestiges of the simple eyes (*ocelli*), and the fore shins have only one spur. Larvae, like those of the Horntails, bore in plant stems.

Although 'large', the four species of this family are only just over the half-inch in length.

♀

The larvae of ***Janus femoratus*** [thighed Passage] (*p. 15*) feed in the twigs of the lower branches of oaks, into which the eggs are inserted by the mother. The larvae make a spindle-shaped swelling in the twig, which sometimes, but not always, withers. They feed throughout the larval life inside the twig and make a well-lined cocoon in the branch within which they spend the winter. When the adults emerge they leave the cocoon at the base of the swelling through an opening made by the larva. This extends to the bark which the adult insect gnaws through.

Most of these species utilize reeds or cereal stems, feeding upon the pith, and one 'small' species is a menace to wheat crops, as the larva works up and down the straw, weakens it, and prevents the growth of the ear.

ORDER *DIPTERA* [Two Wings]

TRUE FLIES

Some 5,000 *British species, of which about* 330 *are 'large'*

CHARACTERS. The usual three changes, each fly passing through four distinct stages: egg, larva or maggot, pupa, and adult fly. There is one single pair of, usually transparent and scaleless, wings (the fore wings). The hind wings are replaced by a small pair of half-dumb-bell-like balancers (*halteres*). The mouth-parts are adapted for sucking and, sometimes also, for piercing. The three parts of the thorax are fused together. The head is borne upon a narrow neck.

The larvae are legless and often with little or no visible head.

The pupa may be enclosed in, and completely hidden by, the last larval skin, retained for the purpose (the *puparium* of the *Cyclorrhapha*) or may be free, and even agile, as are those of the *Culicidae*.[1]

ANATOMY. The **larvae** of the Diptera show much diversity. They are mostly tubular in shape, frequently tapering towards the head end and at their largest at their tails which give the impression of having been cut off sharply. All are legless, though some have either spines or soft fleshy protuberances on their bodies which enable them to move. The number of segments in their bodies varies, the greatest number found being twelve, though sometimes, owing to subdivision, there appear to be more. A very few have spiracles for breathing all along their bodies, but they mostly have either four such openings, two at each end (when they are said to be *amphipneustic*), or else only two at the tail end (when they are called *metapneustic*). The latter is the case of most if not all of the aquatic larvae, in some of which there are also hair-like gills.

The greater number are headless, the forward end of the gut, of which they almost wholly consist, having at most a pair of horny hooks withdrawn within the next segment. Some families have visible heads (e.g. *Culicidae*) and others (e.g. *Tipulidae*) retractile heads equipped with chewing mouth-parts.

[1] To many of the characters above stated there are some exceptions. Some flies produce living larvae, the hatching of the eggs taking place within the mother (e.g. *Sarcophaga*); some have two extra stages (e.g. *Bombylidae*); some (small species) are wingless and lacking the balancers; some have the mouth-parts completely atrophied (e.g. *Oestridae*).

The following sketches (much enlarged) give an idea of two contrasting forms of fly larvae: those of the House Fly (left) and the Common Gnat (right).

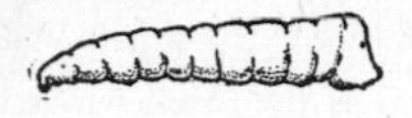

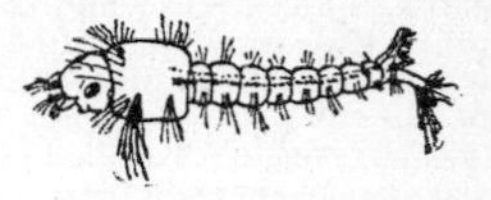

Their habits differ as much as their shapes. Some live upon the leaves or stems of plants, burrowing leaves, or creating galls by their presence (these are all 'small' species). Some are parasites upon insects (e.g. *Larvaevoridae*). Others are true internal parasite supon the vertebrates, living inside their bodies and upon their substance (e.g. *Oestridae*). The greatest number feed upon decaying matter, vegetable or animal. Of these some specialize in excrements, some in carrion, some in rotting vegetation, while others are more catholic in their tastes and are satisfied with any form of putrescence or nastiness. A number are aquatic, living upon impurities in the water.

The **pupae** differ according to the way in which that stage is assumed, as has already been stated; whether, that is, the larval skin is hardened into a leathery bottle to protect the pupa, or discarded. Further reference will be made to this distinction, but for the present it will suffice to give

a rough sketch of two pupae of the contrasted forms: again those of the House Fly (left) and the Common Gnat (right).

The **adult Flies,** all those at any rate which are 'large' insects, are easily recognizable and distinguished from other insects by the one trait from which they get their name of *Diptera* [2-wings]. They have only one pair of wings, the hind wings being replaced by the balancers (*halteres*), hereafter described.

Their bodies are distinctly divided into the usual three parts, head, thorax, and abdomen, and, in all the 'large' flies, these three parts are united to each other by a narrow neck and waist. The following diagram on p. 120 gives the main outlines of the form of a fly with the names of its parts.

The **head** is usually large and, owing to the narrow neck, very mobile. A great part of its surface is taken up by the two compound eyes, which are often much larger in the males than in the females. They are often hairy. There are usually three simple eyes (*ocelli*) in a triangular space between, or behind, the compound eyes. No attempt will be made to describe the mouth-parts in detail. There are two palps, which are sensory organs, and beneath them from two to six dagger-shaped blades resting in a grooved lower lip (*labium*) which forms a trunk or proboscis. The end of this usually takes the form of a pair of lobes. In the blood-suckers the lower lip is a mere sheath and most of the blades act as piercing daggers. In the more numerous species, and in the males which are not blood-suckers, the lobes of the lower lip are toothed so as to rasp the food, while the dagger-shaped blades are usually reduced in number and, being

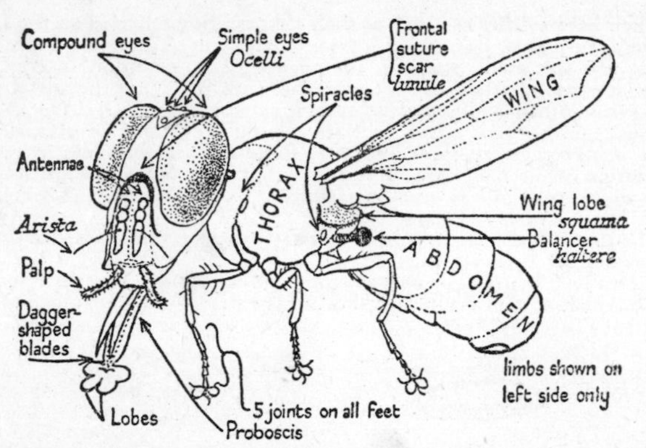

grooved, act as tubes for conveying digesting saliva to liquefy the food and to suck it up. Different blades perform different functions in the different families.

Thus it appears that the mouths of the flies, all of which are adapted for sucking, tend towards two different types. One of these (of which those of the gnats form the best example) is formed for piercing and sucking, while the other type (exemplified by the House Fly) is formed to suck up liquid from the surface of the food. Owing to the fact that the blood-sucking habit is almost always confined to the females, these two different types of mouth are sometimes to be found in the two sexes of the same species.

One indication in the above sketch requires some explanation. Above the antennae, and as it were surrounding the face of the fly, is a fold at what is known as the frontal suture, often called the *lunule*. The greater number of those flies which keep the larval skin as a *puparium* (see p. 118) and emerge from it by pushing open a circular lid in its horny case, have a special organ for the purpose (called a *ptilinum*). This is a hard-skinned and rough-surfaced bladder which, at the time of emergence, is thrust out of this frontal suture, by being filled with blood from within, and thus increases the size of the head, protects the delicate antennae, and pushes off the lid of the capsule in which the fly is imprisoned. When once the fly is out, by alternately filling and emptying this organ, it displaces the earth above it and makes itself a way to the surface. Then the bladder, having served its purpose, is reabsorbed into the head and is no more seen. The only sign of its having existed is the ∩-shaped scar into which it has been withdrawn: the lunule indicated in the sketch.

The **antennae** vary much in shape and are useful in classification. They may be roughly divided into three types. The most primitive type consists of numerous (at least six or more) segments all alike. This is the type usual with the *Nematocera*. The second type has all the segments after the 2nd either fused into one, or, if the segmentation between them is still visible, diminishing in size so as to resemble a single 3rd segment tapering to a point. Such antennae are comparatively short and are characteristic of the *Brachycera*. The third type, which is that of the most highly developed flies (the *Cyclorrhapha*), has only three segments and a bristle, which sprouts, not from the end of the 3rd segment, but from its upper side or, as the antennae are usually drooping, from the front of the last segment and not far from its base. The following sketch

will give an idea of the three types of antennae (Nematocera type, left; Brachycera type, centre; Cyclorrhapha type, right). The bristle in the third type may be thick (a *style*) or a mere thread (an *arista*) and may be feathery or not.

The **thorax** of a fly has its segments so closely united as to make any observation of them difficult. The central segment with the wings and their muscles forms almost the whole. The fore and hind segments are reduced to mere bands each carrying its pair of legs and the hinder the balancers. Much of the discrimination between different species depends upon the bristles found on the bodies, and to these a large vocabulary has been attached, while their study has been awarded the sonorous name of 'chaetotaxy'. This science must be left to its own votaries.

The thorax, then, carries the wings, the balancers, and the six legs. The wings are present in all 'large' species, though absent in some parasitical and ants'-nest species, which are all 'small'. Their veining is of use in distinguishing the various flies, but little mention of it will be here needed. As regards the shape of the wings, there is one point which must be mentioned. In many flies the wings have a projecting bulge or lobe, close to the body on the hindmost edge of the wing. Often there are two or even three such lobes in succession before the main sweeping curve, which surrounds the wing, begins. It is, however, the lobe nearest the body (called the *squama*) to which attention must be drawn. Some flies have this lobe so large as to cover and conceal the balancers, while in others these lobes are small or lacking. The following sketch gives extreme instances of the two types:

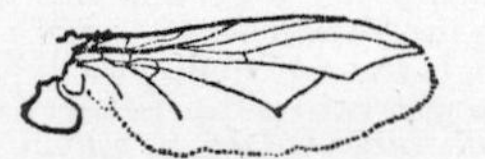

Sarcophaga
Large lobe. Balancer hidden

Tipula
No lobe. Balancer seen

The balancers (*halteres*) represent the hind wings of other insects. In shape they are tiny balls at the end of short sticks thrust outwards and backwards from the thorax: short and minute knobkerries: half dumb-bells: collar-studs without their bases. In function they have evidently something to do with the sense of balance (hence the name), as some flies, when deprived of even one of them, are incapable of flight. They are present in all except a few 'small' and degenerate flightless species.

In the **abdomens** of the flies the 1st and 2nd segments are usually small or lacking. Often four or five segments are visible. In the highest types the segments from 7 to 10 go to make up the egg-laying tube (*ovipositor*) in the female, and are small and curled up under the body in the male.

The legs are immensely variable in length and usefulness in walking or running. They have all five joints in the feet (*tarsi*), and the main difference used in distinguishing families lies in the arrangement of the 'toes' at the end of the last joint. Almost all have two claws, but some have three similar lobes, or flat pads, upon which they walk, while in others the central 'toe' (*empodium*) is lacking, or replaced by a mere thread. These three types are here sketched.

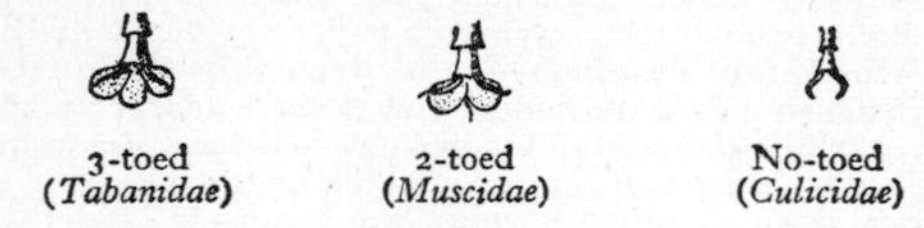

3-toed (*Tabanidae*) 2-toed (*Muscidae*) No-toed (*Culicidae*)

HABITS. Like other insects which have the usual three changes, the only period of growth in the fly's life is the larval stage. It is a common mistake to believe that when we see a swarm of small flies or gnats we are looking at the young of some larger species and that they will grow up. They will not. Once they are flies, they are full grown. Any food that they take in the adult stage is used only to replace the moisture lost by evaporation, and to supply the material wasted in the energy of movement or the processes of procreation. Thus it is found that the females, which have to build up the substance of their large masses of eggs, are almost always more voracious than the males.

Very few male flies suck blood, human or animal. The males of none of the 'large' flies do so, and there is only one family, containing 'large' species, in which the males of any of the 'small' species do so (three species of the *Muscidae*). The 'small' parasitical *Pupipara* is the only group in which both sexes are blood-suckers. All other blood-sucking flies are females only.

The great majority of the Diptera are diurnal (the main exceptions are among the *Culicidae*), and flight is necessary to them as a preliminary to pairing. Often the males will be seen to fly, or to dance in formal patterns, weaving in and out or up and down, or swooping in questing dashes from a chosen perch, seeking or awaiting a mate. The males are usually shorter-lived and soon die after once they have paired. After pairing the females begin to feed much more than before. In the case of the blood-sucking-female families it is at this stage, apparently, that the habit develops. Of the families here treated, these are the following: the *Tabanidae*, *Culicidae*, and some of the *Chironomidae*. The males of all these content themselves with flower nectar, or other sweet, or putrid, liquids. The females, when they have fed and the eggs are ripe for laying, seek out a suitable place where the larvae hatching from their eggs will find their appropriate food. This usually demands warmth, moisture, and decay of some kind, or, in the case of those whose larvae require an insect or other living host, the eggs must be laid on or near the creature needed. Those which lay in or on water must find a pond or pool, however small, in which the water has impurities to feed the larva. When all the eggs are laid the mother usually dies, but before the eggs are all ready to be laid the fly may have to return several times to her sources of food.

Most flies need a fairly high temperature to sustain life.

They get through our winter either by finding warm places or by a retardation of the immature stages which carries them over the cold months. Some produce several generations a year, others only one.

CLASSIFICATION. Of no Order of the insects is the classification so confusing to the learner. Even the main groups, or sub-orders, into which they are divided seem to have no perceptible differences between them. The reasons for this state of things are two. In the first place the structural differences between flies of different families are visible only under a powerful lens. Have the antennae three or more segments? Is there a frontal suture between forehead and antennae? How large are the wing lobes? What is the form of the toes? Is the trunk soft, or hardened by a horny plate on its under side? How are the wings veined? Where are there bristles on the body? &c., &c. In the second place many of the most important distinctions—those indeed upon which the great groups depend—are not matters readily perceptible in the adult flies, but differences in the form and behaviour of the immature stages—matters of past history when you have the fly before you. Did it emerge by lifting a lid in the pupal case, or by bursting the skin in a slit? Had the fly a bladder covering its head when it emerged, and for a few minutes afterwards? Had it, when it was a maggot, a head, and, if so, did it have jaws which worked up and down, or sideways? As well try to sort out a batch of Chelsea Pensioners by the regimental badges they wore forty years ago!

After this apology to the beginner, all that one can do is to set out the classification of those of our families which contain 'large' flies, and hope that he may either master it as he gets to know the creatures—or invent a better.

CLASSIFICATION OF THE *DIPTERA* OR TRUE FLIES

CYCLORRHAPHA Pupa rests in the larval skin, hardened.	*SCHIZOPHORA* with a bladder to help the fly to emerge from the pupa case, which leaves a scar on the face of the fly.	*CALYPTERAE* with large lobes, covering the balancers.	*Muscidae*	House Fly, &c.
			Larvaevoridae	Flesh Flies and Parasites
			Oestridae	Warble Flies
		ACALYPTERAE Balancers not so covered.	*Gastrophilinae*	Bot Flies
	ASCHIZA with no such bladder or scar.		*Syrphidae*	Hover Flies
ORTHORRHAPHA Pupa free, the larval skin having been discarded.	*BRACHYCERA* Larval head incomplete. Mandibles work vertically. Short antennae.	*HETERODACTYLA* Two similar lobes on each foot, between them a mere hair or nothing.	*Bombyliidae*	Bee Flies
			Asilidae	Robber Flies
		HOMEODACTYLA Three similar lobes on each foot.	*Tabanidae*	Gad Flies
			Rhagionidae	Snipe Flies
			Stratiomyidae	Soldier Flies
	NEMATOCERA Larva with head. Mandibles bite horizontally. Long, many-jointed antennae.		*Culicidae*	Gnats
			Chironomidae	Midges
			Tipulidae	Daddy-Long-Legs

GROUP *CYCLORRHAPHA* [Circular suture]

FLIES EMERGING FROM A LID

CHARACTERS. This group is distinguished chiefly in the immature stages.

The **larvae** are without visible heads, their heads being withdrawn into the next segment.

The **pupae** are inert and formed inside a tough leathery skin which is that of the larva. When the time for the emergence of the fly arrives, there is found to be a thin circular line round the front which, on pressure from within, breaks and thus leaves a round hole for the emergence of the fly. The **adult flies** of this group have a special organ (called a *ptilinum*) which acts as an egg-tooth to force open this lid, and as a pick to open a passage to the surface for the new-born fly. This is a bladder which is forced out through the suture which surrounds the face and is inflated from within. Once the fly is out, this bladder-nose is deflated and withdrawn into the head and is never again seen. The only external sign of its having existed is the scar-like appearance of the face suture (*frontal lunule*).

The **adult flies** have short antennae, consisting usually of three joints, from the last of which springs a thread (*arista*) or a thicker spike (*style*). This is sometimes bare and sometimes feathered and springs, not from the end of the antennae, but from the forward side of the hanging 3rd joint (called the dorsal side). The general appearance is shown in the sketch.

They all have feet in which the central pad (*arolium*) is either completely absent or replaced by a mere thread (*empodium*). Such flies are said to be *heterodactyle.*

The sexes differ markedly in the size of the eyes, those of the males occupying almost the whole of the head, while those of the females are comparatively small.

CLASSIFICATION. Those Cyclorrhapha in which the scar appearance is most marked are called *SCHIZOPHORA* [scar-bearers]. Of the Schizophora that contain large flies, there are three families of *CALYPTERAE* (*Muscidae*, *Larvaevoridae* and *Oestridae*) and one sub-family of *ACALYPTERAE*, the *Gastrophilinae*, here treated with the *Oestridae*.

Other Cyclorrhapha, in which there is little or no sign of the frontal lunule, are called *ASCHIZA* [scarless] and are divided into numerous families of which we are concerned only with the *Syrphidae*.

FAMILY *MUSCIDAE* [Flies] HOUSE FLY, ETC.

(The most recent classification of these flies treats them as a sub-family, *Muscinae*, grouped with the *Anthomyinae* (see p. 129). But the method here adopted seems more convenient for this book.)

Twenty-three British species, all 'small'

CHARACTERS. Flies with comparatively few bristles, lacking those just above the hip-joint of the hind legs. The mouth-parts are fully developed and are strengthened with sclerotized rods and plates. When they have any bristles on the abdomen, these are at the tail end only. The threads of the antennae are feathered to their ends. The wings are shaped with a large lobe near the body (*squama*) which covers the balancers (*halteres*), and the veining is marked by the mid-vein (shown in the accompanying sketch) bending forwards so as to touch, or almost touch, the vein in front of it.

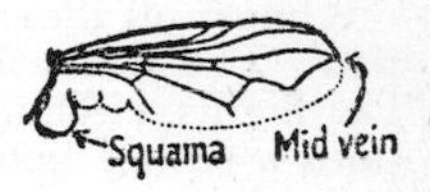

The larvae when first hatched have breathing spiracles only at the tail end, though, later, spiracles are developed at both ends. They pupate, like all the Cyclorrhapha, in the toughened larval skin, emerging through a lid.

HABITS. The **larvae** are mainly filth-eaters. Some eat excrements, others decaying animal or vegetable matter of any kind, cheeses, or carrion. They will also eat meat or fish, and some species eat the festering flesh of mammals. The front end of these maggots, or gentles as they are variously called, is equipped with a pair of hooks, working side by side, to draw the creature forward into its food. These hooks discharge a digesting salivary fluid on to the food which makes it liquid, as in that state alone can the maggots absorb it. Though totally sightless, the maggots crawl away from light, and, when about to pupate, go an inch or so into the ground, or into some crevice, for the purpose.

The **pupae** are enclosed in the last, fully grown, larval skin which is hardened with an additional coat to make it into the pupal case which characterizes the Cyclorrhapha. When the enclosed pupa is ready for the fly to emerge, the nose-bladder is used first to open the lid in the larval skin, then to discard the pupal skin, and lastly to make a vertical tunnel up to the surface. When the fly gets there, the nose-bladder is inflated with blood for the last time, carefully cleaned, and then finally drawn back into the head.

The **adult flies** will usually be found resorting to the same substances for their food as those which the larvae eat, and to which, therefore, the females go to lay their eggs. There are some things, bread and sugar for example, to which flies go rather for their own food than to lay their eggs. They also settle on men and animals to suck sweat.

Almost all flies must fly together before they are able to pair. The males of many species gather together in dance-like flights, circling, or 'weaving', under a tree or chandelier until a female approaches them and joins them, when one male seizes her and leaves the dance to pair. The males of others wait in the sun and fly off upon short exploratory flights whenever another insect is seen or heard, returning to the same spot if it proves not to be an unattached female. The choice of a suitable spot in which to lay the eggs is governed by temperature, moisture, and the proximity of the larval food. After pairing the hunger of the females increases and they feed between the laying of each batch of eggs. Those of the Muscidae which do not bite are, nevertheless, conveyors of disease upon their feet and in their excreta and, particularly, from their mouths owing to a habit of regurgitation before feeding, which is presumably useful in partly digesting and softening their food before it is sucked up by the proboscis. Thus the germs of many diseases are carried by them from garbage, excreta, and midden to milk, sugar, bread, meat, or other food.

Though all the family are 'small', two at least must be dealt with here if only for their nuisance value. The first of these is ***Musca domestica,*** the House Fly. Common as is this most dangerous and disgusting insect, there is some doubt as to its usual life history. There is no doubt that it takes a longer or shorter time to go through the various stages (egg, larva, and pupa) according as the temperature is cold or warm. It is, however, doubtful whether it actually hibernates, or, as seems more likely, continues to breed all through the year in warm or artificially heated places from which the stock which survives the winter builds up again the vast numbers of flies which are found at the end of the summer. The great majority of these die off when the cold comes. The eggs are about 1 mm. long and are laid in masses of 100–150 at a time and to a total of 600–1,000 in human or horse dung, or in any form of decaying animal or vegetable matter. Under hot and damp conditions (77° to 95° F.) the eggs take about ten hours to hatch, the larvae about a week to pupate, and the pupae anything from a few days to a month before the fly emerges.

Three species of the family are (in the adult stage) bloodsuckers, and of them both sexes practise this habit—not, as is usual among the Diptera, only the females. These bloodsuckers are particularly dangerous to man and beast as conveyors of the germs of disease, their probosces, steeped in carrion, filth, or the blood of diseased persons, driving the germs into the blood of the next victim of their bites. Apart from contamination, their bites are innocuous.

The second fly to be described here is one of these, ***Stomoxys calcitrans*** [kicking Sharp-mouth], or the Stable Fly. It can be known from the House Fly by its piercing proboscis which, unlike that of the House Fly, cannot be withdrawn into the mouth. It attacks man and beast, particularly in the legs. Its larvae feed wholly upon horse dung or muck composed of it, and it is responsible for much disease.

The entire family, therefore, may be regarded as highly dangerous to man, and everything possible should be done to destroy them. The most useful steps are the covering, or destruction, of refuse heaps to deprive them of breeding-places, and the ruthless trapping, poisoning, and swatting of the adults.

The *Anthomyinae* [Flower-flies], which are now usually included in the Muscidae, are also all small and very numerous. They differ in the form of the antennae and in their wing-veins, but are otherwise similar. Although some are very annoying to gardeners (their larvae are mainly vegetable eaters), none are such pests as to earn admission to this book.

FAMILY *LARVAEVORIDAE* [Larva devourers] FLESH FLIES AND PARASITES

About 330 *British species, of which about thirty-six are 'large'*

CHARACTERS. In general appearance this family differs little from the last. They are more bristly about the body and, in particular, have a row of bristles on the thorax, just above the hip-joint of the hind legs and beneath the hinder spiracle of the thorax. The three groups, or sub-families, into which they are divided are so different as to require separate treatment.

The *Calliphorinae* [Beauty-bearers] have few, if any, hairs on the upper side of the abdomen and are mostly what are commonly known as Bluebottles or Greenbottles. Their antennae are like those of *Musca* above described. One alone of them is often 'large', ***Calliphora vomitoria*** [emetic Beauty-bearer], the Large Bluebottle (*p. 16*).

This fly is usually found near, rather than inside, our houses, on walls in the sun or, sometimes, on flowers. The females alone usually enter so as to lay, which they do upon meat, fish, or strong cheeses. Their eggs are also found on carrion or other decaying matter. They are laid in repeated clutches, the mother dying as soon as her ovaries are empty.

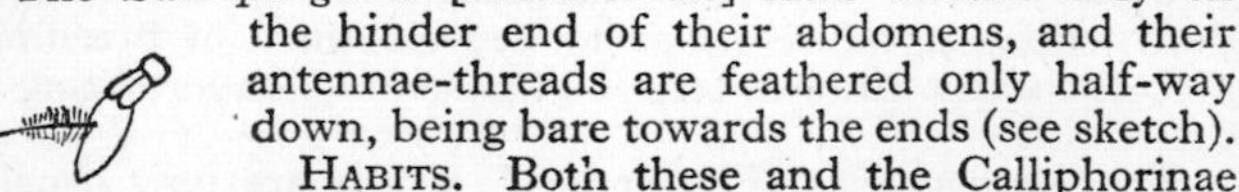

The *Sarcophaginae* [Flesh-eaters] have bristles only on the hinder end of their abdomens, and their antennae-threads are feathered only half-way down, being bare towards the ends (see sketch).

HABITS. Both these and the Calliphorinae have larvae which (like those of the Muscidae) live upon almost all forms of decaying matter, but particularly upon carrion or dead meat. They are often larviparous, that is to say that their eggs hatch as, or before, they are dropped by the mother. Some 'small' species have larvae which are parasites upon insects, earthworms, snails, &c. Many of the larvae are cannibal, and, after the food upon which they are laid is exhausted, they eat each other. This habit is regarded as beneficial to the species, as it ensures the survival of a maximum number of flies from a given supply of food!

Some species drop their new-born young (which are very small) upon meat from a height if they are not able to get nearer to it. Thus Fabre found that ***Sarcophaga carnaria*** [meat Flesh-eater] (*p. 16*) would drop larvae from a height of two feet through a wire 'meat-safe' cover. Such covers are, therefore, useless unless the part over the meat is without holes. This fly is mainly an outdoor species, found on flowers in the sunshine, upon excrement, or upon carrion. It drops as many as 20,000 larvae, in batches of a dozen or so. The larvae have an apparatus for closing and opening the spiracles at the tail end so as to avoid being drowned in the liquefied putrescence. These vast numbers are needed to overcome the wholesale destruction of the maggots by beetles and other enemies.

The *Larvaevorinae* are distinctly more bristly than other members of the family, having not only terminal bristles, but also bristles all over the upper part of their bodies. With very few exceptions the threads of their antennae are bare, thus:

They almost all lay eggs rather than give birth to living young. Their larvae are all parasitical and mainly upon the larvae of butterflies or moths. Some choose hymenopterous larvae and a few other Diptera. A few species live in, and upon, the flesh of adult Coleoptera, Orthoptera, or Hemiptera.

The eggs are laid directly upon the caterpillar or other host (rarely upon its food-plant) and apparently usually upon the head. They must not be confused with the Ichneumon Flies, which are Hymenoptera having similar habits.

In addition to those species which directly parasitize another insect by laying eggs on its larvae, there are flies of this family which destroy one species by laying on the insects of another species which the first has captured and laid by as provision for its young. Thus, as we have seen, the Digger Wasps provide insects for their young. As the mother wasp is taking her prey into the nursery, at the moment when she is half underground and the body of her prey between her legs is still outside the hole, a *Larvaevorid* fly rushes in and lays an egg, or several eggs, upon its body. These eggs develop more swiftly than those of the wasp and thus the fly maggots eat the food provided and then, if still hungry, they eat the wasp grubs themselves, which thus either die of starvation or are eaten by the maggot. In either case from the carefully stored larder of the Digger Wasp will emerge the young of the *Larvaevorid* fly. One of the strangest cases of this sort was recorded by Fabre. The victim was a *Bembex*, a wasp which feeds her young during the larval stage. Though showing clear symptoms of alarm, she not only failed to kill the fly (which she could have done with the greatest ease) but, after the fly larvae had developed in her nest, continued to bring them food.

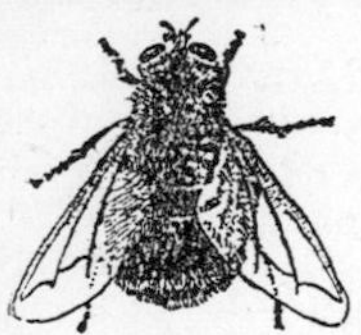

The largest of our *Larvaevorids* is ***Larvaevora grossa*** [fat Larva-devourer] (*p. 16*) which lay its eggs on the larvae of various moths (*Hyloicus*, *Lasiocampa*, and *Macrothylacia*), which are thus destroyed. The adult flies are found on plants of the daisy and parsley families.

FAMILY *OESTRIDAE* [Gad-flies]

WARBLE FLIES AND BOT FLIES

(In this family are included the *Gastrophilinae* [Belly-lovers] or Warble Flies, although many writers separate them because their halteres are not covered by lobes on the fore wings, so that they can be classed with the Acalypterae. They have, however, the same absence of mouth-parts and general habit of life as the Oestridae, and are therefore here included with them.)

Nine British species, of which two are 'large'

CHARACTERS. Mouth-parts reduced to a mere rudiment. Adults ephemeral, living for not more than a day or two. The larvae are internal parasites upon the larger vertebrates. Various species attack the ox, horse, ass, sheep, and red-deer. They fly very swiftly and with a powerful humming which terrifies cattle and may render horses dangerous.

Our largest species is ***Hypoderma bovis*** [ox Underskin] or Cattle Warble Fly (*p. 16*). Its habits are typical of the family as a whole. The adult is very rarely seen, but is said to frequent pasture lands and to fly so low as to be confined within its field, if surrounded with a hedge of moderate height.

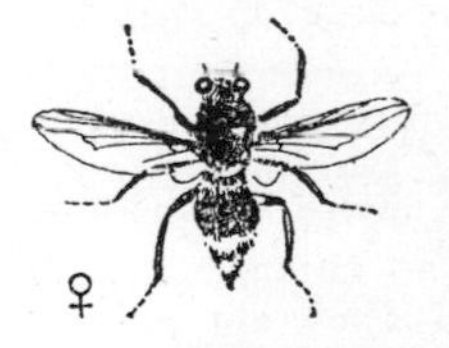

The female lays her eggs, singly, upon the hairs of the legs of cattle. Within four or five days the larvae hatch out and eat their way through the skin of the beast and then travel, inside the body of their host, until they reach the gullet, where they live from late summer until December. They then move, still inside the beast, to the back, where they form ulcerous swellings (or 'warbles') in the hide, on each side of the spine. These warbles destroy the value of the skin to the tanner and ruin the health and milk yield of the cattle. In May the warble-larvae pierce the hide and protrude the hind spiracles so as to be able to breathe the air, and finally crawl out and fall to the ground where they pupate, in a hardened residue of the larval skin, in the same manner as the other Cyclorrhapha. The pupal state lasts from five to six weeks and the adult fly's life is for a day or two only.

As yet no adequate protection against warble flies has been found. The only course appears to be to destroy the larvae after the harm has been done and so destroy the next generation. This course is ordered by the Ministry of Agriculture and may be effected by squeezing the warbles or (better) by washing with a derris wash in mid-March.

The large group of about thirty families known as *ACALYPTERAE* (flies without such lobes on the fore wings as to hide the balancers) are, with the exception of the *Gastrophilinea*, composed of 'small' flies and need not be here treated.

The last group of the Cyclorrhapha consists of those flies which have no bladder (*ptilinum*) for use during emergence, and in which the scar or frontal suture is poorly developed or absent (*ASCHIZA*). Of these again there are a great number of families, only one of which—the *Syrphidae*—contains any 'large' species.

FAMILY *SYRPHIDAE* [flies] HOVER FLIES

About 230 *British species, of which some twenty-five are 'large'*

CHARACTERS. This family forms an easily known group. They are almost always (1) brightly coloured flies often resembling wasps or bees; (2) having the habit of hovering, with swiftly moving, kestrel-like wings; (3) with 3-jointed antennae bearing on the front of the 3rd joint a thread-like *arista* usually unfeathered as sketched on p. 131; and (4) with a characteristic veining of the wings, which is seen in the accompanying sketch. Note, first, the presence of a vein-like thickening (*vena spuria*) in the middle of the wing, dotted in the sketch, and, secondly, a shaping of the veins which gives the appearance of a second wing margin round the outer edge. There is no large lobe at the base of the wing, so that the balancers are clearly visible.

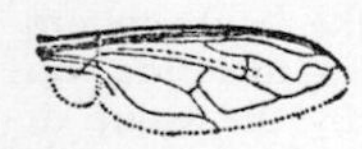

The males have usually large eyes which touch each other, while the females have them wide apart.

The larvae have all very small heads and are of three diverse types:

(1) Eaters of Aphids (Green Fly). These are somewhat slug-like in appearance, being flattened along the under side. They fix themselves upon an Aphis-covered plant, seize the Aphids one by one, suck them dry, and throw away the husks. They have been known to destroy as many as 120 green flies in an hour and feed both by day and night, so that they are most useful to man.

(2) Eaters of filth: dung, decaying vegetation, or foul muddy water. These are short-bodied, with, in the case of the water-dwellers, a long 'rat-tail' breathing-tube at the rear end which is protruded above the surface of the liquid.

(3) Eaters of the refuse from the nests of bees or wasps, which are in form much like the filth-eaters which have not rat-tails.

In addition to the above there are a few larvae of eccentric form, having spines and patterns upon them, and there are a few species which are destructive to vegetation, eating narcissus bulbs.

When about to pupate the Syrphidae either go underground, or else fasten themselves to a leaf or twig, so that the pupae are found among the vegetation. They use the final skin of the larva as a case for the pupa as do the other Cyclorrhapha, but the emergence is abnormal, the fly not lifting a lid and, apparently, not having any *ptilinum* for the purpose, but coming out of a break in the back of the pupa case. The adult flies are usually found upon flowers, or hovering over them in the sun, and their food appears to be chiefly nectar. They do not pierce either animals or vegetables. The greater number of species are smooth and none have bristles, though some, particularly those which do the cleaning of the nests of Hymenoptera, are very hairy.

Two species are here illustrated, ***Scaeva pyrastri*** [pear-tree Sinister] (*p. 16*) as a type of the Aphis-eaters above described, and ***Volucella bombylans*** [buzzing Swift-flier]

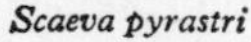
Scaeva pyrastri

Volucella bombylans

which is a bumble bee- or wasp-nest species. Its larvae live in the nests of the Hymenoptera a life which is, apparently, wholely useful to their hosts, as they eat the excreta of the hosts' larvae and any dead or decaying matter. These Syrphidae were long suspected of eating the larvae of their hosts, but it seems to be proved that they are, on the contrary, valuable domestic servants.

The *ORTHORRHAPHA*, or flies emerging from a slit in the skin, are divided into the *BRACHYCERA* and the *NEMATOCERA*.

GROUP *BRACHYCERA* [Short horns]

Flies with short antennae,

which leave the pupal skin by a slit

Characters. This group is distinguished from the Cyclorrhapha by the method of emerging from the pupal stage, and from the Nematocera by the antennae.

The **larvae** are sometimes apparently headless (the heads being retractile and withdrawn into the next segment, as are those of the Cyclorrhapha), and sometimes have visible heads. These are small, and their mandibles are hook-like and move vertically up and down.

The **pupae** are sometimes mobile, or free, and sometimes inert, with all the limbs enclosed in a single undivided skin. The larval skin is not retained (as it is by the Cyclorrhapha) and hardened to form a leathery shell for the pupa during the period of change. It is usually discarded before pupation, or if, as sometimes happens (*Stratiomyidae*), it is retained, it is not hardened but merely kept as a loose covering to the pupa. In the absence of the tough, lidded pupa-case of the Cyclorrhapha, these flies have no frontal bladder (*ptilinum*) or, later, scar into which it has disappeared. The adult emerges from the pupa by a slit, or split, in the head of the pupal skin, made without special apparatus.

The **adult flies** have short antennae, consisting of three segments, though the 3rd, composed of a fusion of numerous segments once possessed by an ancestor, is often marked with rings. Sometimes it ends with a fine bristle. These bristles are, however, at the end of the 3rd segment and continuous with it, and not sprouting from its front as is almost always the case in the Cyclorrhapha. There is no difference between the antennae of the two sexes. The eyes of the males are usually larger and in contact with each other. Those of the females are smaller. The maxillary palpi are turned up and are made up of from one to three segments.

Classification. The main division of the group is as follows: There are species in which the central one of the three toes on the feet is (as in the Cyclorrhapha) reduced to a mere thread, or is totally lacking. These are called *HETERODACTYLA*, and of them there are two families demanding attention here: the *Bombyliidae* and *Asilidae*.

Other species have all three toes, or pads, alike, the central pad (*empodium*) being similar to those on each side of it (*pulvilli*). These are called *HOMEODACTYLA*, and have three families containing 'large' species: the *Tabanidae*, *Rhagionidae*, and *Stratiomyidae*.

FAMILY *BOMBYLIIDAE* [Bumble flies] BEE FLIES

Twelve British species, of which four are 'large'

CHARACTERS. Antennae 3-jointed and thrust forwards. Three simple eyes. Small balancers. Long wings with strong veins.

This family consists of hairy flies, often with bristles on the body, which are mainly concealed in the hair, long and slender legs, and, usually, a long stiff proboscis or beak. They fly swiftly, and sometimes for long distances, and hover over flowers. Their beaks serve to reach the nectar of the flowers from the poised, hovering position, as none of them pierce or suck either animals or vegetables. Many of them bear a strong likeness to the bees or other Hymenoptera of which, in the larval stage, they are parasites.

Their LIFE HISTORY is remarkable. The mother fly lays her eggs, usually dropping them from the hovering position, outside, but near, the nest of the bee to be victimized. From the egg hatches a young larva which is a slender, agile creature with numerous bristles near the head and tail which enable it to crawl, and a coronet of spikes upon its head. This crown makes it possible for the larva to bore its way through the hardest materials, such, for example, as the masonry with which the mason bees build the cells in which their young are enclosed. This provision is needed because the mother fly has no egg-laying organ (*ovipositor*) capable of putting her eggs into the bee's cell. The young larva, as soon as it has wormed its way into the cell, moults for the first time and completely changes its form, becoming a growing larva. In this form, which lasts until the larva is full grown, it is a soft, smooth small-headed maggot, having no spines or power of locomotion, and no mandibles or other mouth-parts except a mere sucking aperture. The need for this stage is explained by Fabre, who first studied the life history of a French species of the same family. In the case which he studied the food of the fly-larva was the pupa of a mason bee. These host-pupae are separately enclosed in hard cells of masonry built by the bee-mother. The fly-larva takes about three weeks to grow to its full size, and this time is spent in wholly consuming the substance of the bee-pupa. The empty skin of its host is left with it in the cell. If, in the process, the pupa were to be killed, it would at once rot and become poisonous. The slightest injury to the pupal skin, nerves, or air-passages would kill it. It can, however, be slowly sucked dry of its substance—through the unbroken skin, and this is done by a toothless, smooth, and treacherous bedfellow. Where the gimlet-headed and spiny form of the young larva would kill it, and therefore the fly larva die, the slow transfusion of substance is successfully effected by a tender, smooth, maggot, master only of the Judas kiss. The substance of the young bee passes into the larva of the fly, and the parasite is ready to pupate.

The first stage of the fly-pupa (or pre-pupa as it is often called) is much like that of many other flies. It is a free pupa, one, that is, in which a form is assumed which is externally like that of the adult fly, while its internal organs liquefy and are regrouped into those of the adult. Now is the time for the fly to emerge; but it cannot escape. It is still enclosed in the cell of its supplanted host. A bee could eat its way out, but a fly, with tenuous legs and a sucking mouth, would be like a nun bricked in. A further change of form is required and duly takes place. The pre-pupa develops a final pupal armature as soon as it has muscles with which to use it. This is once more a crown of spikes upon the head and a bristling hedgehog equipment of spikes along the abdomen. It becomes a hard-shelled battering-ram, breaks down the wall of the cell, and protrudes its forward end, so that the adult fly can emerge.

The species here illustrated is ***Bombylius major*** [greater Bumble-fly] (*p. 16*), and its larvae are parasites upon the pupae of mining bees and solitary bees. Its eggs are scattered, while the mother hovers, over banks where the bees' nests are. The adults hover over flowers and suck their nectar.

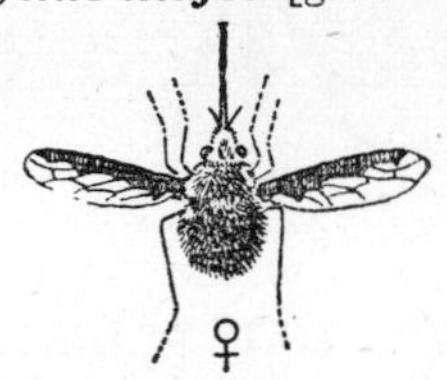

FAMILY *ASILIDAE* ROBBER FLIES

Twenty-six British species, sixteen of which are 'large'

CHARACTERS. Long-bodied, usually large flies, covered with bristles and with long bristly legs, ending in powerful claws, two small pads and a mere thread between them. They have prominent compound eyes, and a hairy beard round the mouth. The sexual organs of the males are noticeable and the females have hard, horny egg-laying organs. Their antennae are 3-jointed with an appendage at the end of the 3rd joint.

The **larvae** are hard-skinned, cylindrical, with small dark-coloured heads and sharp, cutting mandibles. They are usually equipped with leg-like projections and have antennae, but no eyes. They live in the soil or in sand, wood, or mould, and feed upon decaying vegetation or upon the larvae of other insects. **Pupation** takes place under ground, or in wood, and the pupae are also covered with spines.

The **flies** are exceedingly swift in flight, and they seize other insects on the wing and devour them, leaping upon their backs and thrusting their short horny beaks into the back of the head (sometimes the thorax) of their prey, which they then suck dry. There seems to be some evidence of a poison liquid being injected. Even the most powerful of other carnivorous insects are successfully attacked, including wasps, tiger beetles, and even dragon flies. The robber flies usually sit in wait for their prey upon bare patches of ground, logs, or fences, whence they dart out upon them. Both sexes live thus by rapine, though females are more often seen with prey. This is due to the longer life, and greater need for food, which characterize that sex in all the flies.

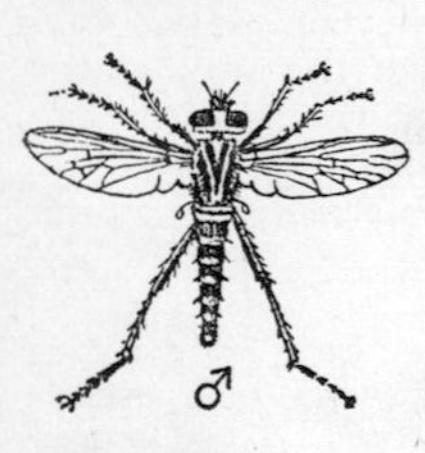

As an example, ***Philonicus albiceps*** [white-headed Lover of victory] (*p. 16*) is here figured. It is a dweller in dry, sandy spots and is common at the sea-side, its larvae living in sand.

FAMILY *TABANIDAE*

GAD FLIES, HORSE FLIES, AND CLEGS

Twenty-eight British species, of which twenty are 'large'

CHARACTERS. Flies without bristles. Antennae of three joints, the last of which appears to be segmented, but does not end in a thread. Eyes very large and spreading sideways. Proboscis short, in our species, projecting and, in the females, equipped with daggers for piercing the skin. The sketch gives the profile of a Tabanid head, much enlarged. They have large lobes (*squamae*) at the back of the wings, near the body, which do not, however, cover the balancers.

The **eggs** are laid upon plants growing in water, or marshy spots, in large masses. The **larvae** taper towards the head, which has visible antennae and powerful mouth-hooks. They have twelve segments, the first three of which are without appendages, and most of the others a

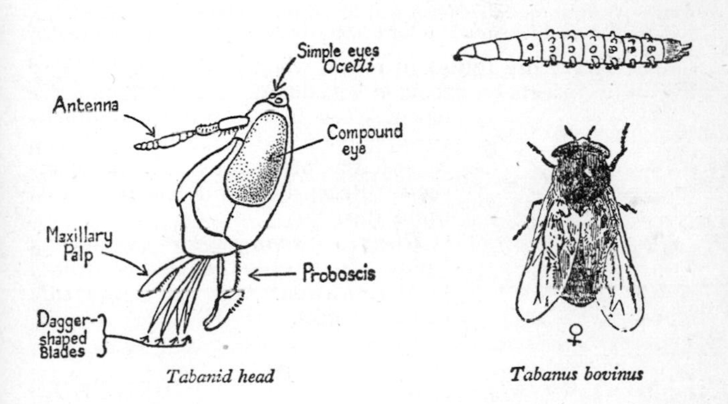

Tabanid head *Tabanus bovinus*

circle of fleshy pro-legs resembling those of a butterfly caterpillar. They breathe in air at the hind end only. They are found in wet soil or damp rotting wood, and all the 'large' species are carnivorous, seizing and sucking worms or insect larvae. Their form is as here sketched. The **pupae** are long and cylindrical.

HABITS. The **adults** are fierce and painful biters of man and beast, at least the females are. The males suck only water, honey dew, or the nectar of flowers. Most species, including ***Tabanus bovinus*** [ox Gad-fly] (*p. 16*) here illustrated, make a loud humming noise when approaching their victims, which, in the case of man, at least, is helpful as a warning. Others, such as the 'clegs' (*Haematopota* [Blood-drinkers]), approach in complete silence and are first perceived when they bite.

FAMILY *RHAGIONIDAE* [Spiders] SNIPE FLIES

(Including the *Xylophaginae* [Wood-eaters] and *Rhagioninae* [Spiders]

Nineteen British species, of which three are 'large'

CHARACTERS. Bristle-less flies. Antennae 3-jointed, often without apparent segmentation of the last joint, which ends in a style. Spurs on some of the shins of, usually longish, legs. No lobes (*squamae*) on the wings. Central toe-lobes (*empodia*) like those at the sides (*pulvilli*).
Their larvae differ much in form, some being flattened, others tubular.

The larvae are found in rotten wood or damp mould and live upon insects or decaying vegetation. The adult flies are harmless as far as biting or blood-sucking goes and have always been regarded as predacious upon other insects. Recently doubt has been cast upon this.

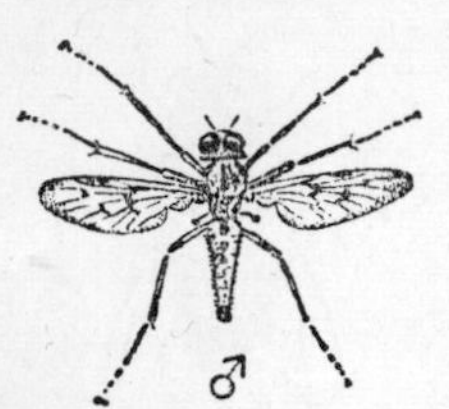

Rhagio scolopacea [woodcock Spider] (*p. 16*) has the habit of sitting, head downwards, on the sunny side of tree-trunks.

FAMILY *STRATIOMYIDAE* SOLDIER FLIES

Fifty-three British species, of which six are 'large'

CHARACTERS. Bristle-less, and mainly smooth, flies. Antennae 3-jointed, with the 3rd joint more or less distinctly segmented and usually ending in a thread. *Squamae* very small. No spurs on the shins. The name of 'soldier' comes from the armature of spikes at the back of the thorax, which is often developed into a hump. The foremost wing veins are thick and crowded. Three similar-lobed toes.

They are sluggish and feeble fliers, often found on umbelliferous plants in damp places.

The eggs are laid on the surface of water or on plants near water, or, in some cases, in dung or soil.

The larvae have thick, leathery skins. Some are flat, others tubular, and they are mostly aquatic. The aquatic species float with the tail up to the surface. The hind spiracles are protected by a crown of hairs, in which, when they dive, they carry an air bubble with them. They feed on living creatures in the water. The terrestrial species eat decayed matter and, sometimes, excreta.

When the larva pupates, it retains the larval skin loosely surrounding the free pupa, as a protection or float.

Among our larger species is ***Stratiomyis chamaeleon*** [chameleon Soldier-fly] (*p. 16*), a common species on plants in marshy ground, the larvae of which are aquatic. Like all other members of the family, it has but an imperfect proboscis, and neither sex pierces the skin, or sucks the blood, of any vertebrate.

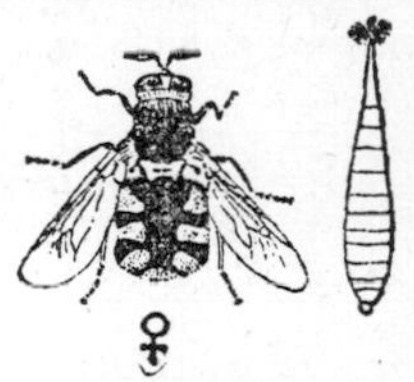

GROUP *NEMATOCERA* [Thread-horns]

Flies with long antennae,

which leave the pupal skin by a slit

Characters. This group is distinguished from the Cyclorrhapha by the immature stages, and from the Brachycera by the antennae.

The **larvae** have well-developed heads, with mandibles which move horizontally.

The **pupae** are free, usually capable of movement, and often rapid movement. The larval skin is not retained by the pupa, and the adult insect emerges from the pupal skin by a slit at the head.

The **adult flies** have long many-jointed antennae, thread-like and consisting of at least ten segments. Those of the males are usually feathered, with longer divergent hairs at each joint. The maxillary palpi are long, erect or drooping, and made up of four to six segments. The compound eyes are alike in the two sexes and rarely touch each other for more than a short distance.

They are mostly long-legged and slim-bodied flies and the females (never the males) are often blood-suckers.

Classification. Here, owing to the small size of most of the flies of this group, only three families are dealt with: the *Culicidae* and *Chironomidae* for the nuisance and danger which they cause to man, and the *Tipulidae*.

FAMILY *CULICIDAE* [Blood-suckers]

GNATS OR MOSQUITOES

Forty-nine British species, all of which are 'small'

This family is divided into three sub-families, *Culicinae*, *Dixinae*, and *Chaoborinae*. The following remarks apply only to the *Culicinae*.

Though 'small', these insects earn for themselves a place in this book by their painful habit, confined to the females, of sucking our blood. One

Culex *Anopheles*

Larvae and Pupae

genus, *Anopheles*, has, by the genius and industry of the late Sir Ronald Ross, been found to be the carrier of the parasite producing malaria. This scourge, which for centuries made vast tracts of fertile land uninhabitable, could, when once explained, be combated and overcome. This has been done so well that the Roman Campagna is rapidly becoming the granary of Italy, and the Panama Canal zone, which sank the fortunes of De Lesseps and slew the workers who went there to dig, has become a winter health resort.

Here it will be enough to mention two of our species, ***Culex pipiens*** [piping Blood-sucker] (*p. 17*), the Common Gnat, and *Anopheles maculipennis* [spotty-winged Importunate], the Malaria Gnat. The larvae of both these gnats are aquatic. The eggs of *Culex* are laid in a mass of 150–300 which forms, as it were, a raft upon the surface of the water, while those of *Anopheles* are laid on the water singly. The **larvae** of both creatures have large heads and hairy bodies and feed upon minute impurities or forms of life found in the waters. The chief apparent difference between them is that, while the *Culex* larvae lie head down in the water, feeding below the surface and breathing through a tube which stretches up to the surface at the tail end, those of *Anopheles* lie flat under and along the surface of the water. Both creatures can do with very small pools of water such as the rain pools retained in the bark of trees, so long as the water contains algae. *Culex* can breed in brackish water. The larvae swim about in the water and feed themselves by fanning it towards their mouths with the palpi.

The **pupae** of both are very similar and very active, swimming with a pair of transparent lobster-like fins at the tail, and breathing at the surface through two small trumpets, one at each side of the head. A film of oil spread on the water enters their breathing-tubes and is one of the most effective ways of killing off these pests, whether those which carry disease, or those which merely make night hideous to the would-be sleeper.

The adults of the family (*Culex pipiens* is here illustrated) are very slender, with six piercing daggers in the mouth as well as a sucking proboscis with which the blood is absorbed. Their palpi are stiff and bent upwards and the antennae of the males densely feathered, while those

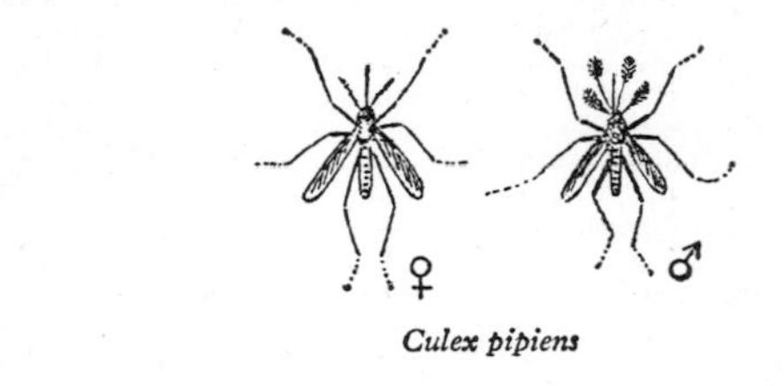

Culex pipiens

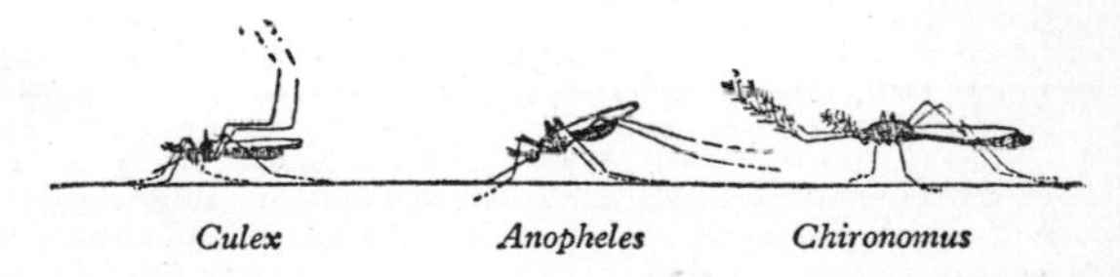

Culex *Anopheles* *Chironomus*

of the females have only a few hairs branching from each segment. The wings are fringed with scales along their veins and round the hinder margin. The position assumed when they are at rest is the easiest way of distinguishing the dangerous *Anopheles* from the irritating, but not dangerous, *Culex*, which, fortunately for us, is far the commoner genus in this country. The almost horizontal position of the piercing mouth-organs and the cocked-up hind legs indicate *Culex*. There is no difference in meaning between the words 'gnat' and 'mosquito', the latter being merely a Spanish word more recently adopted.

FAMILY *CHIRONOMIDAE* [Hand-flourishers]

About 380 *British species, of which one is, sometimes, 'large'*

CHARACTERS. Delicate, gnat-like flies. Antennae feathered in the males and thread-like in the females. No simple eyes. No piercing mouth-parts.

The one species which sometimes attains the length of half an inch is ***Chironomus plumosus*** [feathery Hand-flourisher] (*p. 17*). It, and other members of the family which are like it, lays its eggs, enveloped in a yellowish string of gelatinous matter, fastened to the bank or to vegetation growing at the side of still water. Unlike the *Culex*-larvae, those of *Chironomus* rarely swim. They go down to the bottom of the water, where they crawl about and build themselves mud tubes from which their heads stick out. They feed upon minute animal and vegetable substances floating in the water and become blood-red in colour. They are known as 'blood-worms'. At the end of the pupal stage they come up to the surface, where the adult fly emerges from a slit at the back of the pupa's skin, and the adult, after resting for a moment on the surface of the water, flies off. The flies may often be known from the Culicidae by their habit of resting with the fore legs raised and continually waving, as though they were organs of sense. The males of many species may be seen 'dancing' in clouds of thousands, before pairing, and while awaiting their mates. These clouds appear to be very sensitive to sound-waves, expanding instantaneously if spoken to, as if impelled by an electric current, and then resuming their former shape.

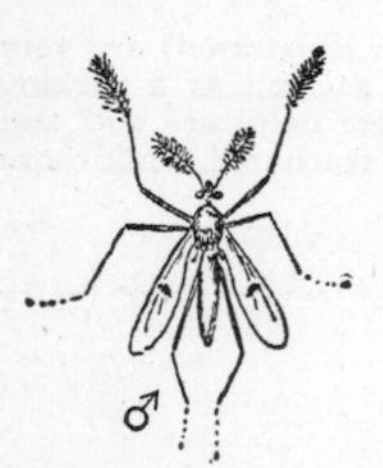

Formerly classified as a sub-family of this family, but now given independent rank, are the *Ceratopogonidae* [Bearded horns] or Midges. These flies are all 'small'; indeed the largest of our species does not exceed 1·5 mm. They are included here as being among the most irritating of all our insects. There are about 135 British species, of which the females of 29 are blood-suckers and, although they are present in England, it is only north of the Tweed that their annoyance is fully felt. They are voracious and with their bite insert an inflammatory fluid which to some is even more irritating than that of the Culicidae, though the ill effect appears to be less enduring. Some species are more venomous than others, and different persons are very diversely affected.

FAMILY *TIPULIDAE* [Water spiders]
DADDY-LONG-LEGS OR CRANE FLIES

Nearly 300 British species, of which 210 are 'large'

CHARACTERS. Mostly long and large flies. Their antennae are long and usually with many segments, though sometimes those which are the longest have only six segments. The antennae of the males are often comb-like, but not feathered. No simple eyes. Legs long and fragile. They have a V-shaped suture in the middle of the back of the thorax. The females have a horny ovipositor. Their larvae usually breathe at the hind end only. The species differ much in shape, in wing-veining, and in colour. Many of the species have clear transparent wings, while those of others are variously stained. The long legs and the V-shaped suture are almost always distinctive. The greater number of species, when at rest, hold the wings outspread and not along the body as do the Culicidae.

Their mouths are sometimes beak-like, but they do not have the piercing daggers of the gnats, and they use them only for sipping moisture, upon the surface of which they are able to stand while they do so.

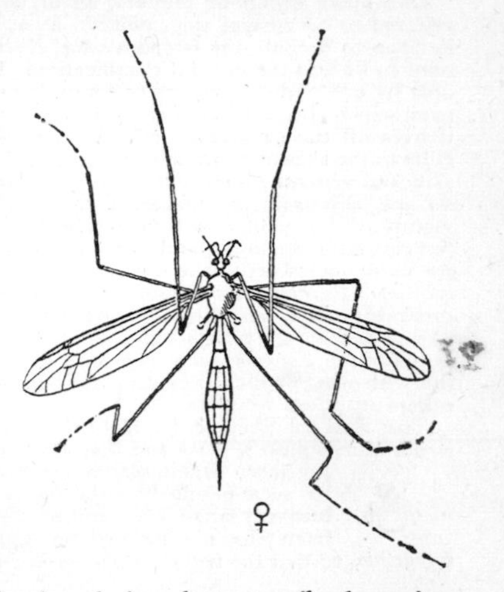

Some of their larvae are aquatic, others terrestrial. Their heads are usually half-hidden in the next segment (though in some they are fully developed and displayed), and they have antennae and chewing mouths, and the aquatic species have gills and a crown of retractile appendages round the breathing-holes at the tail end.

Our commonest species is ***Tipula oleracea*** [vegetable Water-spider] known as the common Daddy-Long-Legs or Crane Fly (*p. 17*). It is found mostly in damp woods or pastures, and the female lays her eggs (by lowering the abdomen vertically into the soil) in crannies in the ground among the grasses, the roots of which feed its larvae (commonly known as 'leather-jackets'). The larvae hatch in about a week and are often very destructive in garden or meadow, remaining underground for almost a year and there pupating. The pupae, also brown or grey, are cylindrical, usually with two horns on the forehead for breathing.

The adults fly heavily and clumsily, mostly in damp woods or fields, and often hang by the fore legs when at rest. There is only one generation a year.

GROUP *PUPIPARA* [Pupa-bearers]
FOREST FLIES AND KEDS

One other group of Diptera, all of which are 'small', will be here referred to because of their oddity. If, as is usually the case, the group is taken to include the *Hippoboscidae*, *Nycteribiidae*, and *Braulidae*,[1] it is hard to fit into the general classification. The *Braulidae* are represented only by one minute creature (1·5 mm. long) without wings, balancers, or eyes, which clings to hive bees and is by them carried into the hive, where it lives off the garnered food. All the others are blood-suckers which cling to the skin of mammals or birds, or else dig themselves in under the skin and remain there. Although sometimes fatal to birds, they rarely do any serious injury to horses, deer, or sheep, which are their chief victims. The peculiarity from which the group gets its name is that the females have feeding-glands which enable the young to go through all the early stages up to the formation of the pupa inside the body of the mother. Immediately before pupation the larvae are dropped to the ground, pupate, and the fully developed fly emerges. The bat parasites (*Nycteribiidae*) are wingless and wait for their hosts at their resting-places. Some of the *Hippoboscidae* have fully developed wings, while others start life with wings which they drop as soon as they have found a host, and others again are wingless.

The Ked or Sheep-tick, ***Melophagus ovinus*** [sheep Sheep-eater], is our commonest species and may be found on the sheep all through the year. It is in search of this delicacy that the starlings may be seen perched on the backs of the sheep. It has normal, but very small, eyes, and no wings. The young are extruded from the mother just as their skin is hardening into the *puparium*, so that the name 'pupa-bearers' is, though barely, justified.

In addition to the above families or groups, there are some forty-eight others (the exact number depends upon the classification adopted) which consist wholly of 'small' flies and are not mentioned in this book.

[1] A. D. Imms has now shown that the affinities of this family are with the *Acalypterae*, see classification on p. 125.

ORDER *SIPHONAPTERA* [*Tube-Wingless*]

FLEAS

Forty-seven British species, all 'small'

No book which has undertaken to notice such insects as attract our attention by the irritation or annoyance which they cause us can fail to give the discredit which is due to the Flea.

Pulex irritans [irritating Flea] belongs to a group which has irritated the entomologist otherwise than by biting him. He has found it hard to classify and has finally been driven to give it the rank of an Order to itself. Its members are wingless and yet they go through the usual three changes, egg, larva, pupa, and sideways-flattened adult being quite unlike each other. They are all suckers of the blood of mammals or birds, and although the different species have their favourite hosts, they will usually make the best of a bad job and take a bite at any other warm-blooded animal to whom their erratic leaps may have led them. Thus the human flea is often found on badgers, foxes, and other mammals, and the rat flea, which is the bearer of plague, bites man. The eggs are laid upon the body of the host, fall to the bedding or carpets, and hatch in from three to ten days. The larvae are not parasites, but eat any organic refuse they can find, including in some cases the excreta of adult fleas. They form a cocoon before pupating, and the adults remain some time in the cocoons after emergence, after which they get as soon as possible to their hosts. The adult flea's jump has been found to exceed a foot in length, and statisticians have taken pleasure in calculating this as equalling a 200-yards long-jump for a man of six feet in height. Others, equally ingenious, have calculated that, if the flea had muscles as efficient as our own, it could hop to a height of six feet!

ORDER *COLEOPTERA* [Case-Wings]

BEETLES

Over 3,600 *British species, of which about* 200 *are 'large'*

CHARACTERS. The usual three changes, every species passing through the four distinct phases of egg, larva, pupa, and adult beetle. The fore wings are hardened into horny or leathery cases (*elytra*), covering the whole of the hinder part of the

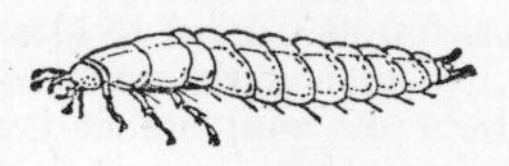

beetle's body, including the folded hind wings. The mouth-parts are adapted for biting and chewing. The fore part of the thorax is much the largest and is separately movable.

Note. There are many exceptions to the above generalizations which will be noted in the sequel. Thus some beetles (e.g. *Meloïdae*) change their form more than three times (*hyper-metamorphosis*). Some (e.g. *Staphylinidae*) have the wing-cases short, so that much of the body remains exposed. Some (e.g. certain *Carabidae*) have the wings rudimentary, or even absent, and the wing-cases soldered together and immovable.

ANATOMY. The **larvae** of the beetles differ greatly according to the life for which they are destined. In all, the heads and mouths are well developed; and in nearly all there are the six legs. They range from those of the *Curculionidae* (left) to those of the *Carabidae* (right). The former are virtually mere lengths of gut—sightless, legless, soft, except for the mouths and heads, with the mouth leading to a digestive tube which ends in a single vent. The latter larvae, which have to hunt for a living, have eyes, sometimes as many as a dozen (single—the compound eyes are reserved for the adults), antennae, and fully developed mouth-parts, six legs with two claws on the feet, and jointed tail appendages, and they have hard plates along their bodies. Between these two extremes is a series showing almost infinite variety and their general form may be long or short, flat, rounded above, or tubular.

The **pupae** are colourless and soft, with the features of the future adult clearly visible and the limbs free from the body; rarely (*Staphylinidae*) the pupae are surrounded by a liquid which dries and fastens the limbs down, though they still project from the body.

The **adult beetles** are, as above mentioned, covered and protected by the *elytra*, or wing-cases, which conceal from view, when closed, the 2nd segment of the thorax (from which, like all the fore wings of insects, they grow), and the whole of the body behind that segment, except for a small triangle (*scutellum*) of the 2nd segment which lies between the wing cases at their forward ends.

As are all insects, the beetles are made up of three parts, the head, the

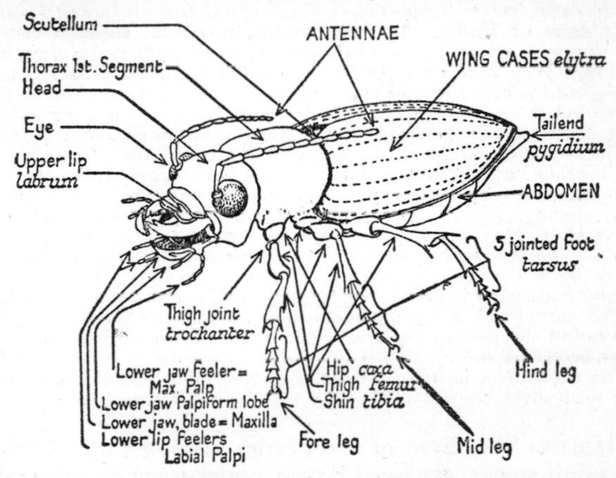

thorax, and the abdomen; but, in their case, the chief mobility lies between the 1st and 2nd segments of the thorax, and it is there, if at all, that there is a waist.

The **head** bears the eyes, antennae, and mouth-parts. The eyes—two in number and compound (some few species have a simple eye in addition)—are sometimes (*Gyrinidae*) encroached upon by the sockets of the antennae and may even be each divided in this way into two (making four eyes). The antennae differ greatly in form, though with very few exceptions they are made up of eleven segments. They may be hairy (*Carabidae*) or smooth (*Tenebrionidae*), long (*Cerambycidae*) or short (*Hydrophilidae*), threadlike, *filiform* (*Cicindelidae*), toothed like a saw, *serrated*, on one side (*Elateridae*), or equipped with long teeth like a comb, *pectinated* (*Pyrochroidae*). They may end in a club owing to the enlargement of the final segments (*Silphidae*), or they may have the last few segments formed like flattened blades, *lamellate* (*Lucanidae*). The segments may be all about the same length (*Chrysomelidae*) or they may differ much. Thus the 1st may be as long as all the others together. The antennae may be sharply elbowed, at right angles, after the 1st segment

(*Curculionidae*) or they may follow each other in a continuous line. All these differences are used in classification.

The mouth-parts of the beetles are always adapted for chewing and consist of an upper lip (*labrum*): two powerful main jaws (*mandibles*) which work from the sides, hook-tipped and often toothed; two smaller lower jaws (*maxillae*) which are forked at the end and, on their outer sides, carry two feelers (*maxillary palpi*); and a lower lip (*labium*) which also has two feelers (*labial palpi*) which spring from it (on either side of the tongue or *ligula*). This equipment, therefore, supplies two pairs of biting jaws and two pairs of feelers. In some families the outer half of the lower jaws is also a feeler, making three pairs. All these parts vary much, but the lower jaw feelers have usually four segments, the lip feelers three, and the outer part of the lower jaws, when it is a feeler, two. All these parts are of importance to the student, but not to us in this work.

The sketch on p. 151 will be sufficient to give an idea of the main parts of a beetle's body. On the under side the three segments of the thorax are seen, each with its leg. The legs may be suited for swimming, running, digging, or only for a slow crawl. The hips (*coxae*) differ much. Above all, the legs differ in the apparent number of the joints in the feet (*tarsi*). The normal number is five and this number is really present in all the 'large' beetles. Often, however, one joint is so small as to be visible only with a strong glass, and certain families became known as 4-jointed. As this forms one of the main distinctions between the groups, I will here forget the microscope and speak as though the tiny extra joint had never been found.

The **abdomen** is usually rigid and immovable and although it may have nine rings, the number visible may be reduced to four.

HABITS. The lives of the beetles, during both the larval and adult stages, are lived largely under cover or in the dark. As a result, we do not see them to anything like the extent that their numbers would suggest. Some are aquatic, the great majority terrestrial. Though most species are winged and can and do fly, they are not aerial in the same way as are the flies, dragonflies, or the Hymenoptera. A few species are carnivorous, the majority live upon plant life, and a large number upon decaying matter or excreta. In fact, there is hardly a substance, animal or vegetable, that has not a species of beetle to consume it.

The egg stage of most beetles is short (1–2 weeks or so), and the length of the larval life depends upon the quality and accessibility of their food. Those which soonest attain full growth and pupate are the kinds which have succulent and unstinted food around them, such as the Burying Beetles; the slowest to develop are those which feed on wood—not because it is scarce, but because it lacks nourishment. Thus the Stag Beetle's larva is said to live in its tree for three or four years before pupating. The pupal stage takes an average of about a fortnight, though it may last a year; and, when the adult emerges, it does so in a soft and uncoloured condition and frequently remains where it is for some months before facing the open air. Pupation usually occurs under ground and frequently in a case built by the larva out of its own dung. They have no silk glands.

Sometimes there are two generations a year and the winters may be spent either as larvae or as adult beetles. The life of the beetle very rarely lasts beyond the laying of the eggs, but in some cases the parents live to provide food for the young. Such is the diversity of habit that this subject must be left for treatment to the separate families.

CLASSIFICATION. No one can be proud of the classification of the beetles. The families are fairly well described and separated from each other. It is the division into the larger groups which is based upon weak distinctions. The following table gives the families which are here described, with the groups to which they are usually held to belong. But they are not in any satisfactory order, nor has any such yet been found.

In addition to the 23 families here dealt with, there are about 63 others found in Britain, containing nearly 1,000 British species.

COLEOPTERA

SUB-ORDERS, SUPER-FAMILIES, AND FAMILIES

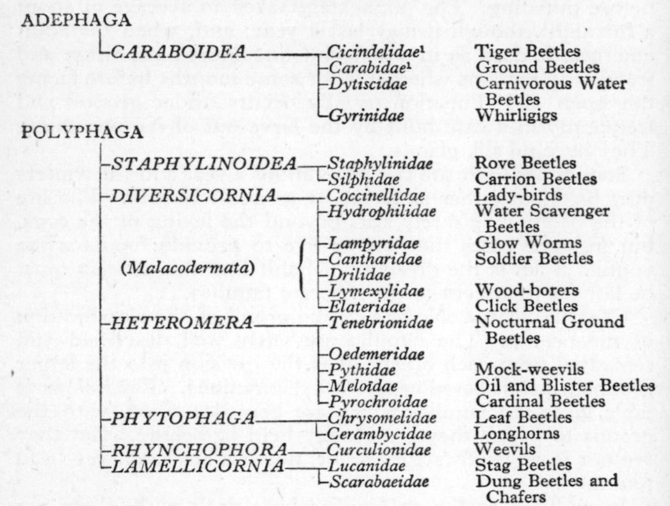

Sub-order	Super-family	Family	Common name
ADEPHAGA	*CARABOIDEA*	*Cicindelidae*[1]	Tiger Beetles
		Carabidae[1]	Ground Beetles
		Dytiscidae	Carnivorous Water Beetles
		Gyrinidae	Whirligigs
POLYPHAGA	*STAPHYLINOIDEA*	*Staphylinidae*	Rove Beetles
		Silphidae	Carrion Beetles
	DIVERSICORNIA	*Coccinellidae*	Lady-birds
		Hydrophilidae	Water Scavenger Beetles
	(*Malacodermata*)	*Lampyridae*	Glow Worms
		Cantharidae	Soldier Beetles
		Drilidae	
		Lymexylidae	Wood-borers
		Elateridae	Click Beetles
	HETEROMERA	*Tenebrionidae*	Nocturnal Ground Beetles
		Oedemeridae	
		Pythidae	Mock-weevils
		Meloïdae	Oil and Blister Beetles
		Pyrochroidae	Cardinal Beetles
	PHYTOPHAGA	*Chrysomelidae*	Leaf Beetles
		Cerambycidae	Longhorns
	RHYNCHOPHORA	*Curculionidae*	Weevils
	LAMELLICORNIA	*Lucanidae*	Stag Beetles
		Scarabaeidae	Dung Beetles and Chafers

[1] The Tiger Beetles and Ground Beetles have been recently reclassified as Sub-families (*Cicindelinae* and *Carabinae*) of the family *Carabidae*.

FAMILY *CICINDELIDAE* [Shiners] TIGER BEETLES

Four British species, of which three are 'large'

CHARACTERS. Long, hairy, slender, swift-running legs, with 5-segmented feet. Long, 11-jointed antennae, threadlike and tapering to a point, with their bases closer together than those of the main jaws (*mandibles*). The inner parts of the lower jaws (*maxillae*) end in a movable joint. There are six visible palpi, the outer part of the *maxillae* forming an additional pair.

The larvae have flat, spade-shaped heads, large jaws (*mandibles*), and eight simple eyes. Their legs are long, with two claws on each, and they have from two to six hooks on the upper side of the 5th segment of the abdomen.

Both larvae and adults are carnivorous.

HABITS. The Tiger Beetles are all useful to man as, throughout their active lives, both as larvae and as beetles, they destroy other insects. They are sprightly and active, very wary and hard to catch, as they run with great speed and readily take to flight to escape capture. They are diurnal in habit and will be found on bare ground or taking short flights in the sunshine. In dull weather they dig themselves into the sand or loose soil. They have an agreeable smell.

They are mostly brilliantly coloured, blue, green, chocolate, or black, with yellow transverse markings, from which, as well as from their sharp-toothed jaws and predatory habits, they have gained their English name. An interesting habit of a continental species of *Cicindela* is recorded: the males help the females in the process of laying their eggs. The female thrusts her abdomen deep into the soil to lay, the male meanwhile grasping her by the body and, when the egg has been laid, helping to pull her out of the ground. For a similar story see p. 264. This process has to be repeated as each egg is laid, because each larva will require its own dwelling.

When the larva hatches from the egg it digs itself a vertical hole by prolonging that in which the egg was laid to the depth of a foot or so below the surface, and in this hole spends all of its life as a larva. As soon as the hole is made, it climbs up it to the top, closing the aperture with its flat head, and retaining its position by the use of the hooks upon its back. In this position it waits for its prey, which consists of any small creature which may inadvertently walk over its head. As soon as this happens, the trap-door, formed by the head, opens, the victim is grabbed by the mandibles, and the larva retires to the bottom of its hole to devour its prey.

The adults use their long mandibles to capture and bite into their prey and they first drink up the fluids thus liberated

from the victim, afterwards eating the more solid parts. The hardest parts may be thrown aside. The Common Tiger Beetle, ***Cicindela campestris*** [field Shiner] (*p. 18*), is the commonest of our species, and I have illustrated it in larval, pupal, and adult stages.

FAMILY *CARABIDAE* [Beetles] GROUND BEETLES

344 *British species, of which thirty-seven are 'large'*

Characters. Long, swift-running legs, with 5-segmented feet. Antennae of eleven segments, threadlike and tapering to a point, usually covered from the 2nd joint onwards with a minute down, their bases being wider apart than those of the main jaws (*mandibles*). There are the usual four palpi, but the outer part of the *maxillae* is 2-jointed and resembles an additional pair. They are distinguished from the *Cicindelidae* by the absence of any movable joint at the end of the lower jaws (*maxillae*).

Many species are without wings, the wing-cases (*elytra*) being permanently closed and fastened together down the back. There are usually nine raised ribs on each of the wing-cases, the furrows between them being sometimes smooth and in others indented with dots, as are also their outer margins. Some are black, others brilliantly coloured with a metallic gloss.

The larvae have long 2-clawed legs and run freely. At the tail their bodies end in a tube with two, often jointed, tails at either side. They have powerful hooked mandibles.

The pupae show the feet of the hind legs projecting beyond their tails.

HABITS. Both larvae and adults are carnivorous, attacking insects, worms, snails, and slugs, and they also feed on dead animal life. A few species are eaters of cereals, plant seeds, and strawberries. Although they are mainly nocturnal, lying hid under bark or stones during the day, some species are about in the daytime.

The larvae spend the day under stones or in the soil and hunt for their food mainly by night, without the concealment afforded by the pit of the Cicindelidae.

The greater number of our large species belong to the genus *Carabus*, of which **C. violaceus** [violet Ground-beetle] (*p. 18*) will serve as an example. They hunt mainly by night, lying up in the soil or under some cover during the day, and are ruthless and voracious destroyers of any living thing which they can master, slugs, snails, other beetles or insects of all kinds. They attack by tearing out pieces of the flesh from any unprotected part, such as the flank beneath the wing-covers of beetles.

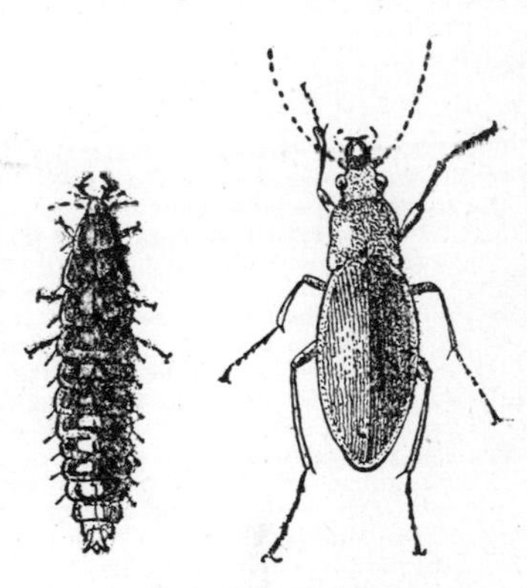

The prey is devoured piecemeal, until nothing succulent is left.

They pair promiscuously and repeatedly throughout the spring and summer, and in the early autumn the females attack and devour the unresisting males. The females dig into the soil until the following spring when the eggs are laid.

They do not usually leave the ground, though other genera climb trees after the caterpillars which frequent them. Other members of the family have wings and are capable of flight.

Many of the Carabids emit an acrid smell when frightened or pursued, and it is to this family that the small Bombardier Beetle (***Brachinus crepitans***) (*p. 18*) belongs. These little creatures have glands in their abdomens containing a few drops of liquid which they blow out in a minute explosion in the face of a pursuer. This tear-gas explosion can be repeated until the liquid is exhausted. The liquid is pulverized by the explosion, is phosphorescent at night, slightly corrosive, and stains the skin.

FAMILY *DYTISCIDAE* [Divers]

CARNIVOROUS WATER BEETLES

110 *British species, of which thirteen are 'large'*

CHARACTERS. Carnivorous beetles living in water, structurally similar to the Carabidae, having the long, threadlike, 11-jointed antennae and the six visible palpi, but adapted to life in the water. They have the hind legs flattened for swimming, while their hip-joints (*coxae*) are large and flat, adhere to the abdomen, and meet in a fork between the legs, the shape of which differs in various species. Their bodies are flat and rounded, and their wing-cases fit to the edges of the belly so as to admit of an air reserve beneath them which the beetle breathes when under water. This air is replenished when the insect projects its tail above the surface. The sexes differ in their fore legs, those of the males having the feet broadened and fitted with suckers with which they hold the females when pairing.

The larvae are also rapacious carnivora, living on small aquatic animals, fish, mollusca, or insects, including each other. They have tubular mandibles through which the juices of their victims are sucked, and they are said to inject a digestive fluid to liquefy the substance. They have eleven segments, with spiracles on the last segment only, which are continued as tubes, and raised to the surface when the larva breathes. The last few segments are often hairy, and these hairs help in swimming and in keeping the tail end above water when in its usual resting and breathing position.

Dytiscus marginalis [margined Diver] (*p. 18*) is the commonest of our large species and here illustrated. It very soon

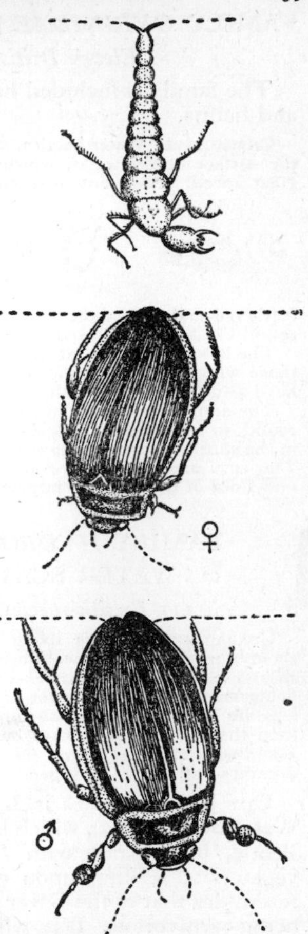

becomes the sole occupant of any aquarium into which it is introduced, as it will kill fish, frogs, or any other living thing which it can master, and it is surprising how large a victim it will overcome. The two sexes differ as here illustrated. The larva hunts its prey in the weeds at the bottom of the water, rising to the surface to breathe, until it attains full growth, when it climbs out of the water into the soil or moss and there pupates. This process takes two or three weeks, plus a further week for the adult to gain colour and hardness. If, however, the pupation takes place in the autumn, it is interrupted until the spring. After this, the beetle returns to the water, where it remains for the rest of its life. This aquatic life is broken by intervals of aerial flight, chiefly apparently at night, when the Divers spread their strong wings and fly to seek other waters where food or mates may be more plentiful.

There are in this species two different forms of the female, one of which has the grooved wing-cases here shown, while in the other they are smooth as in the male.

FAMILY *GYRINIDAE* [Whirligigs] WHIRLIGIGS

Eleven British species, all 'small'

The family is included here because of its oddness of form and habits.

CHARACTERS. Water beetles, small and round in shape, which float on the surface of the water, whirling round and round in figures of 8 at great speed. Their antennae are 11-jointed, the 2nd joint being large and ear-shaped, the others growing from its centre and being short and broad. The two complex eyes are each divided into two by the bases of the antennae, so that the beetle has four eyes, two under water and two above. The hind and mid legs are broadly feathered and very short, so that a stroke on either side spins the body round like a dinghy rowed with one scull only.

The larvae are provided with feather-like gills on each segment behind those which bear the legs. They are carnivorous, and their mandibles have a sucking-tube like that of the Dytiscidae.

The adults are usually in large numbers together and spin round and round, in search of animalculae at or near the surface. They do so only in the sunshine, diving into the water when a cloud passes, or if alarmed. The eggs are laid in horizontal rows on water plants, and the larvae crawl out of the water to pupate.

FAMILY *HYDROPHILIDAE* [Waterlovers]
WATER SCAVENGER BEETLES

111 *British species, of which two are 'large'*

CHARACTERS. Beetles living in water and in general appearance resembling the Dytiscidae. Their antennae are, however, quite different, shorter than the palpi, and heavily clubbed, the last three or five segments being enlarged and hairy for collecting air at the surface. Their hind legs are not flattened for swimming and they crawl under water more than they swim. They have only one visible pair of palpi, which are 4-jointed and long. Some species are terrestrial and live in dung or decomposing animal or vegetable matter.

Our largest species is ***Hydrophilus piceus*** [pitch-black Waterlover] (*p. 19*), which is often called the Harmless Water Beetle, in contrast with *Dytiscus*, because the adult is a vegetarian, feeding upon decaying water weeds. Its larva resembles that of the Diver both in appearance and in habits, being carnivorous. It is, when full grown, larger. The adults are the largest of our beetles (except perhaps the Stag Beetle), and their numbers have been reduced owing to their popularity as inmates of aquaria. In comparison with the swift, predacious Diver, *Hydrophilus* is slow and inert, appearing, as one writer remarks, to devote most of its energy to the preservation of the store of air which it takes under water to

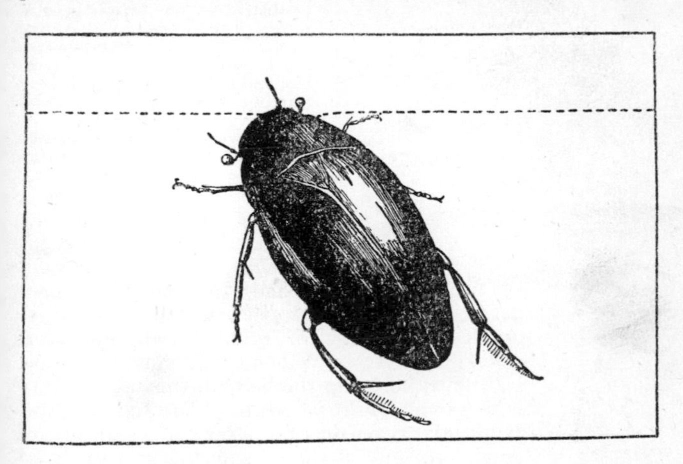

breathe. Certainly the greater part of the attention devoted by observers to the species has been upon this subject. It preserves a bubble under the wing-cases and upon hairs on the belly, and it seems to sweep in the air from the surface with the antennae. In this air collection it contrasts with *Dytiscus*, for it takes the air with the head and shoulder above water, not, as *Dytiscus*, by projecting the tail end.

All the terrestrial beetles of this family are small.

The female lays her eggs (some 50 in number) on water plants in a capsule with a point raised above the water level. When the young larvae are hatched they eat their way through the capsule and get into the water.

FAMILY *STAPHYLINIDAE*
ROVE BEETLES

929 *British species, of which only twenty-four are 'large'*

CHARACTERS. Very short wing-cases, leaving a large part of the abdomen visible. The wings are well developed and folded under the wing-cases. The back of the abdomen is hard-cased and very flexible, so that it can be curled up backwards. The number of foot-joints (five in all the 'large' species) varies much. The antennae are thread-like and have usually eleven joints (rarely ten or nine in some small species).

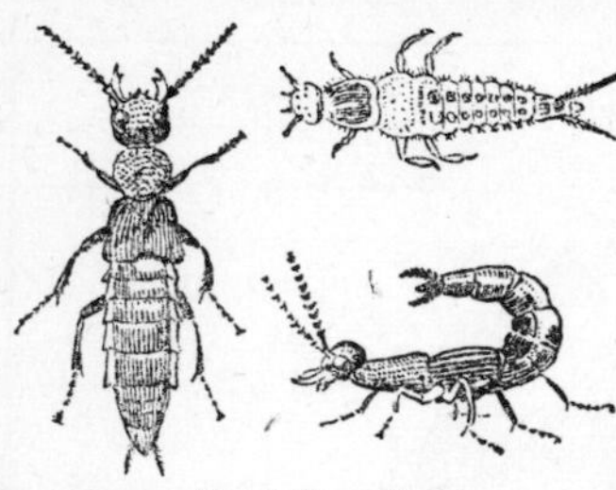

Staphylinus olens

The larvae resemble those of the Carabidae, but have only one claw on the legs. They are mainly carnivorous.

Our largest species, ***Staphylinus olens*** [smelly Parsnip] (*p. 20*), commonly called the Devil's Coach Horse, is usually found lying up in horse-dung or middens where it lives upon other insects. When running, which it does swiftly, it holds up the belly in the air, and, if it is threatened, it lifts both head and tail and from two stink-organs near the latter emits a disgusting smell. In spite of these menacing and unattractive habits it should on no account be destroyed, as it is assuredly of value to the gardener and quite innocuous.

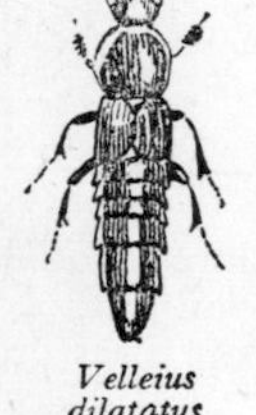

Velleius dilatatus

Several large groups of these insects are to be found only in the nests of some of the social insects —wasps or ants. Their relations with their hosts are very varied. Sometimes they are fed by the ants to the impoverishment of the ants' own young and of the whole nest, sometimes they even eat the ants' larvae, and sometimes they may act as scavengers in the nests. In return for the hospitality received they sometimes exude a liquid which their hosts lick up, but often they appear to be merely tolerated or even feared. Of these latter is our only 'large' species: ***Velleius dilatatus*** [broad-flanged Velleius] (*p. 20*). It lives this life of immune and permanent guesthood in the nests of the most redoubtable of the Hymenoptera—the hornet and wasps. It seems to be protected by its smell, and although it eats the wasp grubs, it is possible that it only eats such as have fallen from their cells and would perish in any case.

FAMILY *SILPHIDAE* [Beetles] CARRION BEETLES

116 *British species, of which only fifteen are 'large'*

CHARACTERS. When dealing with the 'large' species, there are only four genera to be considered—*Necrophorus Necrodes Silpha* and *Phosphuga.*

The first are usually brightly coloured and handsome beetles, of which ***Necrophorus vestigator*** [searching Gravedigger] (*p. 20*), chosen because it was the species studied by Fabre, will serve as an example. Structurally the adults have short wing-cases, cut off squarely at the ends and leaving uncovered the last few segments of the abdomen. They have the last few segments of the antennae enlarged into an almost spherical club-head, and five joints in all the feet.

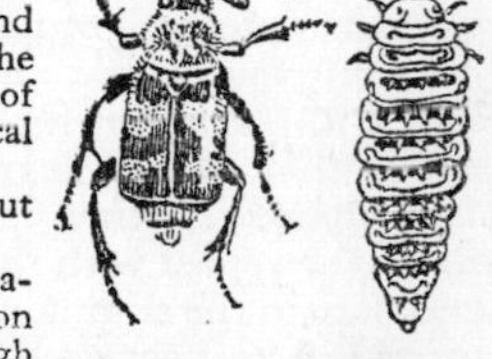

In flight, the wing-cases are held up well out of the way of the wings.

The larvae are broad, soft, blind, white creatures with narrow, hard and spiky scales upon their backs which help them to crawl through the soil to reach the chambers in the ground in which they pupate.

LIFE HISTORY. Most of the adult beetle's time is spent in concealment in a short burrow, about an inch in length, under ground. In the spring they come forth, guided by an intensely acute sense of smell, and, on the wing, make their way towards any dead and decaying meat the taint of which may have reached them. To the quality of the meat they are indifferent: mouse, mole, bird, lizard, toad, or even fish will serve. They are not deterred by its novelty: goldfish and a mislaid mutton chop will do. All it has to do is to stink. If the dead thing is too large for burial, it will be left, perhaps after a short meal, but, where its size makes the work possible, the sexton beetles set about its interment. This is done by burrowing under the body, and digging away the ground from under it until, by its own weight, it sinks into the hole made below. Then again the same process will be repeated: wherever the body presses on the beetle's back as he digs below it, he will dig: whenever it fails to come down to the new level, jerks and heavings of the beetles' backs will sooner or later overcome the trouble, and the downward course be resumed. If all goes well, the carcass will thus be sunk to a depth of a foot or so and covered by the soil excavated from beneath it. The burial is over, the soil enriched, and the air purified. The Sextons have earned our gratitude—see that they get it! But this operation was not for our benefit, nor for the personal benefit of the operators. It is for the next generation. As soon as the burial is over a single pair, male and female, is left alone with the dead. It is the nursery of their young, and all other beetles who may have helped in the burial leave them to their work, and resume their several posts as detectors of far-flung smells.

When the couple are left with the body, they proceed to skin and prepare it for the young and the eggs are laid, after which they usually leave it and come up to take part, if only as helpers, in other interments. Sometimes they stay and share the repast with the larvae, becoming lousy with Acarina and, late in the summer, come to the surface where they sometimes kill and eat each other.

The larvae hatch and attain full growth in about a fortnight after the burial, and, when full grown, burrow into the ground to pupate. Then, after a brief period of autumn life, they settle down for the winter under the surface, waiting to ply their trade in the following spring.

Fabre carried out a series of experiments to test the instincts of these beetles. They inspect the dead thing before beginning to dig and if, after the work has begun, the body fails to sink, they will again inspect it, and will cut any threads or stems by which it is held. If the hitch is traceable to something which they cannot cut, they will even amputate a paw, or any other small part, by which it is attached. They will also move the body, at least for a short distance, on to soil soft enough for their digging. Finally, if the job proves impossible and the body dries up, they will, after perhaps a week's work, leave it and begin again elsewhere.

Other Silphidae are also carrion-eaters, but without any skill as undertakers. They merely assemble to the scent of the dead and eat of its carcass, entrusting their eggs to it. They are smaller, flat, with less markedly clubbed antennae, and much smaller heads. Their larvae are more active, running about to seek their food, and they have a strong likeness to the extinct class of Arthropoda, the Trilobites.

Others again are wholly or partly vegetarians as, for example, the species here illustrated: ***Phosphuga atrata*** [black Light-avoider] (*p.* 20), the adults of which eat slugs while the larvae feed off beetroot, to the injury of those who grow that vegetable.

FAMILY *LUCANIDAE* [Wood Beetles]

STAG BEETLES

Three British species, all 'large'

CHARACTERS. Antennae 10-jointed, the last four segments forming a very distinct comb of which the teeth are long and immobile.

The largest of our species is the well-known Stag Beetle, ***Lucanus cervus*** (*p.* 20), and is so unlike any other species as to need no description beyond the sketch here given. It is the jaws (*mandibles*) of the males which are thus enlarged into stag-like antlers. It is very doubtful whether they have any practical use or are merely ornamental. They may be used to scratch the smaller twigs of the oak-trees, on which the beetles live, to make the sap flow, but the much smaller jaws of the females are far more effective, either for this or for pinching the human finger. The males vary much in size, and the longer the beetle the larger the head and jaws in proportion. The female digs herself in among the decayed wood of the oak and there lays her eggs. The larvae, when hatched, spend several years eating the wood and attaining their full size of as much as four inches in length, before coming down to the bottom of the tree, where they make, in the soil, a chamber of sawn wood in which to pupate. When

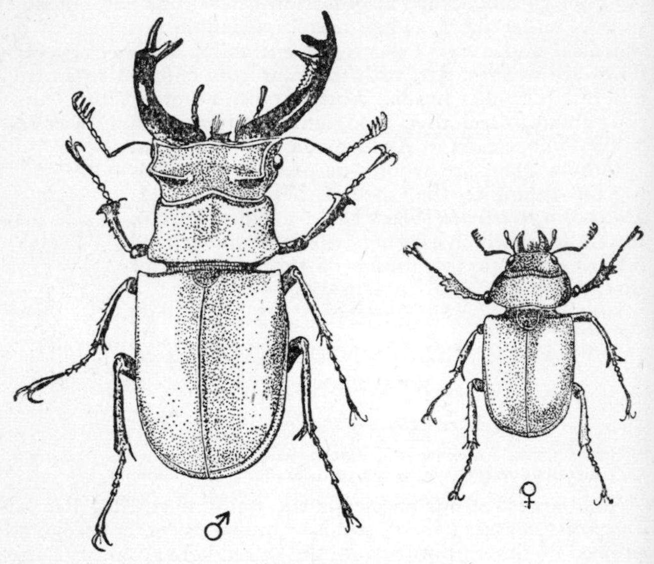

Stag Beetles

the adults emerge they remain for some time in this chamber to gain colour and hardness, not coming out into the open air until summer—about June. Their adult life lasts about a month longer—the only nourishment recorded being exudations from the trees. In captivity they live longer and they can be fed upon honey.

FAMILY *SCARABAEIDAE* [Scarabs]

DUNG BEETLES AND CHAFERS

Eighty-eight British species, of which seventeen are 'large'

CHARACTERS. Antennae have the last few segments developed into blades which are mobile and can be separated, or bunched together at will, by the insect. They differ from the Stag Beetles in this mobility of the antennae tips and in the fact that there is no special development of the jaws in the males.

The family includes a number of very different beetles which are most conveniently divided into those which, both as larvae and as adults, eat the dung of vertebrate animals, mainly the herbivorous mammals, and those which as larvae feed upon the roots, wood, or decaying leaves of plants, while the adults live upon their leaves or flowers.

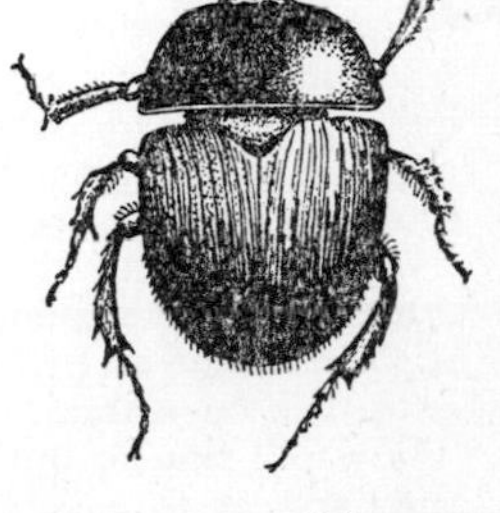

Of the British Dung Beetles we have eight which are 'large'. The commonest is ***Geotrupes stercorarius*** [dungy Earth-borer] (*p. 21*), the Clock, Shardborn Beetle, or Dumble-dor, here illustrated. All but one of our 'large' species belong to this same genus, and it may be considered as typical of them. We have a full account of its life from the pen of Fabre.

These earth-borers are remarkable in many ways. In the first place, their adult life is a long one. The eggs, which are large (8 × 4 mm.), are laid in the autumn, roughly during the month of October, and hatch in about a week or a fortnight unless the cold of winter supervenes, when they will lie dormant and not hatch until the spring. If not so interrupted, the larvae will attain their full growth in December, when, without pupating, they await the spring in a state of immobile hibernation. About April activity is resumed and they pupate in May, earlier or later according to the state of growth attained before winter. The pupal state lasts for a month or so, and the adult beetles remain under ground, gaining colour, hardness, and strength, until September when they come to the surface and begin their useful life of sanitation. Their life is not confined to a single season. They live for several years.

They come out about sunset, on warm and fine nights, and, flying with a slow and buzzing flight, make their way to some newly dropped cow-pator heap of horse dung. These are selected because of their maple size and not for any superiority of quality. Any animal's excrement will serve if amassed in sufficient heaps. Beneath the mass the beetles dig a shaft descending vertically for a foot or more into the soil, and this shaft they fill with a sausage of dung from the store overhead. So quickly do they do their work that the whole cow-pat may be underground before morning. During the day the beetles feed upon their hoard and, if the weather holds fine, they will fly off the following evening and resume their work elsewhere. As the mass of dung so interred vastly exceeds their food-needs, they are of great value to agriculture and sanitation, as they put the manure where it is most useful, just under the surface, and they keep the air pure by freeing the surface of the soil from excrement. Apparently once such a store has been made and left, the beetles never return to it. They will not go out to work unless it is fine and dry, and they appear to have an uncanny prescience of the weather.

The process of egg-laying and accumulating provisions for the next generation is different. For this purpose the shafts are less deep, as a separate shaft is required for each egg, so that the depth of the shaft is about a foot and its bore about an inch and a half. This shaft is bored by the two parents working together, and it is highly remarkable that, throughout the period of nest-making, the male takes a full share in the work. There is no other example of such paternal care for the young in the whole insect world—or indeed (except for a few cases, such as the Sticklebacks among the fish, and a few alien toads among the amphibians) in the rising scale of animal life until we get to the birds and some of the higher mammals. As Fabre says, even some men sink beneath the level of the Dung Beetle in this respect!

The hole made, the couple proceed to line it with dung, the male trampling it hard, and the female bringing down the supplies from above and helping in the work by plastering the inner surface with dung chewed and cemented with her saliva. When thus an almost waterproof lining has been built some six inches up the shaft, the male gets out of the way, and the egg is laid at the bottom of the boring and covered so that it is left in a small cavity protected by a well-cemented dome, after which the whole shaft is filled with provisions up to the top of the prepared lining. This store, again, greatly exceeds the needs of the larva for food (its abundance protects it against wet and cold), and thus again long after the young beetle has left the ground, valuable manure is left in the soil. The young larva eats its way up the centre of the accumulated pudding, pupates in a chamber eaten in it and, finally, the young beetle comes to the surface through the shaft, which, by that time, will have fallen in and be filled with earth.

When the eggs are all laid and winter approaches, the shafts dug by the parents for themselves become deeper and, sometimes at a depth exceeding a yard, the beetles dig themselves in and provision themselves for their winter sleep.

The strength of these *Geotrupes* is very great. It is not possible to hold them in a hand, however horny.

Another 'large' beetle of this family is ***Typhaeus typhoeus*** (*p. 21*), the male of which has an equipment of three horns on the thorax which he uses to push and roll pellets of sheep's or rabbit's dung. Their life history differs from that of the species above described in several particulars. They are not long lived, the males all dying of old age after supplying most of the pellets required for the nest which is dug by the female alone and victualled by her with separate sausages of dung furnished by him. He leaves the deep burrow (which may

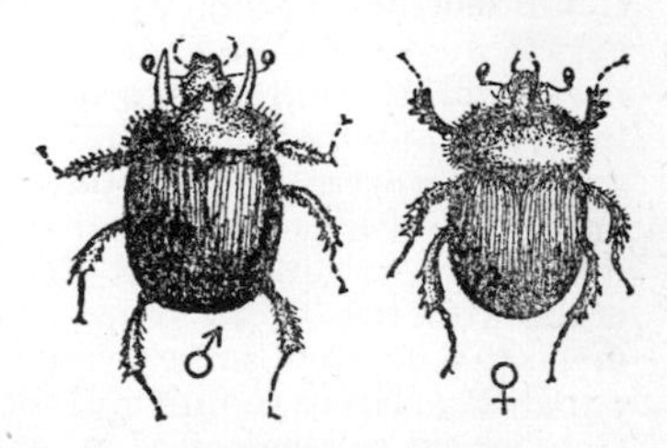

exceed a yard in length) just before his death, and his widow then gathers more pellets and finishes the work alone, placing each egg in a separate chamber, dug at the end of a short passage branching from the bottom of the main shaft and duly provisioned. About a dozen eggs are laid, in this case in the sand below the stores, and before the young are hatched, the mother also dies.

The plant-eating Scarabs, or Chafers, are, from man's point of view, the opposite of the Dung Beetles, as they are

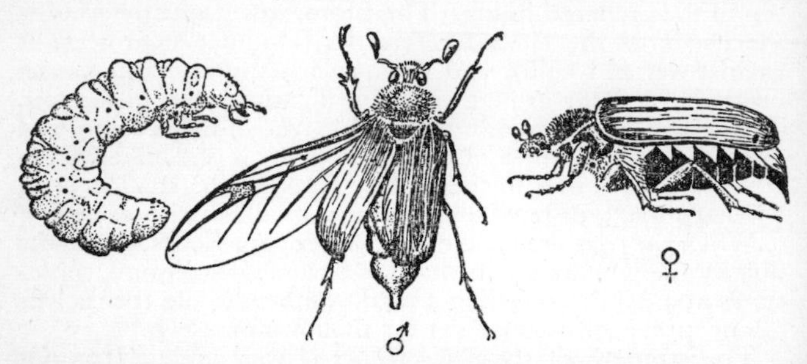

very destructive and of no value to him. The largest, commonest, and most destructive of all is ***Melolontha***[2] [Apple-tree-insect] or Common Cockchafer (*p. 21*). This insect lays its eggs in the early summer about six inches under ground, where they hatch in from four to six weeks and remain from one to four, possibly five, years, feeding upon the roots of corn and grasses near the surface during the warmer months, and retiring to a greater depth for the winters. They are most destructive to young trees. The first sign of their presence is the withering of the crop. When about to pupate they go down to a depth of some two feet and make an oval cell. The pupal stage lasts a month and the beetles stay in the cells from October till the end of May when they come to the surface. As adults they are hardly less destructive, feeding upon the foliage of oaks, chestnuts, and other trees. They lie hid beneath the leaves during the day, flying, sometimes in vast numbers, towards dusk. Rooks and gulls take heavy toll of both larvae and adults, and are probably our best defence against them. Pigs are helpful, and ploughing, and rolling, and beating the beetles from the trees may destroy vast numbers. In France, where rooks and gulls are comparatively rare, they often devastate large areas.

We have fourteen species of these chafers, of which nine are 'large'.

Another well-known member of this family is ***Cetonia aurata*** [gilded Cetonia] or Rose Chafer (*p. 21*). It is a common species and one of the handsomest of the beetles. Its life history shows a curious contrast to that of the Cockchafer. Laid in the early spring in dead leaf mould, the eggs soon hatch and the larvae feed quickly so that they are full fed and ready to pupate in about two months after the eggs were laid. The larvae are in one way remarkable. Though they have small legs, they do not use them for walking. They move about quite freely among the leaves, but always upside down, walking on the scales and hair which cover their backs. When they are about to pupate, the larvae, still among the leaves, build themselves a covering shelter, and here it is that the legs are used. With the legs they gather building material from their own vents, and then, using the legs as trowels, they make the pupal case of it. In the early summer the beetles emerge and all through that year appear to enjoy an idle and greedy life, eating the petals of roses, and enjoying fallen fruit in the autumn. They lie dormant under ground during the hottest part of the summer and again dig in to hibernate through the winter. In the following spring they pair and, deep in the leaf mould, lay their eggs and then die. So long an adult life, and especially so long an adult life before breeding, is most unusual among beetles.

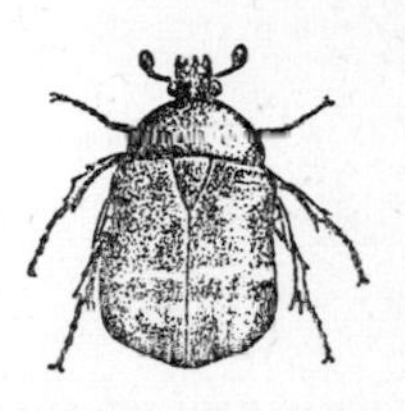

FAMILY *ELATERIDAE* [Drivers]

CLICK BEETLES OR SKIP-JACKS

Sixty-five British species, of which fourteen are 'large'

CHARACTERS. Long slim beetles with short legs and with the 1st and 2nd segments of the thorax loosely articulated. Antennae, 11-jointed and usually saw-toothed on the inner sides, spring from immediately in front of the eyes, which are large and round. The head is usually sunk into the thorax, which has sharp points at its hinder angles.

Under the 1st segment of the thorax is a sharp dagger-like point which, when the segment from which it springs is bent backwards, rests against

the forward rim of the next segment. When, by a muscular effort, this 1st segment is bent forwards, the dagger slips over the edge of the 2nd segment with a sharp click, and comes to rest in a sheath in the front of the 2nd segment. The jerk thus produced, if the creature is lying on its back, throws it into the air and thus enables it to right itself, which, with its short legs, it could not otherwise do. This accomplishment is characteristic of the whole family.

Their larvae are known as 'wire-worms', as are also the Myriapods (see p. 327), from which they can be distinguished by their having only the six legs of the insects. Their food is very varied. The majority live upon the roots of plants, but others seem to eat only decaying vegetable matter, while others again are carnivorous.

Adelocera murina [mouselike Hidden-horn] (*p. 22*) will serve as an example of the family, all the members of which bear a close resemblance to each other. It is fairly common in the south and midlands. It is sluggish afoot, but flies freely and well in bright sunlight. By sweeping grass, or hunting in moss, or garden refuse, they may be found when not on the wing. The skip takes them some three inches off the ground and it is repeated until they land right side up. The adults eat flowers as well as their nectar.

GROUP *MALACODERMATA* [Thin skins]

Ninety British species, of which four are 'large'

This group has been very variously classified, and it contains beetles which have been placed in no fewer than eight separate families. As, however, there are in the whole group only four large British beetles, it is here more convenient to take them together and to describe the four species. In common they have what the name implies, thin and flexible skins, and the same characteristic applies to their wing cases.

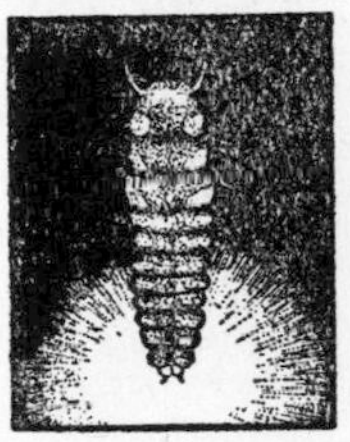

One of these is ***Lampyris noctiluca*** [night-shining Fire-lamp] or Glow Worm (Family *Lampyridae*, *p. 22*). This beetle is remarkable for two characteristics—the bright, bluish, light which it diffuses in the darkness, and the undeveloped and wingless condition of the females which, except for the fact that the claws of the adults are double, while those of the larvae are single, retain almost exactly the larval form. The males are smaller and, after pupation, have all the appearance of true beetles, including wing-cases and wings.

Every stage—egg, larva, pupa, and adult—has the light-giving power; all glow, more or less brilliantly, in the dark. The adults and larvae give out this light from two small organs on the under side of the last segment of the tail, and these points of light are clearly visible in the males in flight. The females, however, are better equipped for the art of self-advertisement as, in addition to the two points of light, they have much larger and brighter areas under the next two segments. The light is clearly, like other green lights, an invitation to come on, and is addressed to the other sex. As it is on the under side, the females, though usually almost motionless, will, when needing attention, climb up a grass stalk and wave their flashing tails with the impatience of an Isolde. The males fly freely at night, and their eyes are larger and more conspicuous.

The lighting system appears, to some extent, to be under the control of the insect, for, though rarely wholly extinct, it is at its brightest during courtship, fades almost to nothing during the act of pairing, and can be affected by treatment which annoys the creatures. The way the insect controls its production of light is not yet very clearly explained, but some process of oxidization connected with the air supply is involved. The light has nothing to do with phosphorus.

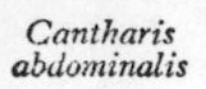

Cantharis abdominalis

Apart from their advertising talents, these beetles are interesting in another way. The larvae live upon snails and they kill and eat them by a method unique among the beetles. They nip them with caressing bites, injecting a secretion which produces instant paralysis of the snail and prevents its withdrawing into the security of its shell. The snail is not killed at first, and, if rescued, will recover in a few days. The secretion, however, ultimately reduces the substance of the snail to a liquid, which the Glow Worm laps up until nothing remains. While eating, it fixes the shell firmly in place, to prevent its falling, with a glue from its own vent, thus replacing the natural stickiness of the snail.

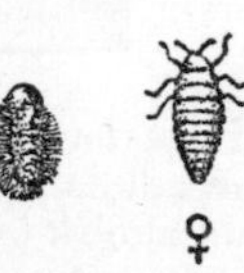

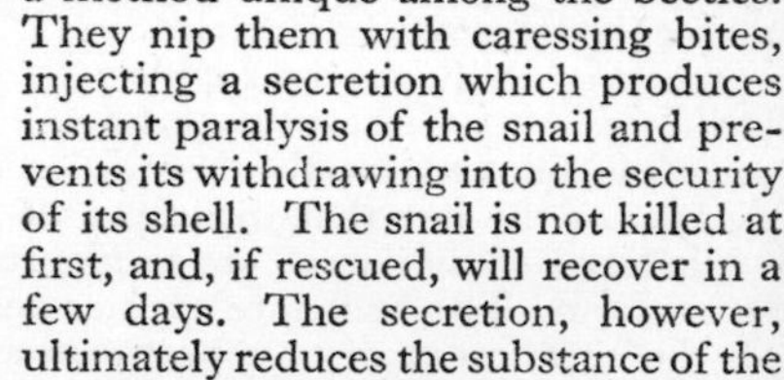

Drilus flavescens

The second 'large' beetle of this group is ***Cantharis abdominalis*** [bellied Corn-pest] (*p. 22*) or Sailor Beetle (family *Cantharidae*, Soldier and Sailor Beetles). It is a tree-dweller in hilly country and, in spite of its soft body, is carnivorous, preying, as larva, upon small worms and other insects, and, as an adult, upon small soft-bodied insects, and sometimes even upon others of its own species. The smaller and commoner species of this genus are found on flowers.

The third 'large' species of this group is 'large' only in the case of the females. This is ***Drilus flavescens*** (yellowish Earthworm, family *Drilidae*, *p.* 22). The males are small and of beetle form, while the females, like those of the Glow Worm, are wingless and larviform. Like the Glow Worm these beetles live on snails and then pupate inside the shells of their victims.

The fourth and last of the group to attain 'large' size is ***Hylecoetus dermestoides*** [dermestes-like Wood-dweller] (*p.* 22) belonging to a family of Wood-borers, known as the *Lymexylidae* [Wood-destroyers]. These are long cylindrical beetles with soft wing-cases, the males of which have very remarkable comb-like *maxillary palpi*. Their antennae are serrated on the inner side. They are to be found on oaks, fir, and birch, and the larvae bore deep horizontal galleries into the wood. The sexes differ in colour, the males being black, sometimes with reddish wing-cases, and the females reddish yellow.

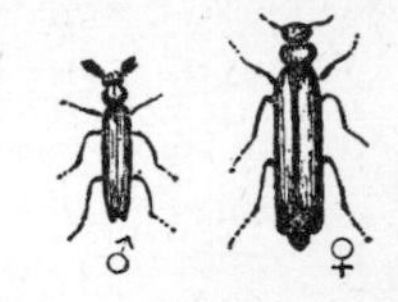

FAMILY *CERAMBYCIDAE* [horned] LONGHORNS

Over sixty British species, of which about thirty are 'large'

CHARACTERS. Large, often handsome, insects, recognizable by the long antennae, which, though they vary much, are often as long as, or longer than, their bodies. Usually the antennae spring from the eyes in such a way as to encroach upon their surfaces at the inner edges.

They are tree-dwellers, and most of the larger species are to be found upon the leaves or trunks of trees feeding from the sap which exudes from them.

The larvae are of tubular form, with small eyeless heads and tiny

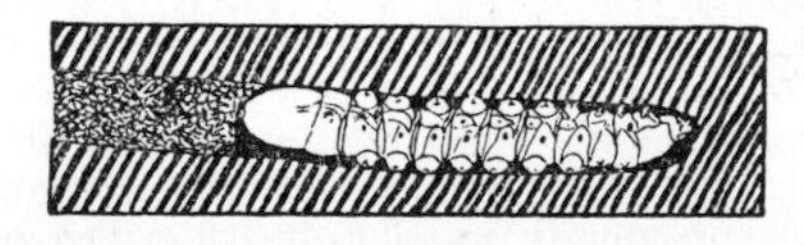

rudimentary legs. They have, all along the body on both upper and under sides, rows of fleshy prominences, or 'false legs', which can be swelled from within, or emptied, at the will of the creature. These organs give the larva its power of locomotion in its narrow tunnel, for they are all wood-borers, eating their way through the wood. Their progress is as follows. When the larva wants to advance, it holds on to its tunnel by filling the hinder false legs which press against the walls and hold it in place. It then draws in the forward 'legs' and stretches its body and head forwards. When a further stretch of the tunnel has been bored by the gouging action of the jaws, the creature swells out the forward 'legs', draws in the hinder, and shortens up the tail end of its body, thus making a step forward. The bore-hole is filled up behind the animal with the rejected fibrous filings, called 'frass', which form its excrement.

HABITS. Some Longhorns live in fresh wood, others (more in number) in decaying tree-trunks, and some in cut timber. The poverty of nourishment in dry wood results in their spending a long time in the larval stage. There is a record of a Longhorn Beetle emerging from yellow pine forty-five years after the felling of the wood.

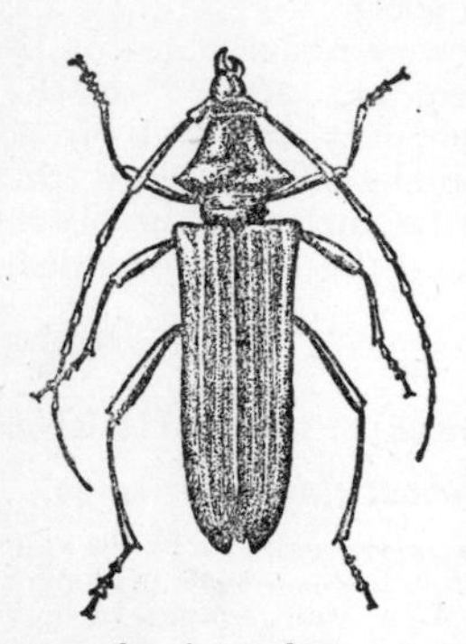

Aromia moschata

These tree-borers differ in their methods. Some bore deep into the heartwood of their trees, others remain in the bark, or just under it, until the time to pupate arrives. Then the exit of the adult beetle has to be provided for. This means that the deep borers must get to within a mere film of the surface, and then return a short distance into the wood to prepare their pupal chambers, in which (with their heads invariably, and necessarily, pointing straight to the prepared exit) they can safely pupate. Surface-borers will, before pupating, strike into the tree for the first time, so as to afford greater protection to their pupal stage. Thus when the adult beetle emerges, it has only to scrape aside the frass which separates it from the exit, cut through, or merely push aside, the film of bark, and come out for its brief breeding-life. There are interesting varieties of structure: sometimes the exit is open and filled only with loose frass; sometimes the pupal chamber is made smooth with a quilting of minute wood dust cemented by the larva; sometimes it is closed with a stony concrete lid, the chalky material for which is emitted from the larva's mouth. But, whatever the variety may be, the exit of the beetle is made safe and easy by the instinctive preparations of the larva before it relapses into the inert pupal state.

The adult beetles vary much in colour and, in minor respects, in form, and a fair number of the species recorded in Britain are importations from abroad introduced with timber. Two common native examples are here shown. The first is ***Aromia moschata*** [musky Scented], the Musk Beetle (*p.* 22), the larva of which feeds as a stem-borer in willows. The adult is unique in emitting an agreeable odour, which, like most scents, is very variously described.

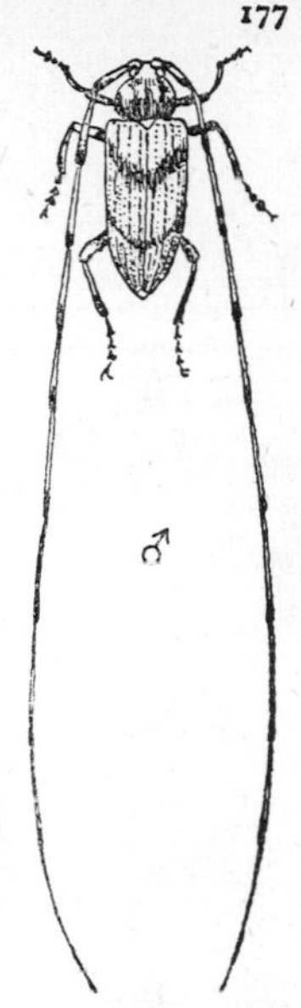

Acanthocinus aedilis

Another example of a Longhorn, which shows how long a beetle's antennae may be, is ***Acanthocinus aedilis*** [edile Spiky one] (*p.* 23), a species found in pine timber. The female has a much shorter pair of horns, barely extending beyond the end of the egg-tube which protrudes at the tail end.

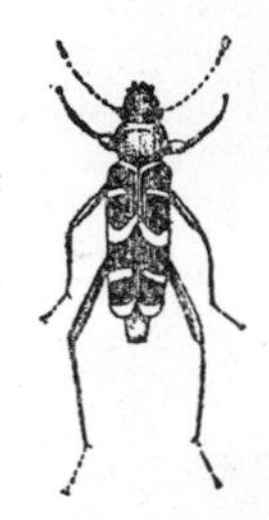

Clytus arietis

The third is ***Clytus arietis*** [ram's Noteworthy] or the Wasp Beetle (*p.* 23), which is commonly seen in May and June upon flowers, and certainly bears a strong likeness to some of the wasps, which is heightened by some waspish attitudes and to which it doubtless often owes its life.

FAMILY *CHRYSOMELIDAE* [Golden apples]
LEAF BEETLES

About 250 British species, of which only three are 'large'

CHARACTERS. In structure no precise line can be drawn between these and the Longhorns. This need not trouble us when considering the 'large' species. They, and indeed the family generally, are much shorter in the antennae, which are thickened towards their ends and never encroach upon the eyes, and they are short rotund beetles. The essential distinction between the families lies in the diet of the larvae. This, in the case of the Chrysomelidae, is not wood but the leaves of plants or their seeds. Almost every form of plant life is attacked by their larvae, most of which are dark in colour and live in the open, feeding in companies on the leaves and pupating underground.

Our three 'large' beetles all belong to the genus *Timarcha* [Censors, so called because of their dignity as the biggest of the family], of which ***Timarcha tenebricosa*** [black Censor] (*p. 23*) serves as an example. The larvae, which crawl with feeble legs and the help of repeated pushes from the tail end, appear to be among the few insects which are satisfied with almost any vegetation. They may, at any rate, be seen eating very various types of low plants by the roadside, without any apparent preference. The adult has earned the trivial name of the Bloody-nosed Beetle from its habit of squeezing out a few drops of its blood round the mouth and at some joints as a defence when handled. It has no wings, and the wing-cases are firmly fastened together.

The smaller species usually specialize upon some one plant or another, and one (the handsome but infamous Colorado Beetle, ***Leptinotarsa decemlineata*** [10-lined Thin-feet] (*p. 23*) earns mention here because of the fear it has aroused for the safety of the potato crop. A native of Central America, it first invaded Europe in 1875 or 1876 and did some damage in this country and more abroad. It has, so far, been successfully stamped out each time it has appeared, except in parts of France, whence there are recurrent fears of its reaching

Britain, as, indeed, it does from time to time. It lays its orange-yellow eggs in masses on the potato leaves. The larvae are brick red with black spots. In spite of the conspicuous appearance of the creature in all its stages, it is hard to exterminate, for the birth-rate is high, there are two generations a year, and periods of under ground sleep, both in summer and winter. Warnings are issued whenever it appears, usually with pictures of the beetle of the size of a hedgehog, and anyone finding a specimen is urged to report the fact at once to the authorities. Folly and contumacy must be combined in anyone who neglects this duty.

FAMILY *TENEBRIONIDAE* [Darkness-dwellers]
NOCTURNAL GROUND BEETLES

Thirty-five British species, of which four are 'large'

CHARACTERS. Feet of fore and mid legs 5-jointed, those of the hind legs 4-jointed. Claws smooth, without lobes. Front hip-joints (*coxae*) small and inside their cavities. Usually wingless, or at least flightless, with the wing-cases more or less fastened together and generally black and hard. They usually live in the dark and their larvae feed on mainly dry vegetable substances.

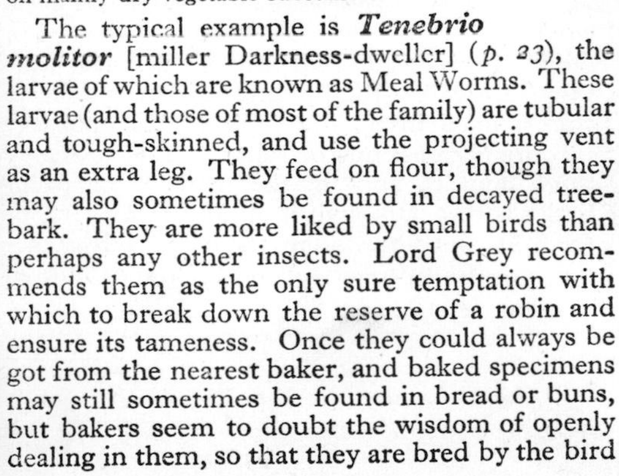

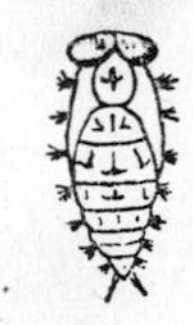

The typical example is ***Tenebrio molitor*** [miller Darkness-dweller] (*p. 23*), the larvae of which are known as Meal Worms. These larvae (and those of most of the family) are tubular and tough-skinned, and use the projecting vent as an extra leg. They feed on flour, though they may also sometimes be found in decayed tree-bark. They are more liked by small birds than perhaps any other insects. Lord Grey recommends them as the only sure temptation with which to break down the reserve of a robin and ensure its tameness. Once they could always be got from the nearest baker, and baked specimens may still sometimes be found in bread or buns, but bakers seem to doubt the wisdom of openly dealing in them, so that they are bred by the bird

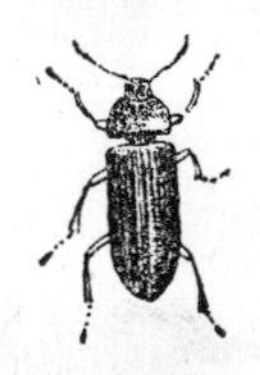

fanciers. They pupate in the flour and the adults also spend their lives in the same material, in mills or bakehouses.

Another common species is ***Blaps mucronata*** [spike-ended Harmful] (*p. 23*), or Churchyard Beetle. These are slow-crawling, black creatures, fairly common in caves, vaults, cellars, and dark stables, or bakeries where there is decaying vegetable matter for the larvae to eat. Their depressing names come rather from their haunts than from their manners, though they do excrete a stinking liquid the smell of which fills places where they are present. This liquid irritates the skin of man or beast.

FAMILY *OEDEMERIDAE* [Swollen thighs]

Seven British species, of which one is 'large'

CHARACTERS. Long, narrow bodies. Wing-cases with three or four ribs, strongly 'shouldered' and tapering towards the ends. Antennae threadlike and long. They feed on flowers, and their larvae feed in old wood.

Our only 'large' species is ***Oncomera femorata*** [big-thighed Swollen-thigh] (*p. 23*). It is a delicate thin-skinned insect found in woods upon ivy bloom and sometimes on sallows. The thickened thigh appears only in the male. One peculiarity is that, although it sucks the flowers for food, it is nocturnal in its habits. It sometimes comes to sugar set out for the capture of moths.

FAMILY *PYROCHROIDAE* [Fire-coloured] CARDINAL BEETLES

Three British species, of which two are 'large'

CHARACTERS. Long flat beetles, larger towards the hinder end and having, in the males, long-toothed comb-like antennae. Those of the females are only strongly serrated. The larvae are found under the bark of various trees and are carnivorous, eating the larvae of those species which eat wood.

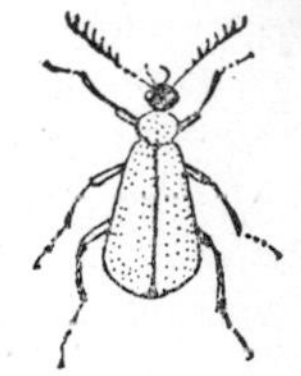

One of our 'large' species is ***Pyrochroa coccinea*** [vermilion Fire-colour] (*p. 23*), usually found under the bark of oaks and other trees, though occasionally upon grass stems or upon flowers.

FAMILY *PYTHIDAE* [Apollos] MOCK-WEEVILS

Thirteen British species, of which one is 'large'

Our only 'large' species, ***Pytho depressus*** [flattened Apollo] (*p. 23*), occurs under the bark of conifers in Scotland. Its wing-cases vary in colour from blue to purple. Little or nothing seems to be known of its habits. The larvae are flat, with parallel sides.

FAMILY *MELOÏDAE* OIL AND BLISTER BEETLES

Twelve British species, of which eight are 'large'

CHARACTERS. These beetles vary much in form, but all have a chemical called *cantharidin* in their blood and genital organs which was much used in medicine for raising blisters. Used internally as a love potion it was found dangerous to health.

Our commonest species is ***Meloë proscarabaeus*** [early appearing Meloë] or Oil Beetle (*p. 24*). It is an ugly ungainly creature which suggests an obese waiter in an ill-fitting dress coat. It is wingless, clumsy, and, in early life, possessed of only one accomplishment as a defence—that of exuding its blood, an evil-smelling, oily slime, from all its articulations. It crawls about in the sunshine on open heaths and rough ground, chiefly in the south of England, and makes its appearance early in the spring. It takes cover whenever the sun is overcast.

The females are remarkable for a vast fertility. The eggs are laid in holes dug by the mother with her fore legs in the ground among composite flowers, such as dandelions, and in

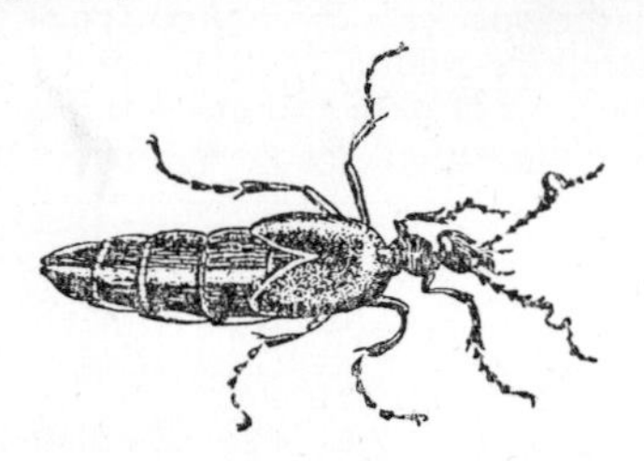

places frequented by some of the solitary bees, which have the habit of providing for their young by laying their eggs in cells stored with honey. The eggs laid by one Meloïd in a single hole have been estimated at over 4,000, and several batches are laid. The need for this fertility will appear later. Within a short while the yellow eggs hatch out into tiny active larvae. These were for long not recognized as the larvae of the Meloïds and they were called *Triungulids* or Bee Lice. They are about 1 mm. in length and, when highly magnified, they have the general appearance of the larvae of the Carabidae beetles (see p. 156). They are bright-eyed, somewhat long-legged, each leg having three gripping claws, and at the tail end exude a drop of strong adhesive liquid. By the help of this drop, and their long extensible bodies, they can crawl over and cling to the smoothest surfaces.

These tiny Bee Lice, in vast numbers, climb up to and cling on to the flowers of the dandelions and there await the visits of their future hosts, the solitary bees.

Their story, thenceforward, is told by Newport and by Fabre as follows. When anything touches the flower they instantly take a grip of it and unhitch themselves from the flower. They do not seem to know a straw or a piece of velvet from the bee which they need and will grasp anything with equal fervour. If, however, it is not an insect, they somehow see their mistake and make their way back to the flower. But if it is any kind of insect—beetle, bee, fly, wasp, or even spider, and even if it be a dead specimen of any of these, they remain upon it, awaiting transportation. Here is another need for the tremendous fertility, for unless the creature seized is a bee, and one of those which hoards honey on which to lay its eggs, the Bee Louse has gone astray and will die. If the Meloë has merely chosen the wrong sex of a suitable species, there seems little doubt that it takes advantage of the opportunity to transfer to the female at the moment when the bees pair.

When the young larva does get on to the bee, it makes its way to the top of the bee's thorax—the one part of its mount which is not reached in the incessant combing and cleaning to which every other part is subjected by a bee in its toilet.

Once the Meloë larva is thus astride its victim, it remains with a tenacity worthy of a cow-boy throughout the process of building, preparing, and victualling the cell for the young bee, and, at the moment when the bee lays the egg, one, not more, of the Triungulids hastily rushes to the bee's abdomen and boards the egg, on which it floats upon the honey. The bee, unconscious of any danger to her race, closes the cell and goes off to prepare another. Every cell thus infested with a Meloïd larva will in due season produce, not a bee, but a beetle.

Sometimes a Meloïd Bee Louse which has chosen a creature other than the proper type of bee may make good an apparent mistake. Thus it may choose one of the parasitic Hymenoptera which make their way into the cells of the provident species and lay eggs destined to produce larvae which will eat up the legitimate owners. Then the Bee Louse will get on to the egg of the parasite and eat both it and its destined victim. The robber is in turn robbed, both householder and burglar are burgled, and the honey goes to feed the young of the Meloë.

Once alone with the bee's egg in the cell, the larva uses the egg as a raft, because were it once to touch the treacherous honey, in its then state, it would be entangled and drowned. The egg is not only its raft, but also its first and essential meal. With its piercing jaws it tears open the covering of the egg and slowly devours its entire substance. When nothing but the case is left the larva must adapt itself to a totally new life.

No longer does it need eyes, legs, body-hairs or adhesive anal liquids. All it now wants is a pair of paddle-shaped jaws to push the honey into its mouth, and a smooth body which will float with a freeboard high enough to keep its breathing port-holes above the entangling honey. It moults, and assumes a form completely different from the first and exactly suited to its need. Its back is flat and deck-like, its belly rounded and deep, its whole body smooth except for the grooves which indicate the segments, its legs minute, and its spiracles along the sides just below the decks. The rest is bowel. In this form (known as the 2nd larval form) it crawls into the honey and stays there until the entire store is eaten.

After this a still further series of moults producing yet further forms (the uses of which are as yet unknown to us) take place. The 2nd larva, above described, becomes what is called pseudo-pupa—legless, sightless, and inert, generally resembling the pupal case of a fly.

This pseudo-pupal skin splits (without being discarded wholly) and a 3rd larva appears—very like the 2nd larva, but this time with its belly less swollen and its breathing-holes placed lower, its back rather than its belly rounded. This 3rd larva again splits its skin and the true pupa appears which shows the form of all the organs of the coming adult and looks like the pupa of any other beetle. From this 2nd pupa the adult beetle finally emerges and bites its way out—the graceless Oil Beetle with which we started—to seek a mate and breed.

Thus in its life (excluding the egg stage) it undergoes no fewer than five metamorphoses and presents six different forms. This is hyper-metamorphosis with a vengeance.

A complete series of these Meloïd forms has been figured and described only in the case of the smaller species, ***Apalus muralis*** [wall Tender

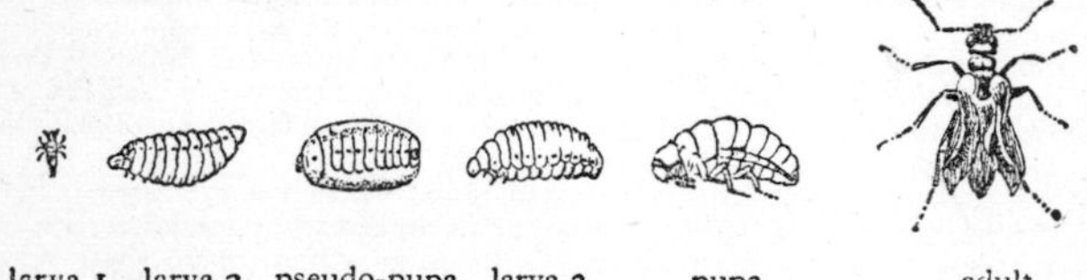

larva 1 larva 2 pseudo-pupa larva 3 pupa adult

one] (*p. 24*), which Fabre studied, and therefore, although a 'small' species, it appears here. It seems to be typical of the family and at any rate gives a good idea of the wealth of forms adopted by the family in growth. The resultant beetle is winged and is handsomer than most of its relatives, owing to the yellow spots on the wing-cases.

FAMILY *CURCULIONIDAE* WEEVILS

About 500 British species, of which ten are 'large'

CHARACTERS. Only four joints on all the feet. (There are minute 5th joints, but these are barely visible under the microscope.)

The head is prolonged into a long snout at the end of which come the mouth-parts. Of these only the jaws (*mandibles*) are visible, the palpi being very small and hidden inside the mouth.

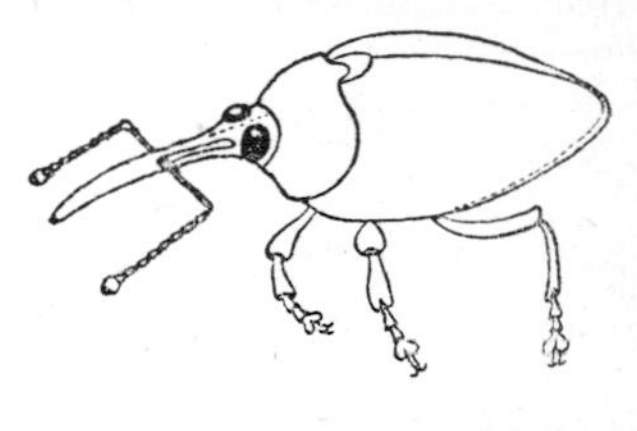

The antennae grow from a point at a varying distance down the snout and have one long 1st segment, followed, at a right angle, by numerous short joints, so that they may not interfere with the use of the snout as a boring implement. There are usually grooves (called *scrobes*) running backwards from the root of the antennae towards the eyes, in which the first long joint of the antennae is laid when the snout is in use.

The larvae are fat, curved, and without legs.

As above stated, the vast majority of this large family are 'small' beetles, and even those which are 'large' only just exceed the half inch measure.

HABITS. They are all purely vegetarian feeders in both larval and adult stages and their larvae, with few exceptions, feed where they are when they hatch from the eggs. The female lays her eggs, therefore, in the plant which is to form their food. She first uses the snout to bore a tunnel reaching to the spot where the egg is to be placed and then, turning about, extends from inside her body an egg-laying tube (*ovipositor*) and deposits her egg in place. The male's snout, which is often shorter, does not seem to be useful to him. His activities seem to be confined to attendance upon the female. He seems to be rarely away from her and the couple constantly repeat the act of pairing. When (as often happens in boring into hard nuts or acorns) her feet slip and she is left balanced on her nose and groping helplessly in the air, there are records of the male coming to her help and saving her life by levering her out.

Almost every seed, fruit, bud, flower, stem, leaf, bark, and root is food for some weevil and the beetles show an instinctive knowledge of the relationship of plants which enables them to select those which will suit their young.

One group of leaf-rollers is particularly remarkable. Their larvae need dying leaves, and the mothers supply these by cutting across leaves, leaving the mid-ribs, and then laboriously rolling them into cigars, in the heart of which the eggs are laid.

Though most weevil larvae spend their lives as such where they hatched, a few species crawl on to the leaves from the heart of buds where the eggs are laid and feed upon the leaves of the same plant. The oddest part of these exceptions is their method of locomotion. Their total absence of legs is replaced by a sticky glue which has the property of not drying, and is exuded from their vents. This enables them to crawl over their plants and adhere to them while feeding.

When the time for pupation comes, some species remain where they are, in thistle head or tree bark, others drop or crawl to the ground and bore their way into it. They pupate in a case, built and cemented within from materials got from their own excrement.

Many of the weevils are very destructive to our crops and useful plants.

One of our largest species, ***Hylobius abietis*** [pine Woodliver] (*p. 24*), is figured here. In its case it is the adults rather than the larvae which do us injury. The larvae feed mainly upon the roots of conifers (other than Scots Pine which the adults prefer) which are decaying after the trees have been cut. The beetles, however, work up young trees of the same family and strip the bark off them to get at the sap running under it. The best defence against this pest seems to be to trap the young by leaving a few logs and twigs lying about, to be carefully burned when well infested. Intervals between cutting and replanting, and the use of insecticides, have been tried with varying success.

Although all its members are 'small', there is one further family which demands attention here for the odd reason that, unlike most insects, it is popular. This is the

FAMILY *COCCINELLIDAE* [Scarlets] LADY-BIRDS

Forty-five British species, all of which are 'small'

CHARACTERS. The commonest of our Lady-birds is ***Coccinella septempunctata*** [7-spotted Scarlet] (*p. 24*) and is well known. The others of the family are usually very like it, though mostly smaller and very different in their colouring and particularly in the number and position of the spots. All, except one species which feeds on leaves, are carnivorous, both as larvae and as adults, and they are remarkable in having only three joints upon their feet.[1] They have the head sunk into the thorax so as to keep unbroken the circular outline of the creature, the general shape of which is that of half a sphere.

Their great contribution to our welfare lies in the fact that their food consists mainly of Aphids (the hated Green Fly), of which they are among the most assiduous destroyers.

The beetles live through the winter, under dried leaves or bark, in the adult stage, and there, early in the spring, lay packets of eggs, which soon hatch out into exceedingly active black larvae. These at once attack the aphids and soon grow into grey creatures with red and yellow markings. After moulting three times they pupate in a way which is unusual among beetles, making a hard, leathery pupa, which is fixed by its tail to the leaves of the bush upon which the larva has fed.

Lady-birds will, if alarmed, exude from between the joints of their legs drops of yellow and evil-smelling blood.

[1] A 4th joint is visible under the microscope.

ORDER *LEPIDOPTERA* [Scale Wings]

BUTTERFLIES AND MOTHS

2,187 *British species, of which about* 1,000 *are 'large'*

CHARACTERS. They have the usual three changes, that is to say that they go through four stages each quite different from the last: egg, larva or caterpillar, pupa or chrysalis, and, lastly, imago or adult.

The adults (males always, females usually) have wings, and both wings and bodies are covered with minute scales, forming a delicate dust which gives them their colours.

The mouth-parts of the larvae are adapted for chewing, and those of the adults of all but the 'small' group for sucking liquids only.

ANATOMY. The **larvae** are usually tubular in shape and consist of a head and thirteen segments.

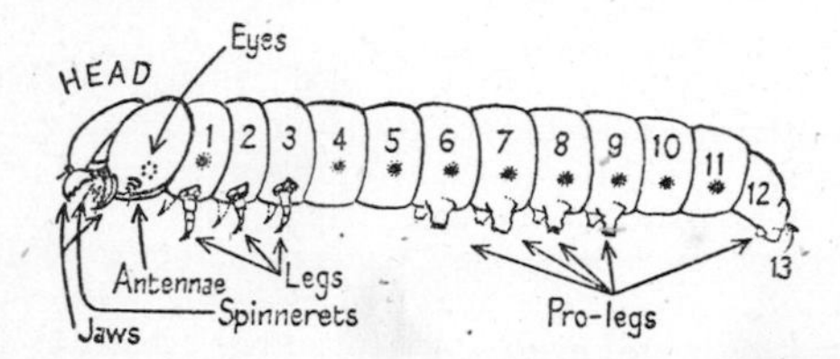

The head has half a dozen very small single eyes on each side, two short antennae for detecting smell, and all the other mouth-parts are adapted for chewing or for spinning silk. There are breathing holes (*spiracles* or *stigmata*) on both sides of all the segments except the 2nd, 3rd, 12th, and 13th. Segments 1, 2, and 3 (which form the thorax of the adult) have each a pair of jointed legs ending in a claw. Five of the abdominal segments (nos. 6 to 9 and 13) have usually each a pair of what are known as pro-legs, soft fleshy protuberances ending in a circle of hooks. The last pair, known as 'claspers', are almost always present. All the larvae, except those known as 'loopers' (p. 219), walk with the pro-legs and claspers rather than with the legs at the forward end. Of all the stages of the insect's life the larva alone grows. All larvae have silk glands and, in the head, under the lower lip, two so-called spinnerets from which the liquid is poured out which, on drying, makes the silk. Silk is used by the larvae for very various purposes: the construction of a carpet on which to walk safely; of a covering tent, or nest; the attachment of leaves, or other materials, to make a shelter; the production of a rope by which they let themselves drop, and up which they climb; and for the fixing, suspension, or envelopment of the pupa.

The greater number of **pupae** are almost inert bundles, having a faint power of moving the last few segments, though some have considerably more mobility. They consist of a continuous hard coating which shows the outer form of the organs of the future adult insect.

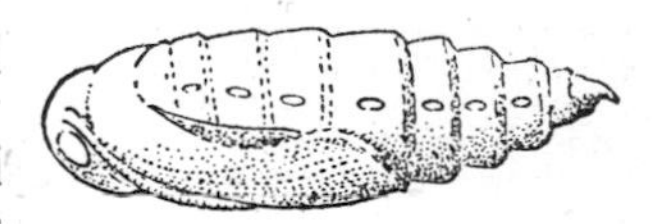

Usually the envelope shows no projecting limb, wing, or other organ, though some are less rigidly enveloped and in some cases the tongue is separate. Pupae are found in the open, hanging from silken pads or fastened with a silk girdle round their middles, or else hidden from view under the ground or in timber, or plant stems, or in twisted leaves. The hidden pupae are usually covered and protected by a more or less complete cocoon.

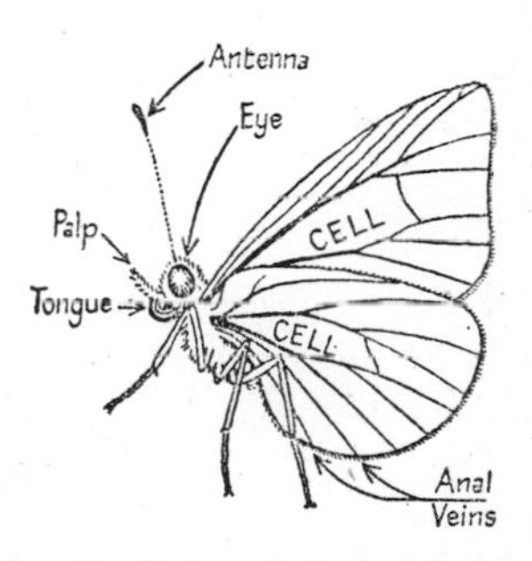

The **adults, or imagines,** crawl forth fully grown from the pupal skins and after an hour or so, during which their wings are inflated and dried, they can fly. Their bodies consist of the head, three segments in the thorax, and ten in the abdomen. The head has two large complex eyes, each made up of several thousand separate lenses, and, often also, a few separate single-lensed eyes (*ocelli*) on its summit. It has also a pair of long antennae, horns or feelers which are the main organs of smell. Almost all the mouth-parts except the lower jaws (*maxillae*) have either completely disappeared or are reduced to mere rudiments. The lower jaws are much lengthened and, being grooved along their inner sides and held together, form a long 'tongue', or *proboscis*, through which liquids (the only food) are sucked. Their *labial palpi* are retained as 3-jointed feelers, perhaps used to clean the tongue.

The 1st segment behind the head carries the fore legs, the 2nd the middle legs and the fore wings, and the 3rd the hind legs and the hind wings. In a very few moths the females have only mere rudiments of wings. Some moths have no tongues, and in some families of butterflies the fore legs are rudimentary and useless. The wing-veining varies greatly in different Lepidoptera, but, as it varies little between members of the same genus, it is much relied upon for classification.

It is not possible in a book of this kind to give any such idea of the veining of the wings of the Lepidoptera as would be required to explain the classification which depends upon this character. The main difficulty lies in the nomenclature. Hardly any two writers use the same terms, or, if they number the veins, the same numbers. And yet without numbers or names it is only possible to tell of the different schemes of veining by sketches which would have to be as numerous as the genera. All that will be attempted here is to give a few general ideas which may help a reader to understand books which give greater detail.

In the most primitive Lepidoptera the veining of the two pairs of wings (fore and hind) is much the same. Far the greater number of species have fore and hind wings veined differently; the hind wings, which are usually the smaller, having fewer veins.

Usually there is only one single cross-vein in either wing and the space enclosed between it and the two veins which it connects is called the 'cell'. There is, almost always, one vein (and only one) in both wings, which lies in front of the vein which forms the forward edge of the cell. This vein (which most writers call the 'sub-costal') varies in its behaviour. Sometimes it rises independently of the one which forms the front edge of the cell and, running along the foremost edge of the wing, never approaches its neighbour. Sometimes it approaches or touches its neighbour and runs with it for a short distance before leaving it again. Sometimes it starts with the vein which borders the cell and thus appears to branch from it when it does leave it.

Behind the vein which forms the hindmost edge of the cell there may be one, two, or three more veins. These are called 'anal veins', and their number, or absence, in the wings of different species has to be noticed.

The cell is sometimes divided into two by a vein running lengthwise along its middle. Sometimes, by itself forking into two before it reaches the cross-vein, this vein divides the cell into three spaces. A general idea of the veining of the lepidopterous wings can be got from looking at that of the butterfly sketched on p. 189.

In a few butterflies the cell on the hind wing is not closed by any cross vein and it is then recognizable only as being the space between the two main veins, each of which forks into several branches.

The word 'vein' is used here as being the most convenient, but these struts which strengthen and support the wings, and which are sometimes called 'ribs' and sometimes 'nerves' (or, where they branch from others, 'nervules'), are not veins in any way similar to those which carry the blood of the vertebrate animals.

The legs have usually five joints in the feet and a pair of final claws.

The segments of the abdomen have no signs of the pro-legs seen in the larvae and are in appearance mere rings; the last two (or in the males three) are adapted to form some of the sexual organs and are not seen from the outside. The whole body and wings are covered with scales which vary in shape from that of a hair to that of a small racket and, on the wings, are laid so as to overlap like the slates on a roof. In these scales, which are tiny bags, are some of the colours, while other colours are made by the texture of their surfaces. The colour patterns arise from the fact that the scales mature at different times in the pupae and the colouring blood changes its composition, so that scales filled at different times show different tints.

Life History. Speaking generally, in our climate, the Lepidoptera live through all their stages in a year. Of this about a month may be spent in the egg, two months as a larva, a fortnight as a pupa, and a month or so in the adult stage. To this very rough time-table must be added some six months or more of enforced quiescence due to the rigours of our winter. This six months of wintering must be added to the time spent in the stage when it occurs, which, oddly enough, differs in the different species. Some winter as eggs, some as larvae, some as pupae, and some as adults. Many species vary this time-table by producing two, three, or even four generations a year—short-lived except for the one wintering generation. Others by a long retarded larval growth which postpones the emergence of the adult insect for two, three, or even four years after the laying of the egg from which it is born. This is seen mainly in those species of which the larva is a wood-borer slowly gnawing its way through the solid trunk of a tree.

Food. It is only in the larval stage that the insect needs food for growth. The adult does not grow, and needs food only to renew the matter consumed by evaporation, movement, and reproduction. When the food-plant of a moth is spoken of, the plant eaten by the caterpillar is meant, not that from which the adult sucks nectar. The main business of the Lepidoptera in life is twofold: as larvae they destroy, and as adults they pollinate various forms of plant life by carrying the pollen from flower to flower. In death (and remember that there is a death-rate of over 99 per cent. per annum, mainly in the earlier stages) they provide food for countless other insects, birds, bats, spiders, and other small creatures. The larvae eat voraciously of practically every type of plant life. There is hardly a plant which is not the chosen food of some caterpillar. As a rule, however, the menu of any single species is restricted to a few kinds of plant, usually of a single family, and sometimes to one species only. The majority eat the buds, flowers, seeds, or leaves, though some live on the roots and on the bark or timber of trees. A few species are eaters of animal substances, fur, feathers, leather, and woollen cloths.

HABITS. The eggs are laid on or near the plant or other substance which is to be the food of the larva, either singly or, more rarely, in a large mass. They are always numerous, often several hundreds in a clutch, and are of very various shapes, usually typical of the particular family by which they are laid. They also vary much in colour and change as the young larva develops within them. When it is fully formed it eats its way out of the transparent shell and then, in most cases, proceeds to eat the shell from which it came, before turning to its plant food. Some feed by day, some by night, and others almost without intermission until their growth and the need to rid themselves of their old 'skin' calls for a moult. A few hours' rest and some wrigglings split the skin behind the head and the larva crawls out. A further period of rest hardens the new skin, and the creature sets to work again to feed and grow. This process of moulting is repeated several times until, when the caterpillar is full grown, it prepares for the pupal stage. This, as already stated, involves very different preparations according to the position of the pupa. Perhaps the most remarkable display of instinct in this respect is that of the wood-borers. They have, all through their lives as caterpillars, slowly gnawed their way through timber deep in some tree. The tunnel of eaten wood is left behind them filled with digested filings. Even if it were not so filled there could be no return to the surface by that way, because it tapers as it leads backward to the minute size of the newly hatched larva as it first entered the tree. Yet the moth, which will emerge from the pupa, has no jaws with which to chew even a particle of wood. It must have an exit. Behaving as if it knew this, the larva about to pupate digs its tunnel outwards until it reaches the surface of the bark. There it leaves a tenuous lid uneaten to hide the exit, secures that lid with a few strands of silk, which the efforts of even the soft and toothless moth will be able to dislodge, and then, spinning itself a cocoon for warmth, shuffles back its larval skin and goes through the internal magic of the pupa. When the moth emerges, it is at the door and can push it open.

Of the adult Lepidoptera little can be said which applies to all. Some females cannot even fly and of these some never leave the pupal cocoon. Some love the sunlight and fly by day: some only at night or at dusk. The majority seem to suck nectar from flowers and are attracted to 'sugared' tree-trunks. Many night flyers are attracted to bright lights. All mate during the adult stage, and in the case of some families it is evident that it is the smell of the unmated females by which the males are drawn to them. The process of attracting the males by keeping a newly emerged female in captivity is known to collectors as 'assembling'.

They are usually completely silent at all stages. One or two species can make a faint creaking sound in the pupal stage and a hissing sound by wing movements as adults, and one squeaks by blowing air through its proboscis.

GAIT AND POSTURE. When the adults have six walking-legs it is usual for them to move by alternate steps of the middle leg on one side together with the fore and hind legs on the other side. The 4-legged species step with an ungainly, ponderous gait, each fore leg in unison with the hind leg on the other side. The flight of the night-flying species is rarely seen, and when it is, it is usually only when they flutter round a light. Those which fly by day vary greatly. Some seem to elude capture by birds by adopting a wobbling, or fluttering, flight like that of a dead leaf blown by the wind. Others fly swiftly and straight, hovering to feed at the blooms as does a humming-bird. Others settle to feed on the flowers, often choosing blooms which match their colouring. This may be accidental, or it may be that they are attracted to the colour hoping to find a mate.

Although most Lepidoptera only fly for short distances, others are capable of long flights and we find certain butterflies, and a few moths, which fly to our shores from the Continent. One species actually flies to our shores from Norway, only to die of our treacherous winters, with their false promises of warmth. Such flights are helped by the fact that they can rest upon the sea and rise again from its surface unwetted.

CLASSIFICATION. The Lepidoptera are, like all other Orders of insects, undergoing a process of re-classification at the hands of experts. Here it has been thought better to adhere to what many now regard as an out-of-date system, rather than to try to guess which of the newer systems will gain the upper hand. The separation of the *Rhopalocera* (Butterflies) into a sub-order is to-day unpopular and the subdivision of the Moths into *Macrolepidoptera* (Big ones) and *Microlepidoptera* (Little ones) is not regarded with favour. It is, however, here followed, not from any mere conservatism, but because it is convenient.

The following table shows the division here adopted:

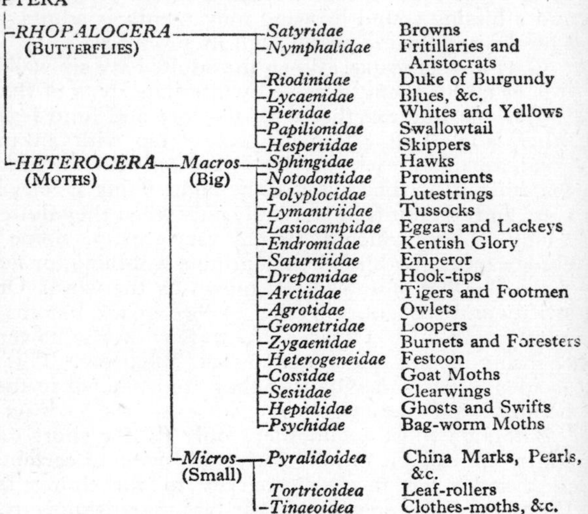

SUB-ORDER *RHOPALOCERA* [Club-horns]
BUTTERFLIES

Fifty-eight British species (excluding occasional migrants), all 'large'

All butterflies fly by day, though possibly some, particularly the migrants, may also fly at night. Most fly only in the sunlight. Almost all settle upon flowers to feed, with the wings wide open, often gently fanning them up and down. When resting, in dull weather or at night, they sit with the

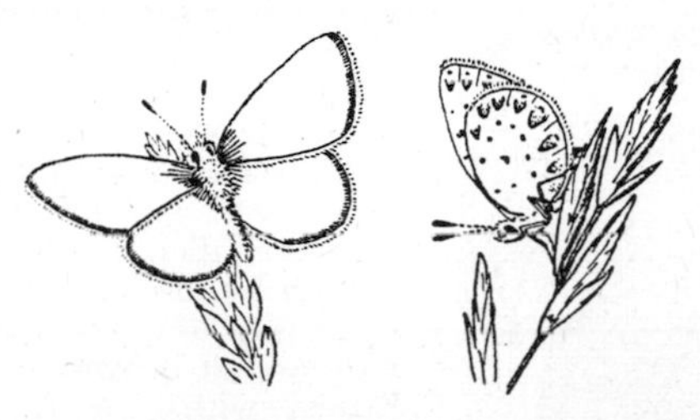

wings closed over the back, usually with the fore wings almost covered by the hind so as to show only the under surfaces of the hind wings and of the tips of the fore wings. Most species are brilliantly coloured. Their bodies and heads are relatively slender and small, and the fore wings are generally triangular in shape while the hind wings are rounded. The wings are roughly the same size, and overlap slightly, but are not otherwise connected. All have one anal vein in the fore wing and (except one family) two or more in the hind wing. There is never more than one closed cell in either wing.

All have antennae which end in a definite thickening or club, thus:

Almost all the larvae are feeders on buds, flowers, or leaves of growing plants. None eat coniferae and very few eat evergreens. One or two are cannibals if they meet, and one species eat the larvae of ants (see p. 199). None are wood-borers. All the larvae have ten pro-legs. Their pupae are found hanging, girt, or slightly cocooned.

FAMILY *SATYRIDAE* [Satyrs] BROWNS

Eleven British species, all 'large'

CHARACTERS. The front vein in the fore wing, running along its forward edge (and sometimes one or two others also), is thickened at its base, where it leaves the body. This seems to serve to give additional strength to the wings which are otherwise weak and feeble. The Browns are 4-legged, the fore legs being small and rudimentary, held up under their heads and almost hidden by the hairy scales on the under side of the body. In colour they are all brown or yellowish-brown with few if any other colours. Usually there are some black spots with white centres, resembling eyes, somewhere on the wings.

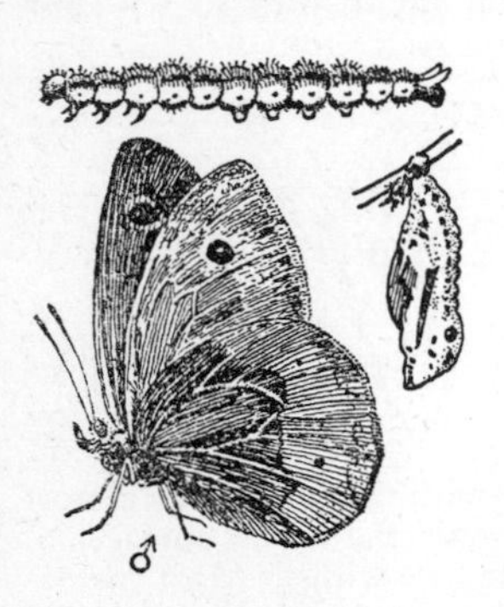

The larvae are all grass-eaters, and the butterflies are mostly woodland or hedge species. Most species have one generation a year, and they all winter as larvae.[1] Theirs is, however, not a complete hibernation as they only sleep intermittently, waking to nibble at the grasses on warm winter days. Their pupae hang or are laid down in a slight cocoon on, or just under, the ground.

Our commonest species is ***Maniola jurtina*** [Jurtina Bugbear], the Meadow Brown (*p. 25*), here illustrated.

[1] The species, *Pararge aegeria* [Egeria Near-white], the Speckled Wood, is alone among our butterflies in that, though sometimes wintering as a larva, it also sometimes does so as a pupa. It is the only species that is known to winter in two different stages.

FAMILY *NYMPHALIDAE* [Nymphs]

FRITILLARIES AND ARISTOCRATS

Sixteen British species, all 'large'

CHARACTERS. These, like the Browns, are 4-legged butterflies, with rudimentary fore legs, but they have no distended veins in their wings, which are stronger and more thickly veined than those of the Browns, and they are amongst our most powerful fliers.

The Fritillaries form a very obvious group, all very similar in colouring; on the upper surface a rich fulvous orange marked with black, and many of them having on the under sides metallic silver spots or splashes. The other members of the family are large insects of very varied and brilliant colouring and include most of our purely immigrant species: those which arrive here from the Continent and are killed off by our winter, so that our stock has to be yearly renewed. Of these immigrants the Red Admiral (***Vanessa atalanta***) is a common and markedly handsome insect (*p.* 25).

The larvae are almost all covered with sharp and complex spines which defend them against some possible enemies. Those of the Fritillaries feed chiefly on the dog violet or plantains. The larvae of the other genera feed mainly on nettles or on the leaves of deciduous trees. Their pupae are all found suspended and, as a defence against injury from swinging against other things, they are almost all covered with prickly projections. Many of them are also sprinkled with metallic gold and silver spots which give them the look of dew-dotted leaves.

The Nymphalidae, other than the Fritillaries, comprise all the British species which winter as butterflies, with the one exception of the Brimstone. Most of the Fritillaries winter as larvae.

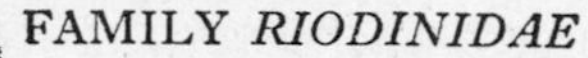

FAMILY *RIODINIDAE*

Of these we have only one example here, or indeed in Europe—***Hamearis lucina*** [Lucina Vernal], the Duke of Burgundy Fritillary (*p.* 25)—which looks like a small Fritillary but has the unique characteristic that the males use only four legs (fore legs abortive) while the females use all six.

♀

FAMILY *LYCAENIDAE*

BLUES, COPPER, AND HAIRSTREAKS

Fourteen British species, all 'large'

Characters. These are all 6-legged butterflies, though the fore legs (particularly of the males) are short and lacking in some joints of the feet.

The Blues are hard to tell apart. The males differ much from the females, and their delicate grey under sides are marked with 'eyes' which are very characteristic.

The larvae of the whole family are short and woodlouse-shaped, and their short, fat, pupae are girt to their food plants by a girdle of silk. Most of them produce two or more generations a year, and the larvae of the Blues usually feed on the pod-bearing plants of the pea family. Many of the larvae of the Blues have special organs on their backs, towards the tail end, which secrete a sweet, honey-like substance beloved of ants by which they are in consequence spared, and even protected, against many of their enemies.

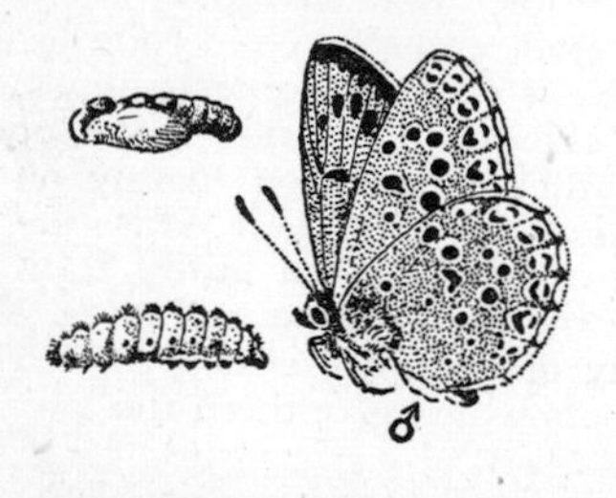

Among those which benefit from this ant-protection is the one British species which has a truly extraordinary and dramatic life story—the local and rare Large Blue, ***Maculinea arion*** [Arion Spotted] (*p.* 25). This lays its eggs on the wild thyme, where they hatch in a week or so. Until after its third moult, the young caterpillar feeds off the wild thyme and behaves like that of any other butterfly. Then it deserts the food-plant and wanders off. The first ant (*Myrmica*

scabrinodis or *M. laevinodis*) which meets it after this caresses it and eagerly licks up the sweet liquid which we call honey-dew, and which is secreted in an organ on the larva's back. After an hour or so of this, the larva hunches itself up and the ant hoists it off the ground and bears it away and into the ants' nest and lays it in one of the lower compartments, among the ant larvae. From that time onwards the *arion* larva produces no honey-dew and gives no return for its lodging, or indeed for its board, for, on the contrary, it lives henceforward for the next five or six weeks by eating the larvae of the ants' nest in which it is lodged. Then, replete and somnolent, it spends the whole winter in the ants' nest and there pupates and, on emergence as a butterfly, crawls out of the nest. After drying its wings on a neighbouring plant, it flies off for its fortnight of adult life in which to breed future generations of ant-destroyers—models of fraud and ingratitude. The discovery and relation of this amazing story are due to the patience and skill of Mr. F. W. Frohawk.

FAMILY *PIERIDAE* [Muses]

WHITES AND YELLOWS

Seven British species, all 'large'

CHARACTERS. The butterflies of this family are distinguishable by the full development and use of all the six legs in both sexes. Not only have both sexes all the five foot-joints on all the legs, but the claws on the feet are each forked so as, under a glass, to give the effect of four minute claws on each foot. The next two families to be named have also the use of the six legs, but not the doubled claws, and they have also other peculiarities which will be mentioned in due course.

In the field the Pieridae are easily recognized. No other of our butterflies is either pale yellow or white in general appearance except only the Marbled White, *Melanargis galathea*. This latter is a Satyrid, having only four developed legs and the distended vein of that family. All members of the Pierid family are almost wholly white or yellow.

The commonest species is ***Pieris rapae*** [rape Muse], the Small White (*p. 25*).

This, and its relative, *P. brassicae* [cabbage], the Large White, are the only enemies of man among the butterflies, because their larvae feed upon the Cruciferae—of which one, the Wild Cabbage, has been developed by human cultivation into many of the main vegetable crops with which man

Pieris rapae

feeds himself and his beasts. The result of this development has been that gigantic acreages are covered with crops of cabbage, cauliflower, broccoli, turnips, swedes, and other roots, all of which are to some extent related to the sea-cabbage, and thus the species which feed upon it have correspondingly increased.

The family has tubular larvae, sometimes gregarious (the eggs being laid in a single clump), sometimes solitary (the eggs laid one by one), and as they produce several generations a year, and are also migrants to our shores in vast numbers, the main salvation to our crops comes from another insect—a small member of the Ichneumon group, *Apanteles glomeratus*, which lays its eggs in the Pierid larva from the corpse of which about thirty Ichneumonoids are bred instead of the destructive butterflies.

FAMILY *PAPILIONIDAE* [Butterflies]

Of these we have only one, ***Papilio machaon*** (*p.* 25), the Swallowtail, and it is confined to a small district in the Fens, its larva feeding off Milk Parsley. The family character is that

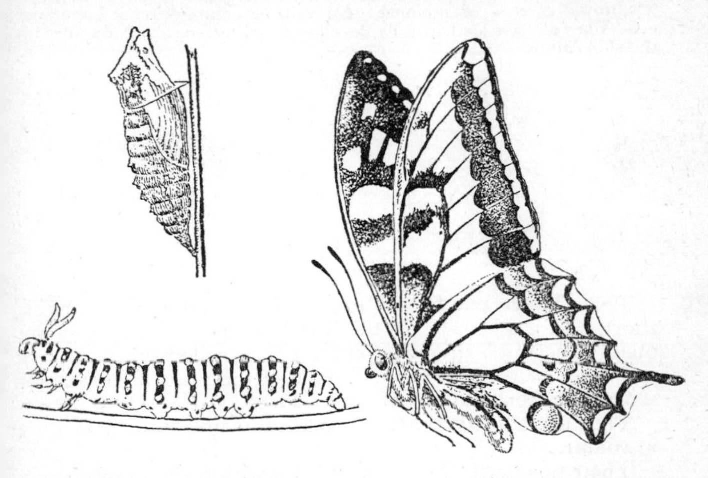

there is only one vein behind the cell in the hind wings, so that instead of the body lying in a groove formed by the hind wings (as in all our other butterflies) the wings stand away from the body and are concave at their hinder edge so as to let the body stand clear of them. They have also all six legs fully developed in both sexes, but no doubling of the claws as in the Whites. *P. machaon* is of course also remarkable for the swallowtails to which it owes its English name.

FAMILY *HESPERIIDAE* [Duskies] SKIPPERS

Eight British species, all 'large'

The last group of butterflies is in some respects mothlike.

CHARACTERS. Heads and bodies large, wide space between the eyes, 'eyebrows' at base of antennae. No vein branching after it leaves the cell. They all have six legs fully developed and, often, unusual spines on the shin joints.

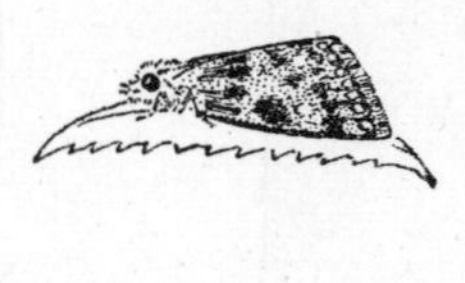

Their larvae usually eat grasses and their flight is swift, short, and jerky—whence the English name. The pupae are mainly cocooned among vegetation or in rolled tubes of grass and some of them have the tongue of the pupa standing out separately from the rest of the body.

They are all little butterflies and all mainly brown or grey in colour.

Their positions when at rest differ within the family, most of them basking with hind wings flat and fore wings half closed, while ***Erynnis tages,*** the Dingy Skipper (*p.* 25), rests in the position of an Owlet moth.

SUB-ORDER *HETEROCERA* [Horns of other shapes]

MOTHS

About 2,000 species, of which about half are 'large'

Characters. Mostly fly by night or in the twilight, though some fly by day. Many settle on flowers to feed, others hover over flowers to feed, some do not feed at all. When resting, some lay the wings back flat, so that the fore wings cover the hind, showing only the upper surfaces of the fore wings. Others wrap their wings round them like the outer leaves of a cigar. Others cover the body with the fore wings which slope down to the surface on which they are resting like a tent. Others spread the wings out flat. Only a very few hold the wings up as do the Rhopalocera (Butterflies). Most moths are dull-coloured, though some, chiefly the day-fliers, are brilliant. Even these have the bright colour usually on the hind wings so that it is visible only in flight. The wings vary much in shape and size, the hind wings being often the larger.

Nearly all have some mechanism for holding the fore and hind wings together in flight. This takes the form either of a projection from the fore wing (*jugum*) which grips the hind, or else of one or more bristles (*frenulum*) at the front edge of the hind wings, and a strap (*retinaculum*) at the rear of the fore wings under which these bristles pass. A few species are (as are the butterflies) without these gadgets. Their bodies are often (not always) fatter and hairier than those of butterflies, and usually without the distinct waist between the thorax and abdomen.

The antennae are of almost any shape except that of the butterflies. Some few moths have antennae which are thickest at the ends, though this is very unusual, but in these they thicken gradually to the end, instead of abruptly swelling to a club. Where, as is often the case, the two sexes differ in the shape of the antennae, those of the males are the larger and more feathery.

Habits. The great majority of the **larvae** feed on vegetation in its soft and growing state, but there are some which eat dead leaves, others which eat living timber, boring through stems or tree-trunks, and others which eat dead wood already carpentered by man. Others again, mostly small moths, feed on animal substances, woollen cloths, hair, skins, and the like.

There are some records of cannibalism and of some form

of feeding off living animals. Most of the larvae have sixteen legs, others only ten.

The **pupae** are sometimes fully cocooned (sometimes with silk only and sometimes by a binding of wood or other hard substances together), and in many cases are merely laid underground without cocoon. They are never horned or angular and are not found girt, and rarely suspended.

FAMILY *SPHINGIDAE* [Sphinxes] HAWKS

Seventeen British species, all 'large'.

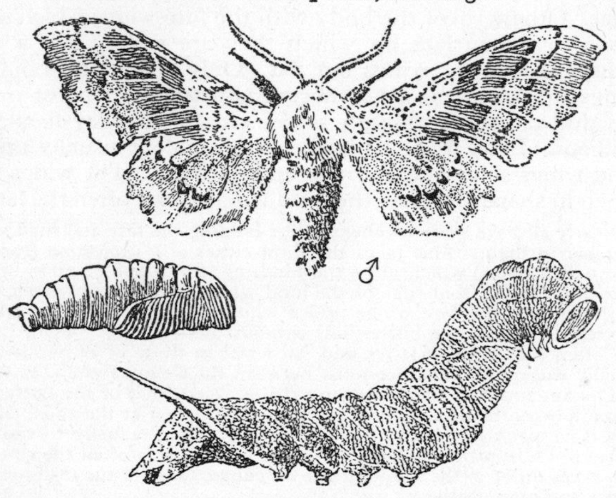

CHARACTERS. Large handsome moths with long pointed fore wings and small hind wings. Heavy bodies usually tapering to a point. Fly swiftly and well, mostly at dusk or about dawn. They usually suck blooms without settling, hovering as does a humming-bird. Many are brilliantly coloured. Their antennae gradually thicken towards the end and usually end in a hook. They have no ears (*tympana*) on the body.

The larvae are very large and ornamental, smooth and equipped with a 'tail' on the 12th segment, and marked with diagonal stripes. They have a trick of raising the head, as here depicted in the sketch of ***Laothoë populi***, the Poplar Hawk (*p. 26*), in its various stages. Some (not *Laothoë* *populi*) have eyelike marks behind the head giving them the appearance of a snake when the head is so raised. This probably serves as a defence.

Some of the species are rare vagrants from abroad. Only six are fairly common here, the Poplar Hawk the commonest. They are all plant-eaters as larvae, our commoner species feeding on deciduous trees and shrubs. Those that breed here produce but one generation a year. When about to pupate most of them dig in at the roots of the trees. The pupae are small and usually without cocoons, though some species form slight cocoons at, or near, the ground surface. The antennae widen in the middle and have often hooked bristles at their ends. Those of the males have comb teeth along the under side, those of the females have not. The tongues vary greatly, some being very long, to reach the nectar of long flowers from the hovering position, others very short.

Among the Hawks one is in several ways remarkable: *Acherontia atropos*, the Death's Head Moth. This rare and local species sucks tree-sap and honey inside bee-hives (which it enters for the purpose with impunity) instead of the nectar of flowers. It also has the unique power of making an audible sound, crackling (with its jaws ?) as a larva and squeaking with its proboscis as an adult.

Its larvae feed mainly upon potato plants.

Two smaller species, the Bee Hawk Moths ***Hemaris fuciformis*** (food-plant honeysuckle) and *H. tityus* (food-plant scabious), and an occasional visitor to southern England, *Macroglossa stellatarum* (the Humming-Bird Moth), fly by day, and of these the first two shed all the scales from their wings in their first flight except those on the borders of their wings. After this they look very like bumble bees. Their pupae have earth-covered cocoons.

Hemaris fuciformis

FAMILY *NOTODONTIDAE* [Back-toothed] PROMINENTS

Twenty-five British species, all 'large'

CHARACTERS. **Larvae** are mostly smooth, or but slightly downy. Many are of fantastic shapes, several are 14-legged, the claspers being replaced by whip-like tails which serve as fly-whisks against ichneumons, from which, however, they suffer greatly. That of ***Stauropus fagi*** [beech Cross-foot], the Lobster Moth, alone of all our caterpillars has long true legs and is among the most eccentric looking of all. Others are 16-legged and more normally tubular, but they often have humps on the 11th segment and almost all have the habit of holding their tails in the air when resting. All are eaters of the leaves and shoots of deciduous trees.

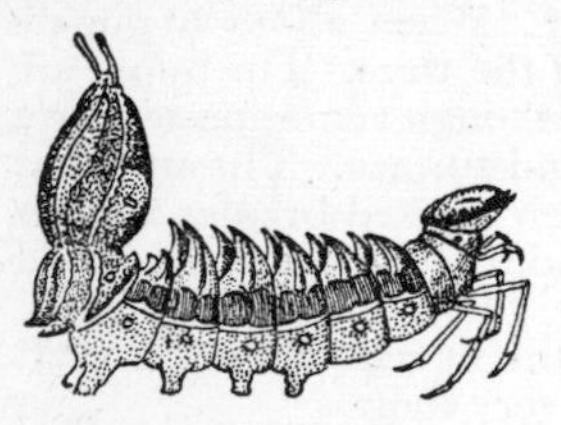

The **pupae** are all smooth and wholly enveloped, and they are very variously posted. Many are cocooned within a stiff coating of bark chips, if on tree or paling, or of earth, if underground. When the cocoon is thus stiffened, the moth's escape is made possible by a sharp edge at the head of the pupa (which acts like an egg-tooth) and a discharge of softening liquid from the emerging moth. Other pupae are cocooned between dried leaves. Others, again, have mere silken cocoons.

The **moths** are large or medium-sized night-fliers, of powerful flight. The wings are long (especially the fore wings) and narrow. They rest, on trees or stumps, with the fore wings laid back, tent-wise, and sloping down to the sides, the hind wings folded beneath them. Some have projections at the back of their fore wings and these stick up, when the moth is at rest, so as to form a peak in the middle of the back. It is either from these or from the spikes on the backs of the larvae that the family gets its name.

They have fat, hairy bodies and heads, and neither waists nor necks. They have 'ears' on the last segment of the thorax, and their 'tongues', though present, are very small. Antennae long, those of the males, toothed.

Few have any colour on the hind wings, which are white. The fore wings are more often brown.

LIFE HISTORY. Mostly one generation a year, though some species, particularly in the south, produce two, and a few, sometimes, remain two years before emergence. All, with one exception,[1] winter as pupae.

[1] This is *Ptilophora plumigera*, the Plumed Prominent, which flies as late as November and winters as an egg.

Among the commonest species is ***Cerura vinula*** [wine Horn-tailed], the Puss Moth (*p.* 26), here illustrated. Like all members of the family, it resorts readily to sugared tree-trunks, and its remarkable larvae are found on willows and poplars. Its flight is from April to July.

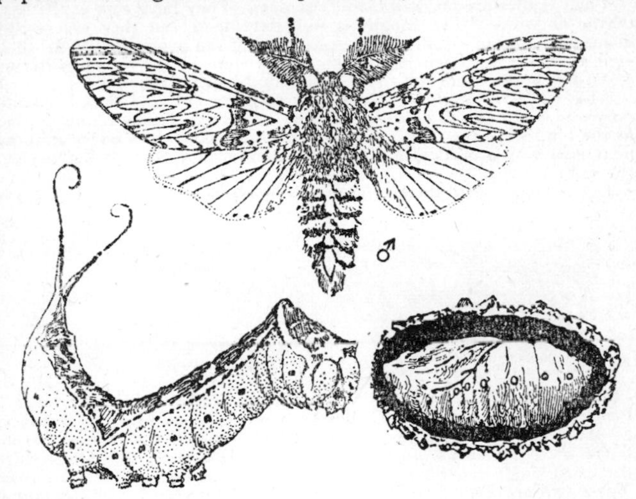

FAMILY *POLYPLOCIDAE* [much tangled]

LUTESTRINGS

Nine British species, all 'large'

CHARACTERS. **Larvae** are naked and 16-legged, having often the habit of resting twisted into the form of a fish-hook or question mark. They are all shrub or tree feeders, eating bramble, raspberry, poplar, oak, birch, alder, or hazel leaves, and many of them make a shelter by sewing together two leaves and living between them.

The **pupae** are smooth and rounded and are found either between two leaves sewn together or (more often) under dead leaves or mosses fastened together by silk threads.

The **moths** are medium-sized night-fliers, having patterns (often of delicate beauty) on the fore wings and little or no marking on the hind wings, which are white or whitish.

The sexes differ little, the females being slightly larger and having mere thread antennae, while those of the males are usually slightly toothed. They rest with the fore wings held roof-wise over the body and folded hind wings.

Their bodies are fat, hairy, and waistless. They have ears at the base of the abdomen. The tongue is well developed and they are readily attracted to sugar. With the one exception of the genus *Polyploca*, their eyes are hairless. Their legs are short, the shins of the fore legs having a leaf-like appendage, and those of the hind legs four spurs.

They all have *frenula* and the fore wings have a second closed cell and only one anal vein. The distinguishing character of the veining is that in the hind wing the foremost vein approaches (but does not touch) the next vein which borders the cell, the point of approach being beyond the cell.

LIFE CYCLE. With the exception of ***Thyatira batis*** [bramble T.], the

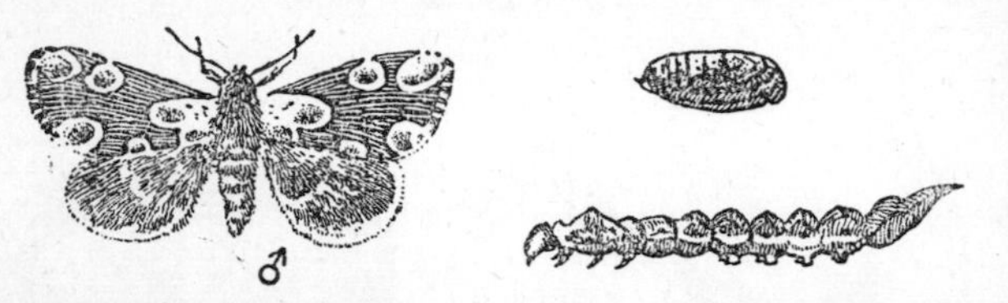

Peach Blossom (*p. 27*), which has been recorded as breeding a partial second generation in the year, and of *Polyploca ridens*, the Frosted Green, which often remains from two to four years as a pupa, they all produce the usual single generation a year. All but two species winter as pupae. These two are *Tethea duplaris*, Lesser Satin Moth, and *Asphalia diluta*, Lesser Lutestring, which winter as eggs.

FAMILY *LYMANTRIIDAE* [Destroyers] (= *LIPARIDAE*) TUSSOCKS

Eight British species, all 'large'

CHARACTERS. **Larvae** all hairy, either all over or in tufts. 16-legged. All feeding on the leaves of shrubs or trees. Often very injurious to fruit-trees. In many cases they live gregariously and spin webs among the leaves as a protection. If frightened or touched they often roll up into a ring and present their bristles as does a hedgehog. Most species are acutely irritating to the human skin, causing a nettle-rash.

Pupae are also hairy and found in loose cocoons, among the leaves or upon the bark of the food-plants. These cocoons are often made up not only of silk but also of the protective stinging hairs of the larval coat.

The fairly common ***Dasychira pudibunda*** [bashful Fluffy-hand], the Pale Tussock (*p.* 27), is typical.

The **moths** of the family are mainly nocturnal, large or medium-sized, with very fat bodies in the case of the females, those of the males being much less so. They have very short tongues and do not come to sugar. They are attracted by light. The antennae of the males are markedly toothed, those of the females less so, or merely threads. Many species are very hairy and have the same power of irritating the human skin as their larvae. The females of several species have tufts of long hair at their tails, which hairs are detached when the eggs are laid and left as a protection for the clutch.

When resting they fold the hind wings, which are without patterns, as a rule, and cover them and their bodies with the fore wings held roof-wise.

The veining which characterizes the family is as follows:

Fore wings: one anal vein and usually (not in all genera) an extra cell formed by the crossing of veins.

Hind wings: the foremost vein starts separately from the one next to it which borders the cell. It touches it, well down the cell, leaving it again to rejoin the costal edge. This forms a second cell of some length.

One of our genera (*Orgyia*) differs markedly from the others. Their females are without functional wings, the wings being reduced to minute stumps. They cannot fly and in fact never move from the cocoons in which the pupae were placed. They there await the males and there lay their eggs, looking, on their silken carpets, like spiders. Their males fly by day and, except for the feathery antennae, are, in flight, somewhat butterfly-like. They rest in the same position as the other members of the family.

The above are the male and female of ***Orgyia antiqua*** [ancient Outstretched-arm], the Common Vapourer.

LIFE HISTORY. All our species have the usual single generation a year except *Orgyia gonostigma*, the Scarce Vapourer, which produces two generations a year, and *Dasychira fascelina*, the Dark Tussock, which may remain in the larval stage for two years. *D. pudibunda* winters as a pupa, *O. antiqua* and the genus *Lymantria* as eggs. The rest of the family winter as larvae.

FAMILY *LASIOCAMPIDAE* [Hairy Caterpillars]
EGGARS AND LACKEYS

Eleven British species, all 'large'

CHARACTERS. **Larvae** hairy, sometimes tufted, and usually gregarious, those of the Lackeys forming silken nests for protection. Their food-plants are very various, including the smaller trees and shrubs (blackthorn, whitethorn, sallow, and fruit-trees) and, in the case of some species, small herbs (sea-wormwood, wild carrot, heath, and grasses).

The **pupae** are short, stumpy, and smooth, enclosed in a true silken cocoon. They are variously placed, on the ground, or among leaves or twigs of the food-plants.

The **moths,** of which ***Lasiocampa quercus*** [oak Hairy Caterpillar], the Oak Eggar (*p. 27*), is shown opposite, are somewhat similar to each other in general appearance, being all of a fulvous brown in colour and decorated only with one or two lines of paler yellow crossing both wings and, usually, a white spot in the centre of the fore wing

They are usually nocturnal, large or medium in size, and

have heavy hairy bodies, with small heads, and short feathery antennae (males), less feathery (females). Their legs are short and have final spurs only on the shins. The tongues are

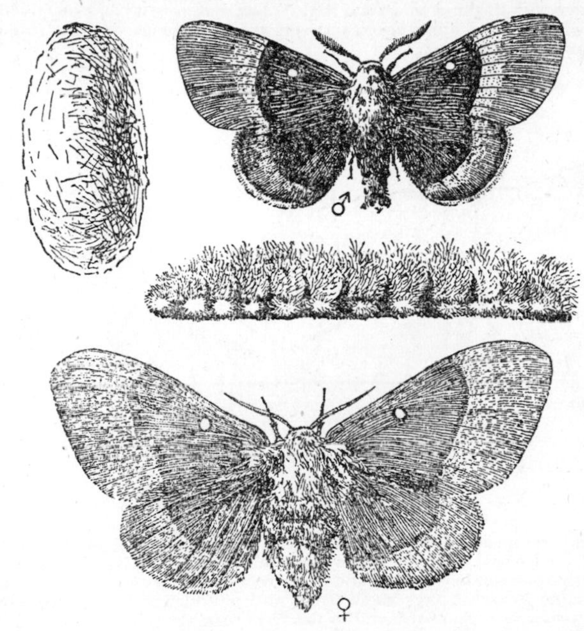

absent or rudimentary. They are noted for the habit of assembling to the smell of a newly emerged female.

Their wings are somewhat small for the size of their bodies, but they are swift and powerful fliers.

The hind wings have no *frenulum* or other connecting devices, the upper lobes of the wings being large as in butterflies. The way in which the foremost veins start differs in the various genera and in some they form an extra cell by joining the next vein as, or after, it leaves the cell.

The Oak Eggar here figured is remarkable in one respect. In the northern part of Britain it has a life cycle of two years, spending the first winter as a larva and the second as a pupa. In this it is unique among our moths.

One species (*Gastropacha quercifolia*, the Lappet) rests in a peculiar position with the hind wings laid flat. When so resting it looks exactly like a dead leaf. The other species covers the hind wings with the fore in the more usual manner.

FAMILY *ENDROMIDAE* [Shaggy coats]

One species

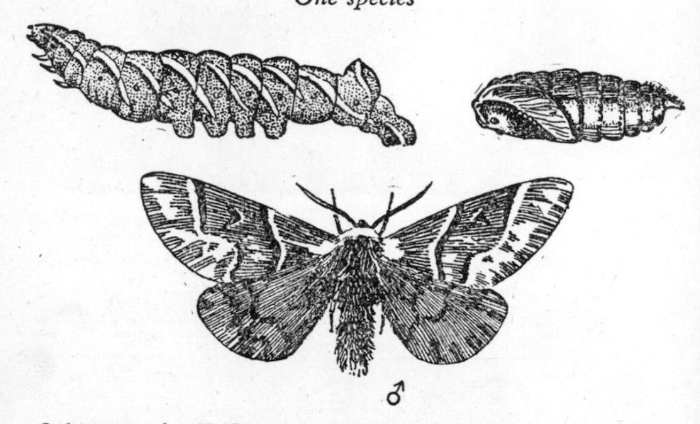

♂

Only one species, ***Endromis versicolora*** [variously coloured Shaggy-coat], the Kentish Glory (*p. 28*), is found in Britain, or indeed in Europe. It is fairly common in Scotland and not rare, though very local, in England. It has no *frenulum*, very small *palpi*, and no tongue. In the fore wing vein 5 rises close to vein 6 and in the hind wing the foremost vein bends towards the next beyond the cell.

The **larvae** are green and white and much resemble those of a Sphinx Moth. Gregarious till after 3rd moult, sitting in groups they look like catkins and where larger and solitary, like leaves.

The **pupae** are in a hard brown cocoon, strengthened with scraps of vegetable matter. They often remain two or more years in the pupal state. Before the adult emerges the pupa ruptures the upper end of the cocoon and protrudes its head.

The **moths** are fat and furry and are remarkable for a great difference between the sexes in appearance and, still more, in habits. The females are pale in colour, being brown and white only, whereas the males (whose pattern is the same) have the hind wings of a bright reddish-yellow colour and far more feathery antennae.

The main difference is in habits. The males fly, strongly and fast, during the brightest hours of the day, seeking the females by scent. If frightened they soar vertically to a great height, out of sight. They assemble in vast numbers. The females remain immobile throughout the day on tree-trunks, dropping to the ground after pairing, and flying only after dark.

FAMILY *SATURNIIDAE* [Saturnia, a synonym of Juno]

One species

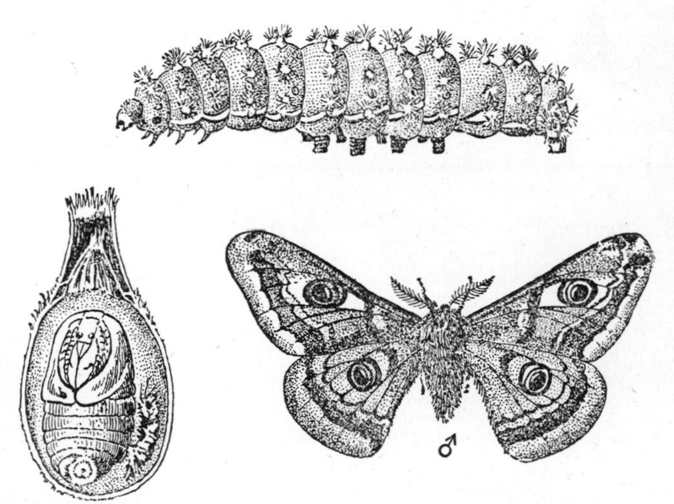

Only one species, ***Saturnia pavonia*** [peacock S.], the Emperor Moth (*p. 28*), is found here, one of our largest moths, though but small among the others of the family, to which the Chinese Silkworm Moth belongs.

CHARACTERS. No *frenulum*, tongue minute, antennae feathery in both sexes but particularly the males. Only one anal vein on both wings. Large fluffy bodies.

The **larvae** are large, green and black, with hairy warts which may be pink, yellow, or blackish. They feed on many different types of plants, including heather, bramble, sloe, or small herbs.

The **pupae** are short and fat with a longish curved tail-spike and are found in a strong brown silk, bottle-shaped cocoon, with an open bottle-neck, the fibres of which are so formed as to give an easy exit, but no entrance. These are placed in a leaf and fall to the ground with it for the winter.

The **moths** differ in habit according to sex. The females are larger than the male here illustrated, with less feathery antennae and with no colour except grey. The males fly by day and assemble to the scent of the females which remain still until after pairing, and, if they fly at all, do so at night.

FAMILY *DREPANIDAE* [Sickles] HOOK-TIPS

Six British species, of which five are 'large'

CHARACTERS. **Larvae** similar to those of the Notodontidae (Prominents). Humped-backed with warts and prominences, 14-legged, having no claspers, pointed or spiked tails, and usually standing with head and tail up.

Pupae, having two spikes at tail, in a loose cocoon among leaves, with which they fall to the ground in winter. They have all two generations a year and winter as pupae. (The Scarce Hook-tip, *Drepana harpagula*, has two abroad, where it is common, though seemingly only one here.)

They are all tree-feeders, on birch, beech, oak, and lime. The Oak (*D. binaria*) and Birch (*D. cultraria*) species fly freely by day. The species figured is ***D. falcataria*** [sickle-shaped Sickle], the Pebble Hook-tip (*p. 28*).

The moths are slender-bodied, with lowered heads, antennae feathered in the males and only toothed in the females, which are otherwise much like the males. They have ears at the base of the abdomen, small tongues and *palpi*, and either two or four spurs on the hind shins.

FAMILY *ARCTIIDAE* TIGERS AND FOOTMEN

31 British species, all 'large'

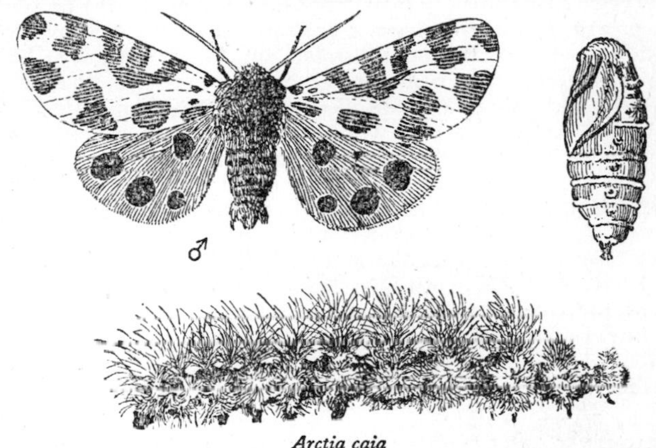

Arctia caia

CHARACTERS. This is a family consisting of moths which differ much in appearance. They are mostly evening- or day-fliers, and are divided into two groups or sub-families, the *Arctiinae*, or Tigers, and the *Lithosiinae*, or Footmen. The family as a whole is distinguished by the veining of the wings. The fore wings have one or two anal veins, and the hind wings two or three. In the hind wings the foremost vein does not leave the one next to it (which borders the cell) until about half-way down the cell, or beyond it.

The **larvae** are 16-legged, more or less hairy (some exceedingly so), and others have longish hairs on warts. They have small round heads. The larvae of the Tiger Moths feed on the leaves of docks, plantains, or other low-growing plants. They are usually catholic in their taste and are rarely confined to one type of plant. They are very hairy. Those of the Footmen (with only one very rare exception) feed wholly upon lichens, selecting those found upon particular plants or stones according to the species. In captivity they can subsist upon other vegetation.

The **pupae** of all Arctiidae are short and fat and are found in loose cocoons made up with the hairs of the larval skin, which are bitten off by the larva before pupating, and the cocoons are placed on, or near, the food-plants.

The **moths** differ very greatly in general appearance. Those of the Tigers are usually brightly coloured, particularly on the hind wings.

Arctia caia [burning Bear], the Garden Tiger (*p. 29*), figured on p. 215, is the commonest example. It often flies by day and is therefore frequently mistaken for a butterfly, but when it settles the brilliant red hind wings and body are covered and disappear from view. The amount of white and dark brown on the fore wings differs greatly in different specimens, and even the two wings are often dissimilar. They may be almost wholly white, or almost all dark with only two or three white dots. The Tigers are normally single-brooded in our climate though, under warm conditions, in captivity, they may produce a second generation. The antennae of the males have visible teeth like those of a comb. The legs are short and often woolly.

The Footmen have long narrow wings and few bright colours. Their antennae are thread-like. Their front shins have a leaf-like appendage, and the hind shins four spurs.

FAMILY *AGROTIDAE* [Rustics][1] (= *NOCTUIDAE*) OWLETS

Over 300 *British species, of which about twenty-five are 'small'*

This family is a very large one. The structural differences between its members are slight, though there is much difference of general appearance, often between those closely related.

CHARACTERS. There is always a *frenulum* and the tongue is almost always fully developed. The antennae are mere threads in the females and usually only very slightly toothed in the males. The *palpi* are normally short, though one small group have long *palpi* from which they get the common name of 'Snouts'. The veining of the wings is as follows: fore wing, one anal vein, the central vein starting low. Hind wing, two

[1] This family is now split into *Caradrinidae* and *Plusiidae*.

anal veins, *frenulum*, and the foremost vein, which starts separate from the next (which borders the discal cell) soon joins it, thus making a small additional cell, and leaves it again about the middle of the discal cell.

They are almost all night-fliers. They are strongly attracted to lights, and to 'sugared' trees. The great majority of species feed upon deciduous trees, shrubs, or herbs, or grasses, either upon the flowers, buds, and leaves, or underground upon the roots. There is a group, of about twenty species (the Wainscots), which are marsh-dwellers and take their food in the inside of the stems of rushes, reeds, or grasses. Apart from these, there are a few whose larvae are exceptional feeders. Thus one species feeds on a conifer, one or two on lichens, and one on fungi.

The **larvae** vary considerably; again closely related species showing much difference, though the greater number are smooth, or nearly so, and 16-legged. About a dozen species have the front pair of hind legs, or even two pairs, more or less rudimentary, so that their progress is like that of the Geometridae, and they are known as 'semi-loopers'.

The **pupae** have usually hooks at the tail end and sometimes hairs on the body. Pupation in the case of some 170 species occurs underground in an earthen cell in which the larval skin is, necessarily, retained at the tail. Some fifty species form a loose cocoon on the surface of the ground, and some sixty-five species form them on the food plants, either on tree-trunks or among vegetation. Two species spin leaves together and pupate between them. The marsh-dwellers (Wainscots) above mentioned pupate inside the stems where they feed, taking care to enable the emerging moth to make its exit at a prepared hole in the stem.

The LIFE HISTORY of the family is comparatively uniform in one respect. Of the 300 species only twenty are recorded as producing two generations a year, with another ten in which the second generation sometimes occurs. Four species are known to spend several years (2–4) in the pupal state before emergence. All the rest have the normal life of one year. As to the state in which the winter is spent, these moths show every variety. About 140 species winter as larvae,

90 as pupae, 50 as eggs, and about 20 as adult moths. One species feeds only on the roots of grass, and it is often a serious menace to farmers owing to the fact that its presence in great numbers remains unnoticed until the grass withers. It pupates in mid-winter underground.

Considering the size of this family, the **moths** do not differ so much in their general appearance as might be expected. Speaking very roughly (there are, of course, many exceptions)

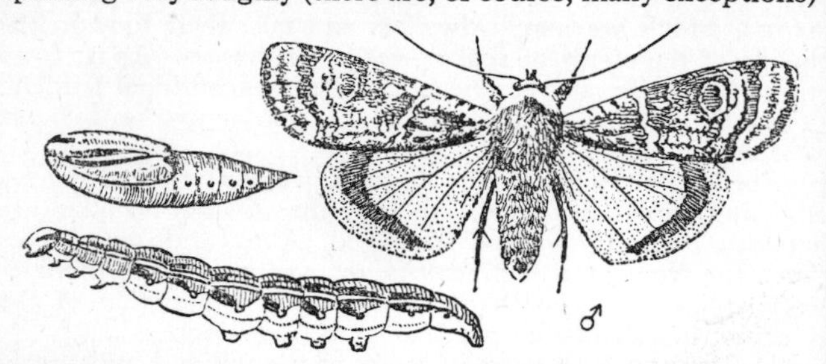

they belong to three types. The most numerous type is that in which the fore wings are brown or grey, and covered with an intricate pattern. This serves as an excellent camouflage when the moth rests on stone or tree-trunk with the fore wings covering the hind, as all Owlets do. The hind wings, which when at rest are folded beneath the fore wings, are, in this type, pale grey or white and with no markings other than a dark smear across the wing. The second type is very similar except that the hind wings are brightly coloured with yellow, red, or blue, e.g. ***Triphaena pronuba*** [affianced Bright-colour], the Large Yellow Underwing, here chosen as the type to be figured in colour (*p. 29*). The third and last type is that of the reed-feeding Wainscots. In these the wings are both without any clear pattern save for some darker lines following the direction of the veins in the fore wings which are of a dry-grass yellow, while the hind wings are mainly whitish. There are a few exceptional species in which green or other colours appear, but these cannot be detailed here.

A small group, of four species containing two 'large' moths, is sometimes classified as a separate family, under the name of *Cymbidae*. The 'large' species are green and white in colour and so unlike any other Owlets in appearance. They show minor differences of veining and one, ***Bena prasinana*** [leek-green Bena], the Green Silver-lines (*p. 29*), is here figured. It flies by night and the larva feeds on oaks and other trees. The pupae make cocoons under the leaves or elsewhere on or near the trees.

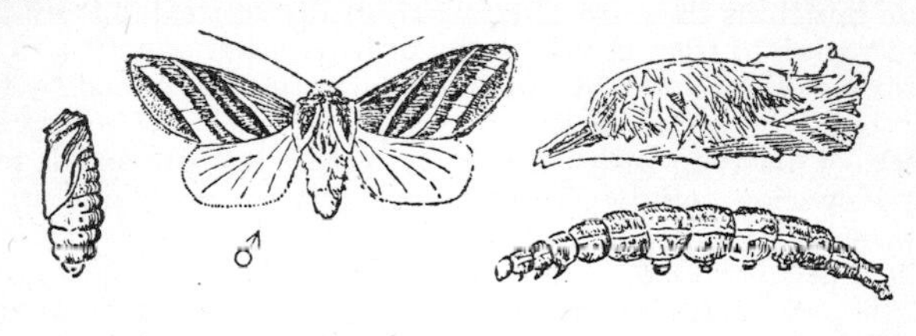

FAMILY *GEOMETRIDAE*[1] LOOPERS

[Land-measurers] (Waves, Carpets, Pugs, &c.)

About 270 British species of which about 160 are 'large'

CHARACTERS. Although there are certain peculiarities of veining which will be referred to later, the main characteristic which distinguishes the family from others is found not in the adult stage but in the larval. The larvae have only ten legs. There are the usual three pairs of 'true legs' on the first three segments and the pair of 'claspers' on the last segment, but of the 'false legs' (usually present on the 7th, 8th, and 9th segments) only one pair (those on the 9th segment) are developed. There are a very few species in which the 7th and 8th segment legs are partly apparent in the early larval stages only to disappear later, but they are useless and may be neglected. Apart from these exceptions, the ten legs are universal in the family.

This results in a method of walking different from that of any other caterpillar. They progress by what is called 'looping'. Holding the bough or leaf on which they are by the four hind legs, they stretch out to their full length and take hold of the twig ahead of them. Then releasing the grip of the hind legs, they draw up the body into a loop and again grip with the hind legs just behind the fore. Repeating this

[1] This family is now split into *Sterrhidae*, *Geometridae*, *Hydriomenidae* *Brephidae*, and *Selidosemidae*.

process they advance as it were by compass strides, whence they have earned the names of geometers [measurers of the land] or 'loopers'.

In addition to their compass progress these larvae have the habit of resting, when not feeding, in rigid positions of which some (not all) simulate the twigs of their food-plants. In these positions they are often wonderfully concealed from the observation of man and of many of their other enemies. The rigidity of these twig-like positions may be maintained by the help of a silk line from the twig to the spinneret of the caterpillar. This twig-posturing is, however, not universal, and many species completely spoil the picture by taking up a station at 'wrong' angles which make them very visible. Others adopt coiled or spiral attitudes on leaf, moss, or twig. Others again hang down, and others lie along twigs, leaf-ribs, or pine-needles. There is often marked variation of colour between the larvae of the same species, some being green and others brown. The way in which the pupae are placed also differ much. The greater number of species pupate either on the surface of the ground among leaves or other vegetation, or else beneath the surface. There is usually some cocoon, consisting either of a loose silken case or, in the earth, of a case made of soil fastened together with silk.

While the chief character of the family is that their larvae are loopers, the following are the structural characters which distinguish the adult moths. They have ears at the base of the abdomen. They have the *frenulum* and the sucking tongue well developed. A very few species lack either the *frenulum* or the tongue, but one or other is always present. The antennae are threadlike in the females and, to varying degrees, feathery in the males.

The wing structure of the various species differs, and in accordance therewith the family has been subdivided and is even regarded as consisting of as many as six different families by some authors. All have, however, in common the following points: (1) in the fore wing, the vein which starts from the cell begins either at the centre of the cross vein or else nearer to the vein in front of it than to that behind; (2) the vein which forms the front of the cell forks into two branches after leaving it; (3) in the hind wing, the hindmost branch of the anal vein is either very short or altogether lacking; (4) the foremost vein leaves the next near the base of the end of the cell and does not come near it again.

In colour there is much variety. A few species are of a delicate apple green, some mottled in black and white and others pure white or generally yellow. The greater number are of various shades of brown. While some species have the hind wings almost uniform in colour, the majority have the pattern of the fore wings repeated or continued over the hind wings.

The species here depicted is ***Abraxas grossulariata*** [gooseberry Delicate-precious], the Magpie (*p. 30*). It is commonly found throughout the country and does much harm to fruit bushes and shrubs generally.

The Geometrids are almost all night-fliers, comparatively thin-bodied and large-winged, and when they rest, they usually do so with the wings outspread and open flat as if spread out in a collection. This rule is, however, only a generalization. A few rest in the way typical of the butterflies (with the wings thrown up, the upper surfaces together), and some again flat, but with the fore wings covering the hind.

Of our 160 larger species, a dozen show a very strange peculiarity. Their females are almost, or completely, wingless. These females have no look of moths at all, but rather of spiders (compare the Lymantriid *Orgyia*, p. 210). What is perhaps the oddest thing is that the males of these wingless female species often closely resemble those of normal species and are in fact nearly related to them. Further, there does not seem any such great change as might be expected in the life history of these species. Most of their larvae are tree-feeders and their eggs are commonly laid at the summits of tall trees, though the wingless females emerge on, or under, the ground. They appear to climb the trees afoot, and it is to prevent this climb by the Winter Moth, *Operophtera brumata*, that the owners of apple-trees band their trunks with sticky substances to protect them against their greatest enemy. It has been suggested that they are lifted on high by the males, but there seems to be little or no evidence of this.

LIFE HISTORY. The great majority of the Geometrids breed only once in the year. Of the larger species here dealt with only nineteen are recorded as producing two generations. A very few (five) are known to spend more than a year of life, all in the pupal stage. Their larvae are mostly feeders by day in the open upon forest trees, shrubs, or low plants. Four species feed on the Scots pine or other conifers. A few (seventeen) feed by night only. Their method of wintering shows every possible variety, though those that winter as pupae exceed all the others in number Those that winter as pupae are 76, as larvae 44, as eggs 27, and as adult moths 3. One species, the 'Winter Moth' above mentioned, emerges in the winter months at any time between October and February. *Theria rupicapraria*, the Early Moth, also emerges in December or January and *Phigalia pilosaria*, the Pale Brindled Beauty, does the same. It is noticeable that all the three species just mentioned have wingless females.

The great majority of the moths of this family are night-fliers, though many of them can be caught in the day, as they will fly from their trees or bushes if these are beaten with a stick. They are greatly attracted by light and even some of the wingless females will climb lamp-posts to get near to the light.

FAMILY *ZYGAENIDAE* [Sharks]

BURNETS AND FORESTERS

Ten British species, of which nine are 'large'

CHARACTERS. The seven Burnets are all very much alike in shape, general appearance, and colour, all having the hind wings, and the spots on the fore wings, red, while the ground colour of the fore wings is a darkish bronzed green. The two Foresters have unspotted green fore wings and white hind wings.

Their **larvae** are much alike, 16-legged, somewhat fat and

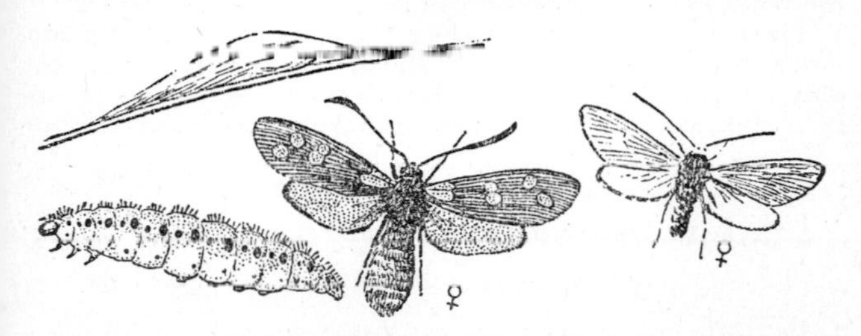

tubular, with small heads. They are dark green, with black and yellow markings and whitish hairs. They all feed upon low plants, the Burnets mostly upon vetches and the Foresters on sorrel.

The **pupae** are soft and more mobile than is usual, and the top of the tongue-case is free. They have a ridge of tooth-like prominences along their backs and they are in hard, parchment-like cocoons tightly fastened to a leaf or stem and, as it were, glazed.

The two **moths** here illustrated are ***Zygaena filipendulae*** [dropwort Shark] (*p. 30*), the Six-spot Burnet (left), with larva and pupa, and ***Procris statices*** [sea lavender Procris] (*p. 30*), the Forester (right). All these moths have long fore wings, while the hind wings are short and round. Their bodies are large and covered with short hair. They have long tongues and a *frenulum.* The antennae of the Burnets are dilated towards their ends, flexible, curved, and pointed at the extreme tips, being thus not unlike those of some of the Hesperiidae, Skippers (see p. 202). They are separable from the butterflies by the possession of *frenula.* The antennae of the Foresters are not club-shaped, but threadlike in the females, and with short teeth on the sides in the males.

All the moths are brilliantly coloured, diurnal—flying only in sunlight—and very gregarious. They rest, often several together on the same flower, with the wings closed, tent-wise, along the body. Both as larvae and as moths they are sluggish, the flight being slow and heavy.

Their Life History is, like their appearance, uniform. They are short-lived as moths, and all winter as larvae, having only one generation in the year. The larvae of two of our rarer species of Burnets sometimes take two years to develop.

FAMILY *HETEROGENEIDAE* [of different race]

Two British species, of which one is 'large'

The only 'large' species is ***Cochlidion avellana*** [Avellan Snail-let], the Festoon (*p. 30*). It is fat-bodied, with thread-like antennae, and flies by night.

The family is remarkable for the form and habits of the larvae. They are most unusual. They are practically legless, the head withdrawn within the body except when feeding, the true legs small and rudimentary, and the usual hind legs completely lacking, replaced by sucker-like projections on the first eight segments of the abdomen. The spinneret is flattened so as to produce the silk in a ribbon, not a thread, and this is used to help locomotion. During the larva's life it pushes out numerous telescope-like spines which are, however, withdrawn again, becoming mere warts before it is full grown. It lives and feeds upon the leaves of oaks, beeches, and other trees and reaches full growth before the winter sets in. Then it ceases to feed and spins for itself a brown cocoon and therein sleeps through the winter. When spring comes it pupates without leaving the cocoon. This is built with a hinged lid at the end, from which the pupa comes out just before the emergence of the moth. There is only one generation a year.

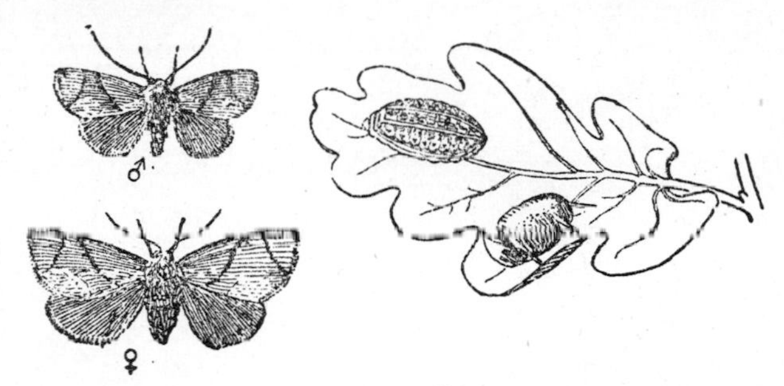

Cochlidion avellana

FAMILY *COSSIDAE* GOAT MOTHS

Three British species, all 'large'

CHARACTERS. The **larvae** are 16-legged, with powerful chewing jaws, smooth and shiny and with only a few hairs, loosely scattered.

The **pupae** are enclosed in cocoons built among, and with, earth or wood chips, either on the bark or at the foot of the tree or reed, on the wood (or pith) of which the larvae live.

The **moths** are stout or slender, with unusually long bodies covered with flattened hairlike scales. They have no tongues, and yet there are records of their being attracted to sugared trees. Their legs are short, with hairy thighs and shins bearing a leaf-like appendage. They are night-fliers and rest with the wings closed roof-wise. The females have a hard ovipositor, sometimes of considerable length.

Veining: Fore wing has two anals. Hind wing: *frenulum.* Three anals. The foremost vein independent at the base and throughout its length.

HABITS. They are all wood-borers, and live for two or more winters in the larval stage. On coming from the egg, they eat their way through the bark, boring a minute channel along which they travel for their two, or even three, years of life.

This channel becomes gradually larger as the larva grows and is filled up behind the larva with the sawdust made up of the part of the wood which even a Cossid larva cannot digest. Larvae enclosed in carpentered wood have even been known

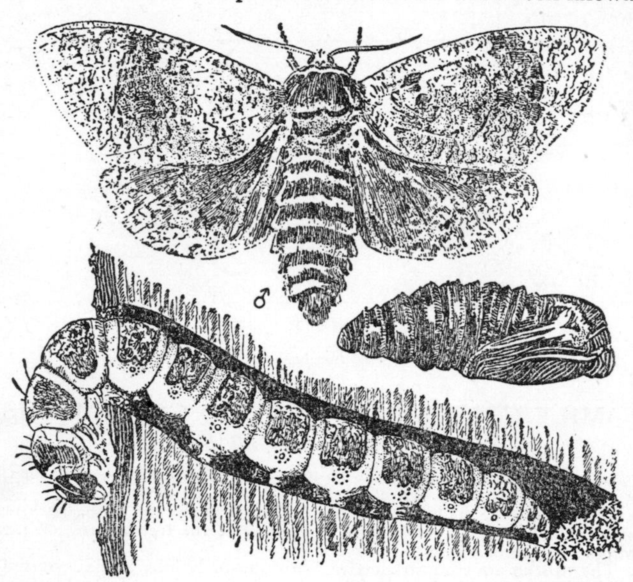

to eat their way through lead sheeting which covered it. Not being able to return through the blocked and tapering passage by which it advanced, and the pupae and emerging moths not being provided with jaws, the larva must (and does) either eat its way out before pupating or else eat its way to the surface, where it pupates behind a thin, membranous, doorway which the moth can push open.

Cossus[2], the Goat Moth (*p. 31*), here illustrated, is the largest and far the commonest of our three species. It gets its name from the evil stink of its larvae, which bore for three winters in the timber of willow, poplar, ash, oak, and other trees, before coming to the surface to pupate. It is a serious pest to the forester. The cocoon is made up of earth or chips on, or under, the trees.

FAMILY *SESIIDAE* (= *AEGERIIDAE*)[1] CLEARWINGS

Fifteen British species, of which three are 'large'

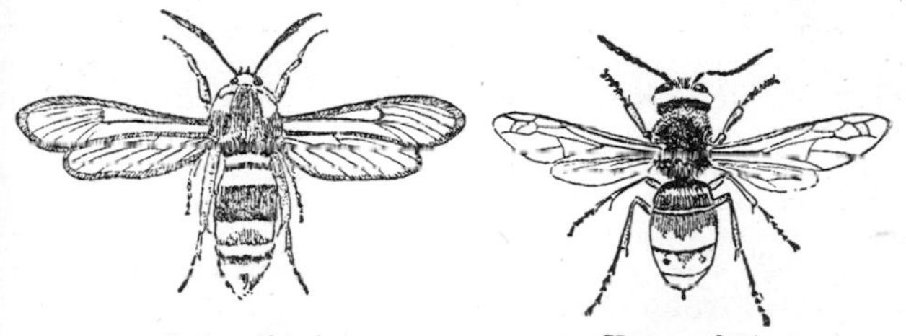

Sesia apiformis *Vespa crabro*

CHARACTERS. The **larvae** are 16-legged, although the claspers are sometimes ill developed. They are almost colourless and hairless and have powerful jaws. They soon bore through the bark and spend some months there. Then they bore deep into the wood of the stems or branches or roots of the forest or orchard trees which form their food-plants. In the tunnels thus made they live for one or two years, at the end of which time they eat their way to the surface of the bark, leaving a thin film of the outer bark to act as a door and cover, and then, in a cavity some inches above the prepared exit, they spin a loose cocoon and pupate.

Their **pupae** are unlike most of those of the Lepidoptera in that they are not completely wrapped up in one continuous sheath of chitin, but have the limbs separately enclosed (*incompletae*). They have the eyes projecting at the end of 'collars', a series of bristles or teeth on the segments of the abdomen, and considerable mobility. Thanks to this, the pupae push through their covering doors and protrude from their holes before the adults emerge.

The **moths**, once recognized as such, are easily distinguished from all others, except the genus *Hemaris* belonging to the family of Sphingidae (p. 205). They look like Hornets or Wasps.

[1] The relationships of this family are with the *TINAEOIDEA*, p. 234.

The sketch on p. 227 shows the likeness between one of our largest species ***Sesia apiformis*** [bee-shaped S.], Hornet Moth (*p. 31*), and the Hornet, ***Vespa crabro*** (*p. 31*). They have long narrow wings, scaleless and transparent except for a few scales round the edges and at the end of the cell. They have very long hind legs, of which the thighs are equipped with spurs. The species are distinguished by their size and by differences in the arrangement of the black and yellow marks on the heads and bodies.

The distinction between them and the wasps or other Hymenoptera (apart from the ordinal differences detailed on pp. 188 ff.) which are most apparent to the unaided eye are that they have no waists and that they have some scales on body and wings. They have, of course, no stings, and they have spiral tongues.

They seem always to emerge in the morning, in sunlight, and may be seen sunning themselves on the tree-trunks or, in the evening, hovering over flowers.

The main differences between the Sesiids and the genus *Hemaris* are in the earlier stages and life history. The wing structure of Sesiids is characterized by: *Fore wing*. The five veins which come from the cell are equidistant. No anal vein, or at most one. *Hind wing*. No vein between the cell and costal edge. Three anals.

FAMILY *HEPIALIDAE* [Fevers]

GHOSTS AND SWIFTS

Five British species, all 'large'

CHARACTERS. Believed to be among the most primitive of the moths.

The **larvae** are 16-legged and differ much in form. They are all underground feeders upon roots of grasses, bracken, or other low plants.

The **pupae** are all formed underground and are unusually soft-skinned and mobile. They are equipped with stiff hairs on the abdomen which enable them to move some distance through the soil, even when it is dry and hard, so as to get to the surface before the moths emerge.

The **moths** show very little difference in structure between the fore and hind wings. Both have the cells divided into three by an intermediate forked vein, and there are as many or more veins in the hind wings as there are in the fore. There are other signs of a lack of characters later developed by most moths. Thus they have not the usual *frenulum* on the hind wing to make a union with the fore wing, nor is this union made good by the hind wing being enlarged at the base, as it is in other Lepidoptera (e.g. the butterflies). The *frenulum* is replaced by a projecting lobe on the fore wing (*jugum*) which is tucked under the hind, but this junction is very imperfect. They have no tongue or other developed mouth-parts, and the *palpi* seem to be differently formed from those of other moths.

One odd fact is that they do not seem to have settled upon the best form of courtship. Among our own five species three very different methods are practised. Our largest species, ***Hepialus humuli*** [hop Fever], the Ghost Moth (*p. 32*), differs

from most moths in that it is the male which attracts the female. This he does by dancing in the twilight, hovering in one place, with quick-beating white wings, rising and falling as if suspended on an elastic thread. He continues this dance until the large yellow female, whose flight is direct and purposeful, seems actually to bump into him. It is not until after pairing and when she is laying her eggs that she adopts a somewhat similar hovering flight. During this hovering flight she scatters her eggs broadcast.

The Gold Swift, *H. hectus*, also hovers and attracts his wife, but in this case the charm seems not only to be the flash of the gold-spangled wings, for he is brown like the female, but also a scent (noticed even by the human nose and compared to pine-apple) which he carries in glands in his swollen hind legs.

In the case of the Common Swift, *H. lupulina*, it is the female which does the 'vamping', not this time by hovering in the air, but by sitting on a stem and vibrating her wings. Sharp suggests that the attraction in this case is sound rather than smell, as the spell seems to extend only to a range of three or four feet. A foreign species assembles multitudes of males in a more usual way, apparently by scent.

FAMILY *PSYCHIDAE* BAG-WORM MOTHS

Six British species, one 'large'

CHARACTERS. They are remarkable for the fact that all the females are completely wingless. The **eggs** are laid inside the sheaths formed by their mothers and hatch there. The **larvae**, after eating up the body of the dead mother(?), come out, and each begins for itself the formation of a sheath composed of grains of sand, or shreds of bark or other vegetable matter. In these sheaths, the head and legs alone projecting, they will live, if males, until after pupation, and if females, until death. The **pupal** stage lasts usually two years. The cases, or baskets, of the two sexes differ in appearance owing to the choice of diverse materials to

compose them. They crawl about in these cases, feeding, and then hang themselves up by the head when ready to pupate, still retaining their sheaths.

The male **moths** then emerge in normal manner. They have fattish hairy bodies, no tongues, combed or feathery antennae, rounded wings of a uniform dark colour, sparsely scaled and almost transparent.

Sterrhopteryx fusca [dark Stiffwing] (*p. 32*), our only large species, is here shown.

The females never leave the larval cases, but, in them, pupate, receive the intrusive males, lay their eggs and await their death. They are small-headed, wingless, legless, thin-skinned maggot-like creatures.

The males fly about in the daylight, seeking the females in their straw bottle-case hermit-cells. Their life as adults is very short, not exceeding a few hours.

SUPER-FAMILY *PYRALIDOIDEA* [Fire-dwellers]

CHINA MARKS, PEARLS, ETC.

163 *British species, of which seventy-six are 'large'*

CHARACTERS. Though half these species are 'large', they are usually classed among the micro-lepidoptera. The various groups have the following traits in common.

The **larvae** are 16-legged, slender and glossy, having but few hairs.

The **pupae** are cocooned, and, with very few exceptions, found above ground. They have from three to five free segments, but do not protrude from the cocoon before the moths emerge.

The **moths** have the peculiarity that the top vein of the hind wing approaches, joins, or is connected by a short cross-vein with, its neighbour beyond the cell and then leaves it again.

With few exceptions they have tongues, and all have *frenula.* Their *palpi* are often long and the *maxillary palpi* are mostly apparent. They are slender, have long thin legs, and the fore wings are often long and sharp-pointed, while the hind are broad and rounded. They fly at dusk.

Within the super-family are several notably peculiar groups.

Pyralis farinalis

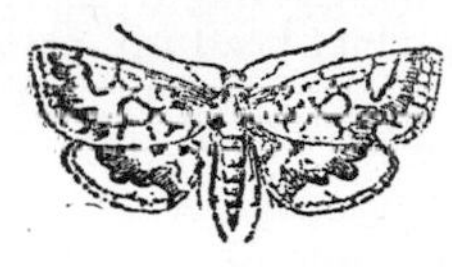

Nymphula nymphaeata

One, the family of *Pyralididae,* is known as the Knot-horns, from a swelling at the base of the antennae. The flour-eating pest ***Pyralis farinalis*** [flour Fiery] (*p. 32*) is here illustrated. Its larvae are said to live two years in silken tubes through the flour.

There is also a group of aquatic moths, aquatic at least in the earlier stages. These are the China Marks or *Nymphulinae.* The life history of ***Nymphula nymphaeata*** [water-lily Nymph] (*p. 32*) is as follows. The eggs are laid on water plants, and the larva when hatched mines into the water plant and remains there for one to three days, breathing through the skin the oxygen in the water. At this time its spiracles are closed. After the first moult—still breathing through the skin—it builds itself a sort of blister by cutting a piece out of a leaf and fastening it to the underside of another leaf. In this blister it spends the winter. In spring it changes its habits. While still remaining in the water, it makes a new kind of movable floating, leafy case out of two oval pieces of leaf. This case is made watertight and is open only at the end. It is filled with air, retained in the hairs newly appearing in the larva's skin, and breathed in through the spiracles, which now, for the first time, open and function like those of any other caterpillar. After further moults it pupates, either under or above the water surface.

Another odd group, called the *Galleriidae*, feed on the wax, or other materials, in the nests of bees and wasps. They are very sociable and even spin their cocoons together.

Another group, the Grass Moths or *Crambidae*, have very long *palpi* and the habit of folding their wings tightly round the body like a furled umbrella and lying, head up, along the grasses which are the food of their larvae. These make silken tunnels among the roots of the grass.

The family of *Alucitidae* (*Pterophoridae*) or Plume-wings also belongs to the Pyralidoidea. It contains thirty-five British species, of which ten are 'large'.

CHARACTERS. These moths have their wings divided into 'plumes' (except in the case of one genus), which, with long fringes on their under sides, look like feathers. The fore wings form two (sometimes three) plumes, and the hind three (rarely four). They have also long spine-like scales on the under side of the hind wings.

The **larvae** are soft and hairy and feed on low plants, living exposed to view on the leaves.

The **pupae** are also soft and hairy and are found hanging from hooks at the tail, like some families of butterflies. Sometimes they are covered with a slight cocoon.

The **moths** fly about sunset and are delicate and feeble in flight, being more wind-borne than self-propelled. They have tongues and no *maxillary palpi*. The male antennae are faintly toothed. They have long and slender legs.

Some of them have yellow or brownish colouring, but the commonest of our largest species, ***Alucita pentadactyla*** [five-plumed Gnat] (*p. 32*), here illustrated, is white.

SUPER-FAMILY *TORTRICOIDEA* [Twisters]

LEAF-ROLLERS

347 *British species, of which ten only are 'large'*

CHARACTERS. A super-family containing many agricultural pests. Some fly by day and some at night. They have relatively large wings, the fore wings squarish. Réaumur called them the 'big-shouldered' moths. Unlike the *Tinaeoidea*, they have narrow fringes to the wings. When resting, the hind wings are carried folded, fan-wise, beneath the fore wings.

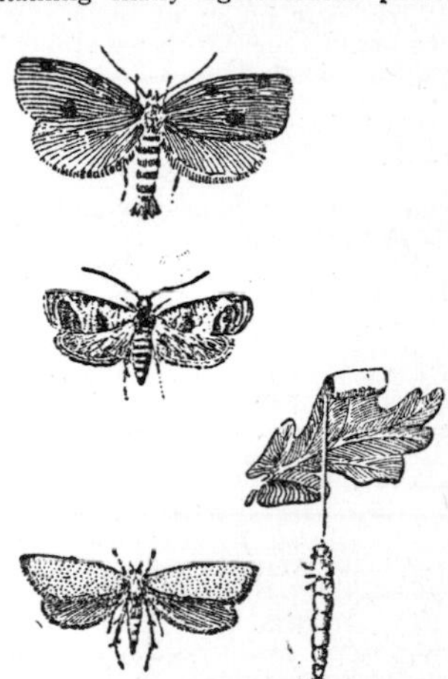

The **larvae** are all 16-legged, long, and with few hairs. They live concealed in their food, either in roots, fruits, or stems, or, if leaf-feeders, within tubes formed by rolling the leaves. In the latter case, if alarmed, they run out and drop by a silk thread. They are all very much alike and, as most species are not restricted to any particular plant, they are hard to distinguish. Those which feed in plant shoots often cause distorting growths of the shoot which help to conceal them.

The **pupae** have four (the males five) free segments and they protrude from their cocoons before the moths emerge.

The **moths** have hairy heads, smooth eyes, and developed tongues. The *palpi* are blunt-ended and the hind wings have *frenula*. Their shins are 4-spurred.

Three moths are here illustrated: one of the 'large' ones, ***Tortrix forsterana*** [Forster's Twister] (*p. 32*), found on ivy, honeysuckle, &c.; ***Ernarmonia pomonella*** [apple Fruit-fitting], the Codling Moth, which bores in apples and pears, from which the pupae protrude before the emergence of the moth; and ***Tortrix viridana*** [green T.] (*p. 32*), 'small' but great in its works, as it often completely strips oaks of their leaves.

SUPER-FAMILY *TINAEOIDEA*

CLOTHES-MOTHS, LEAF-BORERS, ETC.

About 735 *British species, of which all but seven or eight are 'small'*

This vast group of small moths, known to the townsman mainly because of the Clothes-moth of our houses, is variously divided by writers into numerous families. Though spoken of by some as a single family, it seems better to treat it as a major group or super-family. As the number of 'large' species is so small, the group will not here be subdivided.

CHARACTERS. Apart from their small size, they are recognizable by their long narrow wings and the long fringes upon them, and their slender long bodies.

The **larvae** of all the larger species are 16-legged, though some of the smaller have only 14, and a number of the smallest are legless. They differ greatly in habits. Some feed upon every variety of plant life, including fungi, and upon every part of the various plants. Others eat dried vegetable matter, such as stored grain or dead wood, and others again animal substances, wool, cloth, fur, hair, and the like. One species lives as a guest in ants'-nests, cleaning up the refuse, and some are useful in eating scale insects. They mostly feed in concealment, many as leaf-borers, and many in silk cases, which they move about with them. Very closely-related species differ much in their diet.

The **pupae** are cocooned and have usually several mobile and free segments. Many of them protrude from their cocoons before the moths emerge.

The **moths** have long antennae, long shins which are spurred, often developed *maxillary palpi*, usually little or no tongue, and *frenula* on the hind wings.

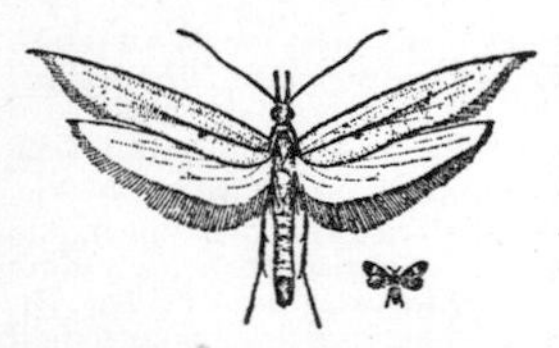

Illustrated here is the largest species of the group, ***Ypsolophus mucronellus*** [pointed High-crested] (*p. 32*), the larva of which feeds on the spindle tree in a slight web on the leaves, and, for comparison only, the smallest, smallest of all our Lepidoptera, ***Stigmella microtheriella*** [midget Spotkin], which belongs to the super-family *Stigmelloidea*.

There is some competition for the place of 'the' Clothes-moth, as three species are about equally destructive in different districts. They differ in the means of concealment adopted by the larvae. Here is depicted ***Tinaea pellionella*** [skin Moth], the larva of which is whitish, with a brown head. It lives in a case on cloth, fur, or feather, from August to May. The moth is found in flight from July to October and when about to lay, the female creeps into drawers or boxes to leave her eggs on our clothes. Clothes which have no eggs or larvae in them are safe if the moth be kept out by paper wrappings or bags with *every* entrance closed by strips of gummed paper. Eggs will not be laid in the air or sunlight, and eggs or larvae in clothes will be killed if the clothes be brushed in the sunlight.

One other British species, ***Orneodes hexadactyla*** [six-plumed Bird-like], the Twelve-plume Moth (*p. 32*), which is 'small', is included here only because of its unique shape. Its larvae are leaf-borers, its pupae cocooned, and its colouring a yellowish-white with black marks.

The following six Orders are amongst those which were included (see pp. 65, 66) in the Linnaean Order of *NEUROPTERA*, and although the modern subdivision is adopted, I have chosen to group these six Orders together.

They are:

Order	*Sub-order*	*Family*	
TRICHOPTERA [Hairy wings] CADDIS FLIES		*Phryganeidae*	
		Limnephilidae	
		Sericostomatidae	
		Molannidae	
		Leptoceridae	
		Hydropsychidae	
		Rhyacophilidae	
MECOPTERA [Long wings] SCORPION FLIES		*Panorpidae*	= Scorpion Flies
NEUROPTERA [Nerve wings]	*PLANIPENNIA* [Flat wings] Lacewings	*Chrysopidae*	
		Osmylidae	
	MEGALOPTERA [Big wings] Alders and Snake Flies	*Sialidae*	= Alder Flies
		Raphidiidae	= Snake Flies
ODONATA [Toothed] DRAGONFLIES	*ANISOPTERA* [Unequal wings] Dragonflies	*Gomphidae*	
		Cordulegasteridae	
		Aeshnidae	
		Corduliidae	
		Libellulidae	
	ZYGOPTERA [Yoke-wings] Damsel-flies	*Agriidae*	
		Lestidae	
		Platycnemididae	
		Coenagriidae	
EPHEMEROPTERA [One-day wings] FISHING FLIES		*Ephemeridae*	= Mayflies
PLECOPTERA [Folded wings] STONE FLIES		*Perlidae*	= Stone Flies

These various groups are so different that there is little that can be said of them all. The greater number are developed from eggs laid in or near the waters of streams or ponds from which larvae hatch which are aquatic throughout the larval life. These larvae have all chewing mouths. Some are plant-eaters, but the greater number are carnivorous, and many of them have some form of gills which enable them to breathe the air dissolved in the water. One group (*Perlidae*) retain traces of the gills even after they have become adults and left the water. When adults they all leave the water and live ashore, breathing, like other insects, through air channels, and using their four wings for flight. The wings are transparent and usually covered with a very close network of veins and cross-veins. If either wings are larger than the others, it is the hinder pair, though this is not true of the Mayfly family. None of their wings are markedly thickened or horny. One group alone (the *Trichoptera* or Caddis Flies) have the wings covered with hairs. They all have, as adults, chewing mouths, though those of the Trichoptera and the Mayflies are much reduced and almost, or quite, functionless.

Life History. There is great diversity in the changes gone through after the eggs hatch. Some Trichoptera and Megaloptera have the usual triple stages of larval, pupal, and adult lives of the most highly developed insects, the rest have no inert pupal stage. The various methods of change will be dealt with under the different Orders. So also will the different ways of carrying the wings, which are characteristic of the Orders.

ORDER *TRICHOPTERA* [Hairy wings]
CADDIS FLIES

188 *British species, of which sixty-seven are 'large'*

CHARACTERS. Moth-like insects with four wings thickly covered with hairs. Their mouth-parts are of the chewing type, but often so reduced as to be useless.

Their wings are held roof-wise over the body when at rest. The fore wings are narrow and long and the hind wings shorter and broader, their hinder parts folding fanwise beneath the fore wings. There are very few cross-veins, and the pattern of the veins is very similar to that of the more primitive of the moths. Their antennae are long, held forwards, and threadlike. Their legs are long and have five foot-joints.

The larvae are (with only one 'small' exception which lives in wet moss) aquatic and usually live in cases, which they make for their protection, of objects collected from the water.

They go through the three usual stages of egg, larva, and pupa before the winged adult emerges. The pupae have the limbs separated from their bodies and powerful jaws (*mandibles*), and they become active and mobile just before the emergence of the adult form.

ANATOMY. The **eggs** are very various in shape, many being patterned as are those of the Lepidoptera, and have threads by which they become attached to objects in the water.

The **larvae** are mostly tubular or somewhat flattened. The first three segments have a hard thick shell and project from the case, while the rest of the body, which is protected by the case, is soft. They have strong main jaws (*mandibles*) and their legs are active and used to walk. Along their bodies, gill filaments are often developed after the first few moults, and at the tail end are two strong hooks with which they grip their cases.

These cases are very variously made according to the materials to be found in the water, and to the species. It is not possible to identify the species by the case alone owing to the variety of these materials, although the choice of material made is helpful. Some cases are mobile, others attached to fixed objects. The sand, gravel, twigs, or leaves used may be built round the larva lengthwise, across, or spirally, and in the form of a tube, a horn, or a berry or bean.

One single species uses a hollowed twig as a case (*Agrypnia pagetana*), and one genus (*Rhyacophila*) lives freely in the water and dispenses with the protection of any form of case.

The typical appearance of these larvae when in and out of their cases is as here illustrated. When wanted by fishermen for bait they cannot be pulled out of their cases, but they can be made to come out by being prodded behind.

The **adult flies** differ little from Lepidoptera. The hairs on their

Agrypnia pagetana

Adult Caddis Fly (enlarged)

wings are sometimes flat and forked, but never have the paddle shape which characterizes those of the butterflies and moths and has earned these the name of scales. Their wings are held together by a device different from that of the moths, though the same result is attained. A fold along the edge of the fore wing grips the forward edge of the hind. Lastly, their mouths, when not purely rudimentary, are of the chewing type and they have not the curled proboscis of the Lepidoptera.

LIFE HISTORY. The eggs are held together in several jelly-like masses each containing some 100 eggs which the mother carries about on her body, finally dropping them into the water. The jelly dissolves in the water and frees the separate eggs. These float until they are held by some weed or other object, and hatch in about ten to twenty-four days.

The larvae and pupae pass their lives under water. To this there are only one or two exceptions. The larvae, until their gills are formed, get their air through the skin. They build their cases with the help of silk spun, like that of a moth caterpillar, from silk-glands situated in the head, and after the gills appear the water is circulated through the case by movements of the insect's body.

The larvae are generally vegetarian, but some species are carnivorous. They live on algae and small animalculae captured in the water, and the larval life lasts for about seven to ten months. When about to pupate, the larva spins a silken sieve at each end of its case, which, if hitherto mobile, it fastens to a stationary object and in which the pupa is formed.

The pupae of the species which have no cases are spun up in a complete silken cocoon. The pupae (or nymphs as, owing to their unusual mobility, they are often called) possess gill-threads like the larvae, but in other respects resemble the adults, and they undergo the inert and secluded stage of their existence. Shortly before the adult is about to emerge, the pupa, or nymph, becomes active. It has powerful jaws (*mandibles*) with which it chews its way out of the pupa-case and it also often has a pair of feathered legs with which it swims to the surface, where, almost immediately, the adult fly emerges.

The life of the adults is brief—a few days, rarely twenty—and dull. They mostly fly only in the dusk or at night and their flight is slow and short. They eat little or nothing, but it has been proved that they can drink and they have been found on flowers or dew-drops, or at the sugar placed by insect-hunters for moths. They have lost the main jaws of the pupae which are left with the pupal slough.

Their legs are long, particularly the hip-joints (*coxae*), and have several spurs on their various segments. They have five foot-joints and either a pad (*empodium*) or two threads (*pulvilli*) between the two claws of each foot. They rarely stray far from the water in which they are bred, which, according to the species, may be swift-running, slow, or even stagnant ponds.

CLASSIFICATION. The British species of the Order are variously divided. The families which contain 'large' species are seven in number, and the distinctions between them are found in the form and number of segments in the maxillary palps, in the presence or absence of single eyes (*ocelli*), the length of the antennae, the number of spurs on the legs, the wing-veining, and whether the sexes differ in structure.

FAMILY *PHRYGANEIDAE* [Bundles of Sticks]

Nine British species, of which eight are 'large'

These are the largest species of Trichoptera. As well as compound eyes they have simple eyes. The sexes differ in the number of segments in the palpi, the males having four and the females five. The larvae are tubular and build their movable cases of plant fragments, often arranged in a spiral. They are found in stagnant or very slow-moving water only.

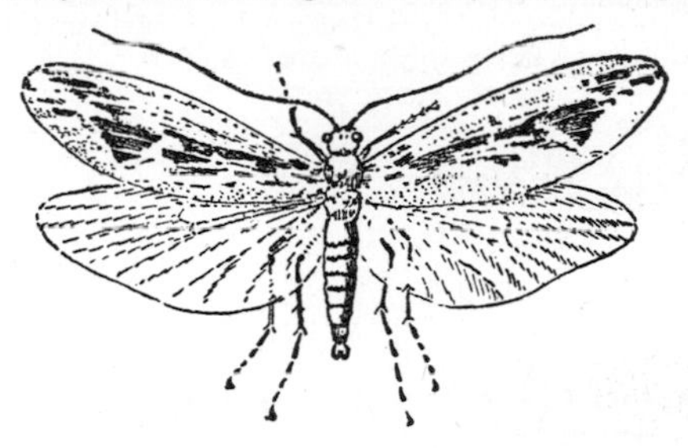

The largest of all our species is ***Phryganea grandis*** [large Stick-bundle] (*p. 33*) which is shown above.

FAMILY *LIMNEPHILIDAE* [Mud-lovers]

Fifty-five British species, of which thirty-nine are 'large'

The maxillary palpi of the sexes differ, those of the males having only three or even two joints, those of the females five. The wings are hairy, but usually with two or three transparent patches on the fore wings. The larval cases differ in shape and materials, sand, stones, shells, or vegetable matter being used. The larvae are tubular and frequent still and running water. The adult of ***Limnephilus lunatus*** [moon-shaped-marked Mud-lover], the 'Cinnamon Sedge' (*p. 33*), is here shown. The larval case is made up of twig pieces laid lengthways, and the adults are found throughout the summer.

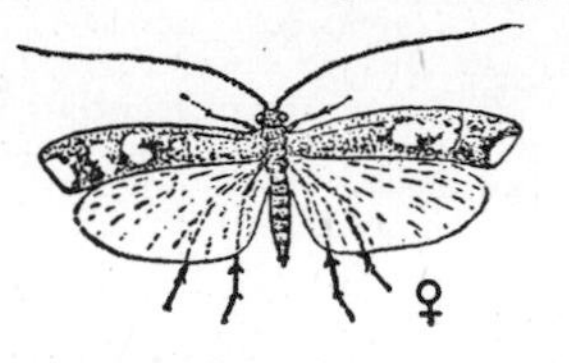

FAMILY *SERICOSTOMATIDAE* [Silk-mouths]

Ten British species, of which two are 'large'

The palpi of the two sexes differ, those of the males being hairy and broad and curled up in front of the head so as to form a mask. The wings are covered with thick hair. They have no simple eyes. They frequent running water. The larvae are tubular, and the larval cases of the two 'large' species differ.

Those of **Goëra pilosa** [hairy Groaner], the 'Medium Sedge' (*p. 33*), are weighted on each side with extra large pebbles.

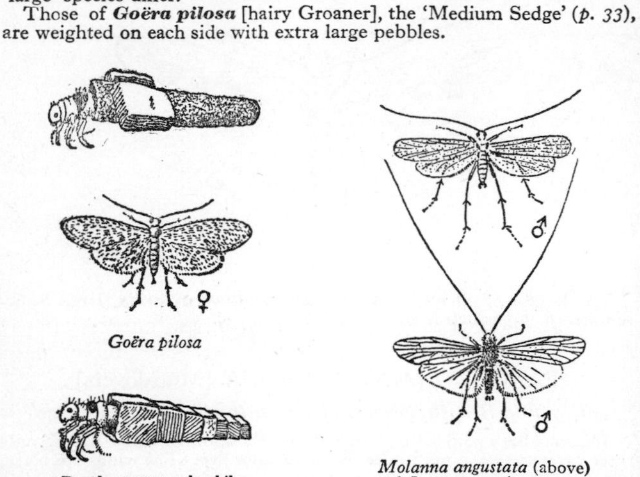

Goëra pilosa

Brachycentrus subnubilus

Molanna angustata (above) and *Leptocerus nigronervosus*

Those of **Brachycentrus subnubilus** [almost-cloudy Short-spur], the 'Grannom', are 4-sided, each side being made of a series of flat, slate-like stones.

FAMILY *MOLANNIDAE*

Two British species, both 'large'

No simple eyes. Sexes alike, legs 5-jointed, and very hairy palpi. The females are somewhat larger. The adults fly by night only. The larval cases are made of sand, tubular and attached to a flat shield of sand. **Molanna angustata** (*p. 33*) is found near lakes or ponds in June and July.

FAMILY *LEPTOCERIDAE* [Thin-horns]

Thirty British species, six 'large'

Antennae very long. No simple eyes. Sexes alike, legs 5-jointed. Wings thickly haired. Larvae tubular. They make long conical cases of various materials. They fly by day, sometimes in swarms, and frequent both still and running waters. ***Leptocerus nigronervosus*** [black-veined Thin-horn] (*p. 33*) is a still-water species (figured opposite).

FAMILIES *HYDROPSYCHIDAE* [Water-butterflies], *POLYCENTROPIDAE* [Many-pointed eyes], and *PHILOPOTAMIDAE*) [River-lovers].

Twenty-seven British species, six 'large'

Philopotamidae have simple eyes, Hydropsychidae and Polycentropidae not. The maxillary palpi are alike in the two sexes. The last (5th) joint is longer than any of the others and scaly like a rat's tail. Their wings are long and narrow, and the antennae short. The larvae are flattened, with heads not bent down, and are apparently carnivorous. They do not build cases, but spin nets, not unlike spiders' webs, in which floating animalculae are caught. Thus ***Philopotamus montanus*** [mountain River-lover] (*p. 33*) spins a tunnel-shaped net at the end of which the larva waits for its prey. This insect has no gills in either the larval or pupal stages. It flies in daylight from April to August.

♀

FAMILY *RHYACOPHILIDAE* [Torrent-lovers]

Ten British species, four 'large'

Having simple eyes. Maxillary palpi similar in the two sexes, legs 5-jointed, the 2nd joints being equal to the 1st, the 3rd much longer. The larvae are flattened and those of the two 'large' species make no cases but live openly and exposed in the water. They are found in swift-running streams. Of these ***Rhyacophila dorsalis*** [dorsal Torrent-lover] (*p. 33*) is an example.

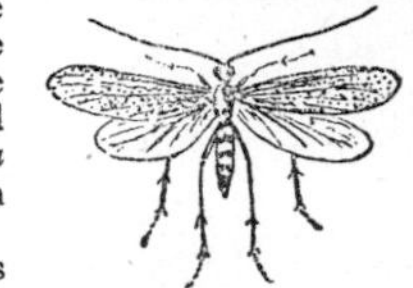

In addition to the above, there are four families containing only small insects.

ORDER *MECOPTERA* [Long wings]

FAMILY *PANORPIDAE* [All-hooks]

SCORPION FLIES

Three British species, all 'large'

CHARACTERS. Sharp, beak-like heads, with the chewing mouth-parts at the extremity of the beak. The larvae are terrestrial, living in the ground, and they greatly resemble those of the Tenthredinidae (Saw-flies) as they are caterpillar-like in form and have eight pairs of abdominal false legs.

Our species have four long hairless wings with many veins, which are carried flat along the body when at rest. The English name is due to the fact that the males carry their bodies curled up over their backs in the manner characteristic of the scorpions, to which their resemblance is heightened by the pincer-like gripping organs at the end of the abdomen. ***Panorpa communis*** [common All-hook] (*p. 34*) is here figured.

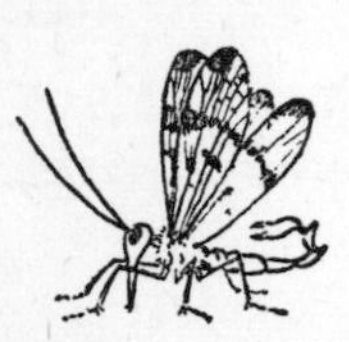

Both larvae and adults are carnivorous, but they are believed to prey upon injured or dead insects rather than to kill for themselves. They are found in damp and shady places, upon bushes in gardens and woods. They pupate in a cavity under ground, and the pupae are able to move fairly freely and make their way up to the surface for the emergence of the adults.

ORDER *NEUROPTERA* [Nerve wings]
LACEWINGS
ALDER FLIES AND SNAKE FLIES

(In recent classifications these are the only members of the old Linnean Order of Neuroptera to retain the name and thus acquire the status of an Order. They are divided into two Sub-orders, *Planipennia* and *Megaloptera*.)

SUB-ORDER *PLANIPENNIA* [Flat wings]
LACEWINGS

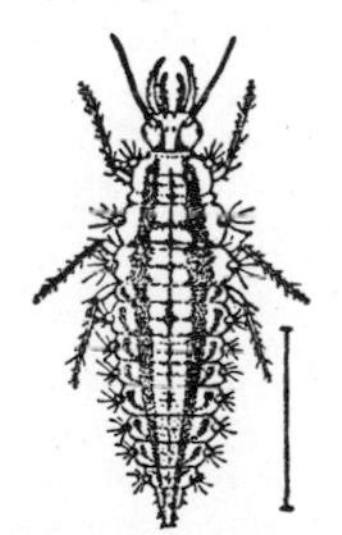

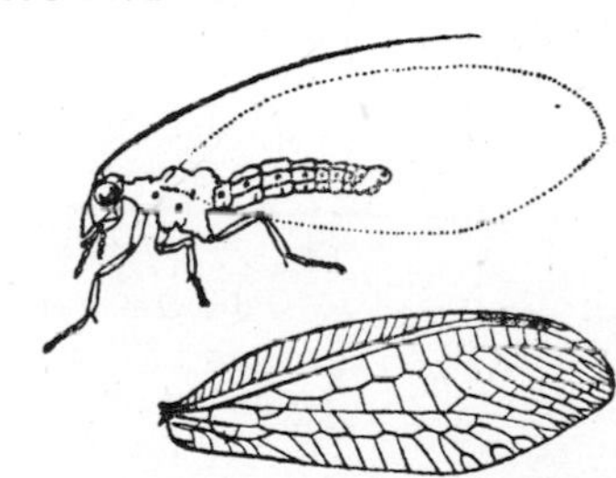

(In addition to the two families described here, there are two other British families containing no 'large' species, and one (*Hemerobiidae*) containing only one 'large' species, so rarely found that the family is omitted.)

Sixty British species, of which fifteen are 'large'

Characters. They have the usual three changes, going through the stages of egg, larva, pupa, and adult. Both larvae and adults are predacious, preying upon small animals, mainly upon Green Fly (Aphididae), and they are therefore of much use to mankind. The adults have two pairs of roughly similar wings which are profusely veined with a large number of longitudinal veins each of which divides into a fork at the end so that the edges of the wings are very thickly veined. There are also numerous cross-veins. Their mouths are adapted for chewing, their bodies soft, and their antennae threadlike.

ANATOMY. The **larvae** are shuttle-shaped, and a general idea of their form can be gathered from the sketch of that of *Chrysopa carnea* (= *vulgaris*) here given. They have tubular sucking-jaws with which the prey is seized and its juices imbibed without its ever entering the larva's mouth. Many of them have a series of tubercles along their sides from which grow numerous bristles, and the last segment of the abdomen (10th) acts as a leg and is used in crawling much as the claspers of the Looper Caterpillars.

Before pupating, the larvae spin a cocoon, using a secretion exuded at the anus, and there is a so-called pre-pupal stage followed by a moult inside the cocoon. The **pupae** have the limbs of the future adult separate from their bodies (*exarate*) and are furnished with powerful jaws and are capable of considerable movement. They come out of the cocoon and go some way before the adults emerge.

The **adult Lacewings** have prominent compound eyes, placed at either side of the head, long, threadlike antennae, and some, but not all, have also three simple eyes (*ocelli*). Their mouths are built for chewing and, unlike those of the larvae, open in the usual way to admit the food. Their legs have five foot-joints and a pair of claws on each. The wings are large and covered with a rich network of veins. The patterns vary, and upon them, and the differences in the external organs of reproduction, the separation of the species mainly depends. When at rest, the wings are held roof-wise, completely covering the body. The sketch on p. 245 with the veining of the left fore wing alone indicated gives a general idea of the form of the adult Lacewing.

HABITS. The eggs are laid upon the leaves or stems of trees, or other plants, the insects frequenting which will form the food of the larvae, and hatch in a week or two, according to the weather. The larvae moult twice before spinning their cocoons. The adults are nocturnal, lying up for the day upon the under side of leaves, which they often resemble. They fly at dusk and during darkness, and their flight is feeble and floating. Their main adult food, like that of the larvae, consists of such small forms of life as their feeble powers of flight and movement allow them to capture. This in most cases means Aphididae. Some have been seen to go to flowers for moisture, and they resort to the sugar preparations set to attract moths, so that they cannot be said to be wholly carnivorous. The adults live for some months, and there is much variety in the number of generations born in a year and in the stage in which the winter is passed.

FAMILY *CHRYSOPIDAE* [Goldeneyes]

GREEN LACEWINGS

Fourteen British species, all of which are 'large'

CHARACTERS. These are mainly green in colour, the transparent wings being also green-veined, though some of them have some black markings on head or body, and some black cross-veins. They have no simple eyes between the bright golden compound eyes, and there are none but the most minute hairs upon the wings.

When laying her eggs the female first touches the leaf or stalk with her abdomen so as to fix to it a drop of moisture, then she raises her body and draws out this liquid which dries on contact with the air, and then extrudes the egg. Thus each egg is found growing, as it were, at the end of a stalk. Some species lay several eggs at the same spot, in which case the stalks stick together for half their length, making the group of eggs look like a small nosegay. This habit of laying the eggs on stalks is probably a protection against ants or other enemies. Most of the family are single-brooded, though such is not the case of ***Chrysopa carnea*** (=*vulgaris*) [flesh-coloured

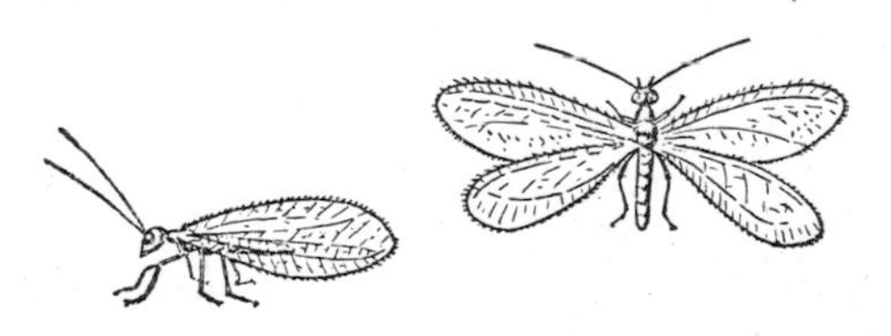

(or common) Goldeneye] (*p. 34*), which is our commonest species and which is here reproduced. This species is unique in wintering as an adult, and thus may be found at all months in the year. There seem to be usually two, or even three, generations in the year, and the last generation winters in hiding and does not pair till the spring of the following year. As autumn advances the green colour is gradually replaced by a russet brown. The first eggs are laid from May to

July, and the generation then born lay again in July and August.

There is another habit of this family which is odd. The larvae of some species, after sucking dry the Aphids or other small prey, entangle their dead bodies among the spines which cover their own bodies and so acquire a protective shield to hide them from their enemies. The Common Goldeneye is not a species in which this accumulation of debris seems to be practised. The larvae of all the family are terrestrial, and they are found on almost every kind of plant. It has been noticed that many species seem to go particularly to coniferous trees, but *C. carnea* is found on most forms of plant life.

FAMILY *OSMYLIDAE* [Stinkers]

One British species, which is 'large'

This is ***Osmylus fulvicephalus*** [yellow-headed Stinker] (*p. 34*), and it differs from the Chrysopidae as follows. The eggs are laid flat upon leaves and not stalked. The larvae, though born ashore upon plants by the sides of streams, are semi-aquatic. They are found in wet mosses on the banks of the stream and sometimes even swim in shallow water to catch their prey, which consist, not of Aphididae, but of the larvae of aquatic Diptera, for which they probe the mud. Their bite is apparently poisonous to the victim. They are not covered with spines, and there is no storage of debris on the back for protection.

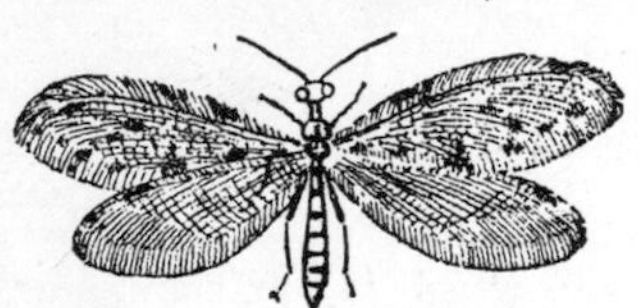

The adult has three simple eyes (*ocelli*) between the prominent compound eyes. The wings are not veined with green, but dark brown, and they have blackish spots upon them. Their veins are crossed by more numerous cross-veins and, in addition to the very minute hairs covering the membrane, there are slightly larger hairs along the veins and from points along the outer edges which are situated between the tips of the veins. Only one brood is born in the year. The adults are on the wing from May to the end of July, and the eggs, then laid, hatch in about three weeks. The larvae winter after their second moult and spin their cocoons about the end of April. In this species the males attract the females, thrusting out from their bodies a pair of scent-glands the odour from which calls their mates to them.

SUB-ORDER *MEGALOPTERA* [Big wings]

ALDER FLIES AND SNAKE FLIES

FAMILY *SIALIDAE* [Bird-like] ALDER FLIES

Two British species, both 'large'

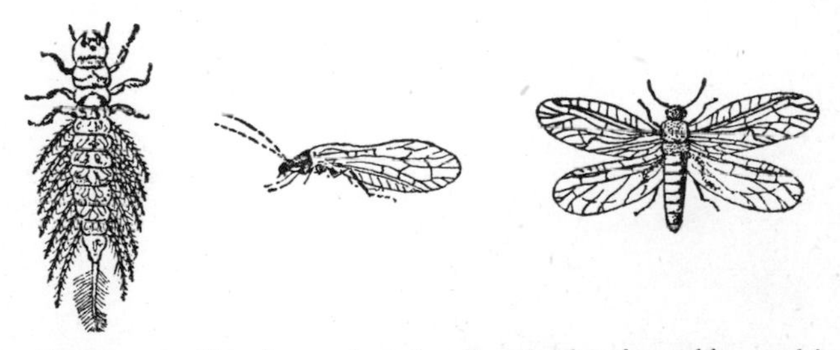

CHARACTERS. Four large wings, heavily veined and roughly equal in size. They are not folded when at rest, but laid back, roof-wise, along the body. Heavy bodies and feeble flight. Chewing-mouths with the mouth-parts pointing forwards. Five foot-segments. They go through the usual three changes, with immobile pupae. Larvae also have chewing-mouths, and both larvae and adults are carnivorous.

ANATOMY. The **eggs** are numerous (200 to 500) and are laid side by side on plants ashore.

The **larvae** are equipped with leg-like appendages all along their sides and at the tail end, each of which is fringed with gill filaments by which they breathe when in water. They are able to live out of water in damp places.

The general form of the larva of *Sialis* is as here shown.

The **adult** of ***Sialis lutaria*** [mud Bird] (*p. 34*) is here shown, at rest and as set in a collection. The bodies of the Alders are clumsy and soft, and their wings without any apparatus for holding them together in flight. The 4th joint of the feet is heart-shaped.

Life History. The Alders deposit their eggs in large clumps, hanging from plants close to water. When the larvae hatch out they crawl to the water where they live, and prey upon other insects or small water creatures, for a year. At the end of this time they leave the water and go ashore, seeking a place underground in which to pupate. The pupa does not move, and the adult insect emerges in due course. The life of the adults only lasts for a few hours. They do not fly far and do so clumsily.

The Sialidae are the most primitive and oldest type of the Order of Neuroptera.

FAMILY *RAPHIDIIDAE* [Needles] SNAKE FLIES

Four British species, all 'large'

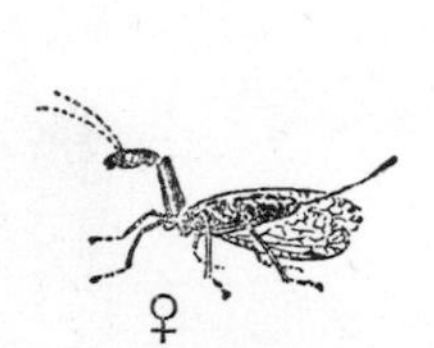

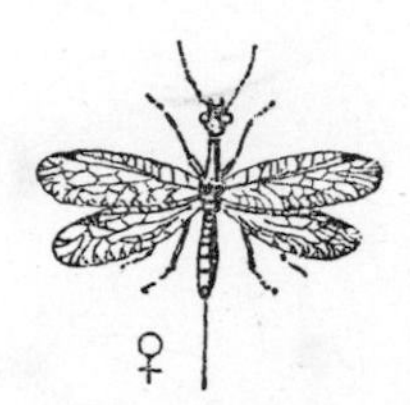

Sometimes regarded as belonging to a separate Superfamily or even Order. The Raphidiidae are wholly terrestrial and found only in wooded regions. Their shape differs much and their long necks (really the first segment of the thorax) have earned them the name of Snake Flies. One of them is shown here, ***Raphidia notata*** [marked Needles] (*p. 34*). The Snake Flies are not amphibious, the larvae, which grow from eggs laid by long ovipositors possessed by the females, in the bark crevices of trees, live on the trees and eat Aphids and other insects found there. They are carnivorous both as larvae and as adults.

ORDER *ODONATA* [Toothed]

DRAGONFLIES

Forty-two British species, all 'large'

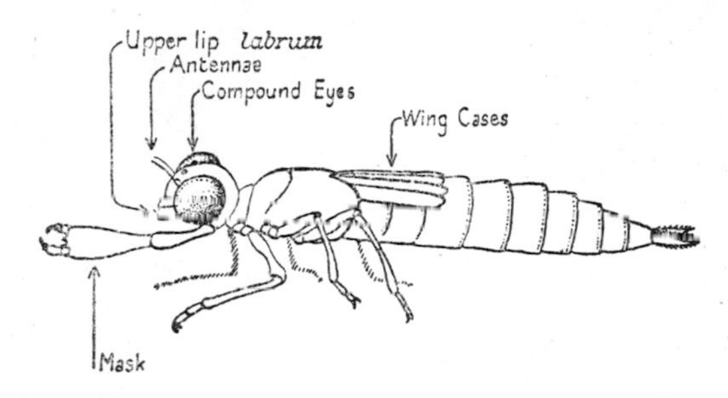

CHARACTERS. Their metamorphosis is not complete: there is no pupal stage, nothing corresponding to the inert chrysalis. From the egg comes a legless and wingless creature (called a pro-nymph) which moults within a few minutes (at most) into a larva or nymph. In the several moults of the larva it develops its wings in cases along the back and from its skin emerges the adult dragonfly, fully formed.

Both larva and adult are wholly predacious, with biting and chewing mouths. The adults have two pairs of roughly equal-sized wings, long, usually transparent, without scales, and with a great number of veins and cross-veins. Their eyes are large and compound, antennae short and thread-like, and bodies long and usually very slender.

ANATOMY. The pro-nymph stage and the earlier states of the larvae will not be described here. The fully grown **nymphs** differ in general appearance chiefly in the length of the legs and the bulk of their bodies. They are all wingless, though the wings are formed and their position shown by the cases in which they are enclosed, and they all live under water which they breathe through gills at the tail end of the abdomen.

The sketch above gives their external appearance.

Two peculiarities of structure in the dragonfly larvae deserve special attention: the gills and the mask. The tail-gills, which in the *Zygoptera* are long and conspicuous, are in the *Anisoptera* inside the rectum and form part of the breathing apparatus, much of which is internal and concealed from view inside the rectal cavity. The so-called 'mask' is a development of the lower lip and chin-pieces of the larva and is unique among insects. As shown in the accompanying enlarged sketches, it is

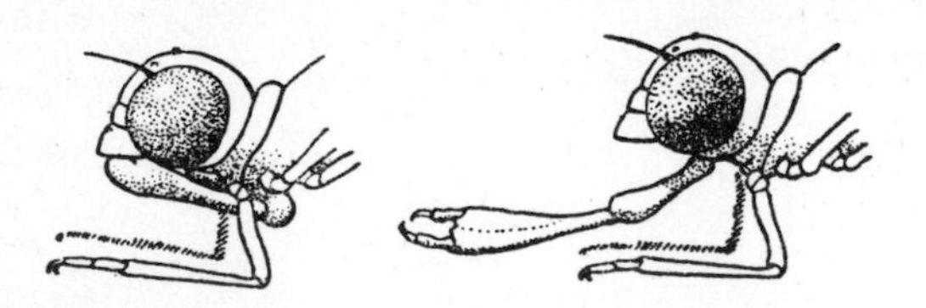

folded back under the head (extending sometimes as far as the hind pair of legs) and then forward again until it covers the mouth, when looked at from below. This is the normal position, and hence the name of 'mask'. When the larva sees any creature which it can capture, it shoots out the mask, opens and closes the pincers upon its victim, and drags it back to the mouth to be sliced and chewed by the mandibles. The movement is very swift and works much as used to do the instrument known to our elders as 'lazy-tongs'.

At the time of the final moult which marks the change to the adult dragonfly or *imago*, the larva leaves the water and, ashore or on a reed, stands, head up, and its skin at the head and neck breaks open. The adult slowly and carefully crawls out and, standing or hanging from its legs above the discarded larval skin, expands its wings and lengthens its abdomen into the complete adult form. For some time it remains delicate and colourless, and during this time is said to be immature or *teneral*. It is, however, already able to capture its food. There is therefore no break in its life of rapine.

The following sketch shows the external form of the **adult dragonflies.** The two Sub-orders differ in shape, as later described, but the differences need not be considered in this diagram, in which the wings are cut off.

It is not necessary to describe the mouth-parts here, save only to say that they are large and elastic, the upper and lower lips both being mobile and standing out from the face like a short megaphone. The mask of the larva has disappeared and is replaced by toothed lower jaws. The antennae are small and appear to be unimportant. The small eyes (*ocelli*) remain on the top of the head, and the huge compound eyes are even larger than in the larvae. In some species they have been estimated to have over 20,000 separate lenses.

The first segment of the thorax forms the narrow neck and allows the freest movement to the head; the other two are fused together and so slanted backwards and upwards that both wings come behind the three legs. The legs are all alike and not adapted for walking. They serve to cling on to plants, but mainly to help in catching the dragonfly's prey on the wing. In flight they are held in the position of a wicket-keeper's arms, and there are six of them instead of two.

The abdomen is long and usually tubular, sometimes very thin. The most remarkable organs (unlike those of any other insect) are those used by the sexes when pairing. Both sexes have, at the tail end, several claspers (or *anal appendages*), and in both sexes the genital apertures are

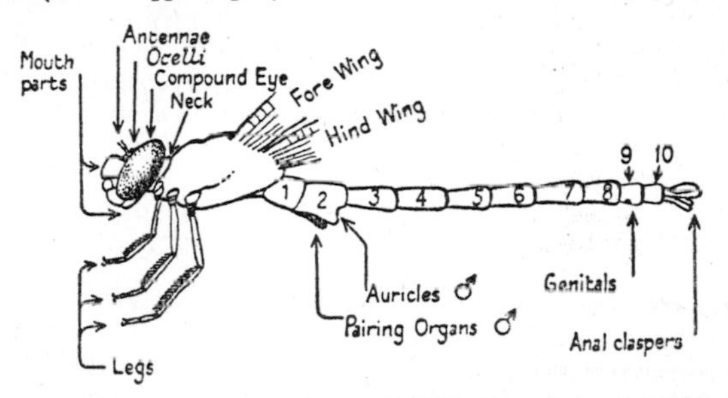

under the 8th or 9th segments of the abdomen, but, in addition, the males have highly complex pairing organs, varying in the different species, under the 2nd abdominal segment, the use of which is described later.

The various species are differentiated mainly by these, and by the veining of the wings which we need not consider here.

HABITS. The eggs are always laid in water or in weeds just above the surface of water. The larvae enter the water as soon as they hatch out and remain there until just before the emergence of the adult dragonfly. They hunt and eat any living creature they can find. Some of them burrow into the mud or sand and lie in wait for their prey, others live among water plants and stalk their victims. They are almost all slow and laborious walkers, but in the process of hunting they have two very remarkable accomplishments. The first is the use of the grapnel or mask above described, which, thrown forwards with lightning speed, gets hold of creatures apparently well out of their reach. The second is an odd means of progress. When haste is needed, the larva of the Anisoptera, discarding the use of its tardy legs, jerks itself forward by squirting out of its vent the water used for its breathing, and so, by the same propulsion as that of a rocket, shoots itself forward through the water. The two sub-Orders of adult dragonflies differ much in their flight. The Anisoptera are among the swiftest and most masterly of all the insects and hunt their prey by greater speed on the wing. They fly with wings often outstretched and can even reverse in flight as well as twist and turn with the utmost rapidity. Few, if any, butterflies, bees, wasps, or beetles can escape them. They hawk in chosen beats over or near their native waters, or dart from a perch upon a passing insect. The Zygoptera, on the other hand, appear to live upon creatures found upon or near the plants to which they hang between their fluttering, feeble, and butterfly-like flights. Almost all are sun lovers and settle whenever a cloud obscures the sun.

The way in which the **pairing** is effected is unlike that of any other insect. Before taking a mate, the male curves down his abdomen so as to bring the 9th and 2nd segments together and so transfers his sperms to the special pairing organs which lie under the 2nd segment. He then seizes the female with the claspers at his tail, either by the scruff of her neck (in the case of the Zygoptera) or by the back of the head (in the case of the Anisoptera). The security of his grasp is strengthened by the female throwing back her head and so gripping his claspers. In this position the couple may fly in tandem to some plant where the male obtains a hold and where the female bends down her long body until it is securely grasped by the pairing organs under the 2nd abdominal segment of the male and fertilization is effected. The coupled pair suggest the figure 69. Sometimes pairing is completed in flight but more usually on plants, always, however, in the manner above described.

This tandem formation as adopted before pairing is also, by several species, employed for a more unusual purpose. These insects lay their eggs under water, sometimes so deeply that the mother has to go wholly under the surface.

To help her in so doing the male adopts the tandem position and so, after the eggs are laid, pulls her up again into the air. This midwifery by the male is found nowhere else in the insect world except in the Tiger Beetle (*p. 155*).

Not much is known about the duration of life in this Order. None of our species live through the winters as adults. It seems probable that the usual life history is that of eleven months' life as larva followed by about a month of dragonfly life, there thus being one generation a year. Some species probably breed two generations in each year, and, probably, some have a life of almost two years as larvae, so that the duration of their lives is two instead of one year.

SUB-ORDER *ANISOPTERA* [Unequal wings]

DRAGONFLIES

Twenty-six British species, all 'large'

These are the larger species of the Order, which hunt their prey on the wing in the adult stage. All our species are at least 35 mm. in length and 55 mm. in span. They have great powers of flight, and rest with the wings outstretched.

There is no need to consider minor differences of wing structure in the adults, or small structural details in the larvae to distinguish them from those belonging to the other sub-Order of Zygoptera.

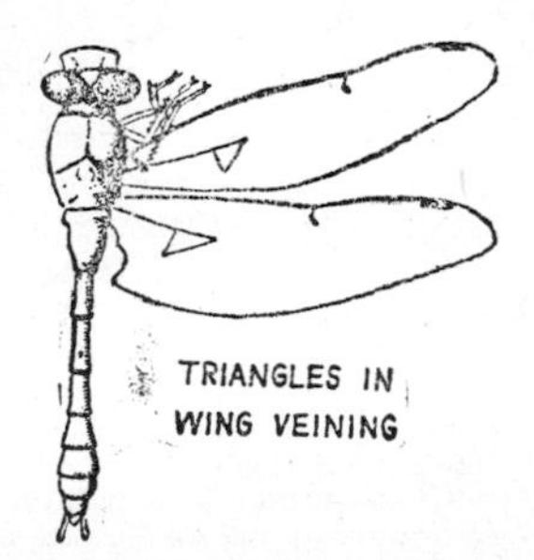

The Anisoptera as larvae have all somewhat fat abdomens and the breathing organs at the tail ends are comparatively inconspicuous.

The adults have the two pairs of wings quite dissimilar in shape: the fore wings being widest beyond the middle and the hind wings widest close to the body. Their general appearance is as here figured.

Note. In the wing structure, about a quarter of the way from the body to the tip of the wing, there will be found, among the thicker veins, a triangle, the shape of which, and of the neighbouring veins, will be referred to when we come to distinguishing between the different families. These triangles, alone of the wing veins, are drawn in the sketch on p. 255.

These Dragonflies are divided into five families.

FAMILY *GOMPHIDAE* [Nails]

Only one British species, 'large'

This fly, ***Gomphus vulgatissimus*** [commonest Nail] (*p. 35*), is some-

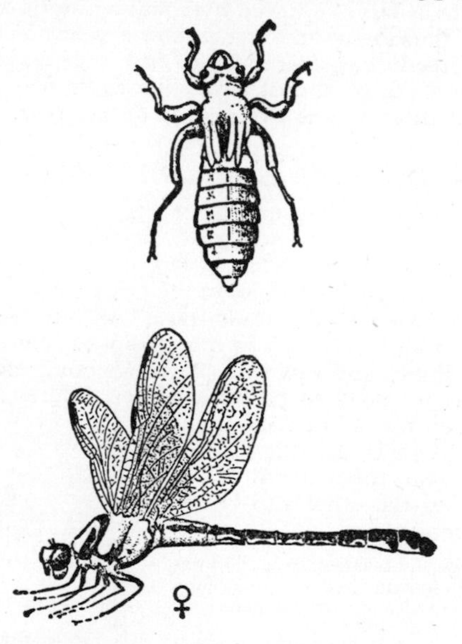

times classed with the family of Aeshnidae and is of medium size among the larger Dragonflies.

CHARACTERS. The nymph has only four segments in the antennae (4th minute) and its legs are strengthened for digging. The 1st and 2nd pairs have two segments in the foot. The mask is flat and does not wholly cover the mouth. The wing-cases are separated at their bases and come together at their tips. It lives in running waters and digs into the sand or mud, crawling out on to the bank for its change into the adult stage. For a very short time after hatching from the egg, it is without legs (a primary larva), and its nymphal stage is believed to last two years.

The adult's eyes do not meet at the top of the head, and the veining of the wings is unique among our large species in having no thin veins crossing the triangles. The triangles of the four wings are all alike in shape, as here drawn: note that there is a defined sub-triangle, and a super-triangle, also free from thin dividing veins.

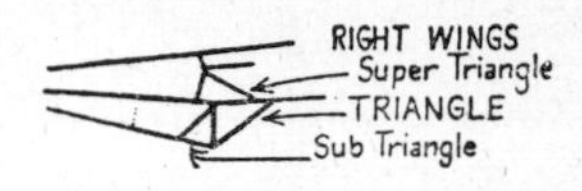

G. vulgatissimus is a rather slow flier, the females keeping away from the water except when pairing or laying. Pairing takes place in trees, and the eggs are dropped into the water of running streams.

FAMILY *CORDULEGASTERIDAE* [Club-bellies]

Only one British species, 'large'

This is ***Cordulegaster boltonii*** [Bolton's Club-belly] (*p.* 35) and is also sometimes classed with the next family (Aeshnidae). It is one of our largest Dragonflies.

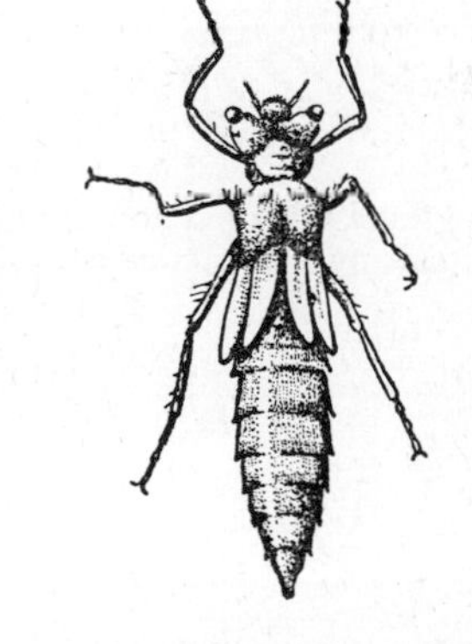

CHARACTERS. The **nymph** has seven segments in its threadlike antennae. Its legs are strong, but well adapted for walking. The mask is spoon-shaped and covers the head. The body is long and the wing-cases, in contact at their bases, diverge at their tips. It lives in the mud or banks of streams or ponds, and crawls out, often to a considerable distance and up a tree, for its final change.

The **adult's** eyes just touch at the top of the head, and the veining of the wings, though generally similar to that of the Gomphidae, differs in having a fine cross-vein in the triangle, and in the fact that the vein which makes the third side of the sub-triangle is a fine one and so placed as to make but an imperfect triangle.

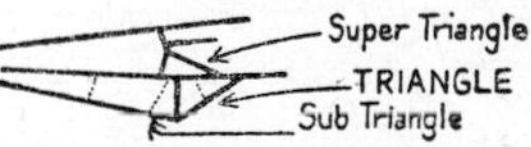

C. boltonii is a powerful and swift flier, hawking low over the water in a set beat, and the female plants her eggs in mud

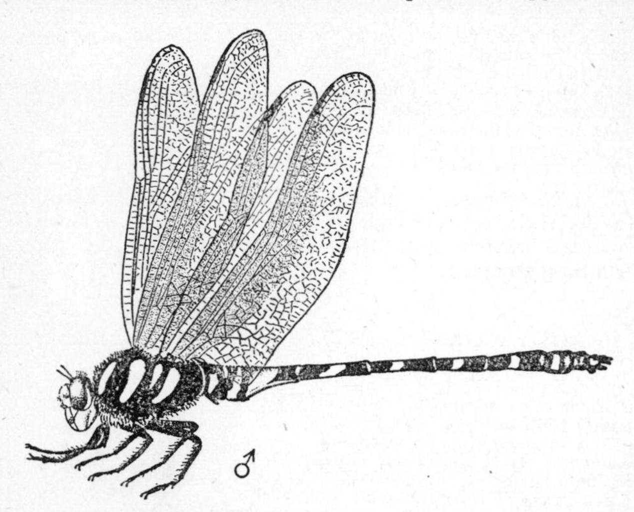

or gravel with her long ovipositor. The males have angular hind wings, the females rounded.

FAMILY *AESHNIDAE*

Eight British species, all 'large'

This family is much like the last two and comprises the rest of our very large Dragonflies.

Characters. The **nymphs** have bodies much longer than their legs (as both preceding families), flat masks, not covering the mouth, and wing-cases meeting at the tips (as Gomphidae), thin 7-segmented antennae (as Cordulegasteridae).

They are mainly confined to still weedy water in lakes, ponds, or disused canals, and they do not dig into the mud. When changing into the adult flies they crawl up on to reeds or other vegetation.

The **adult's** eyes are in contact for some distance at the top of the head, and the veining of the wings has fine cross-veins in both the triangle and the sub-triangle. The super-triangles are bordered on the 3rd side by only a fine vein and are also crossed.

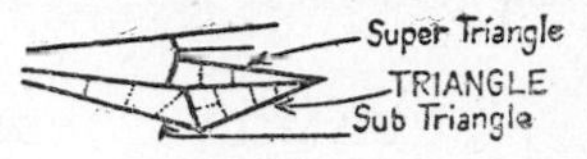

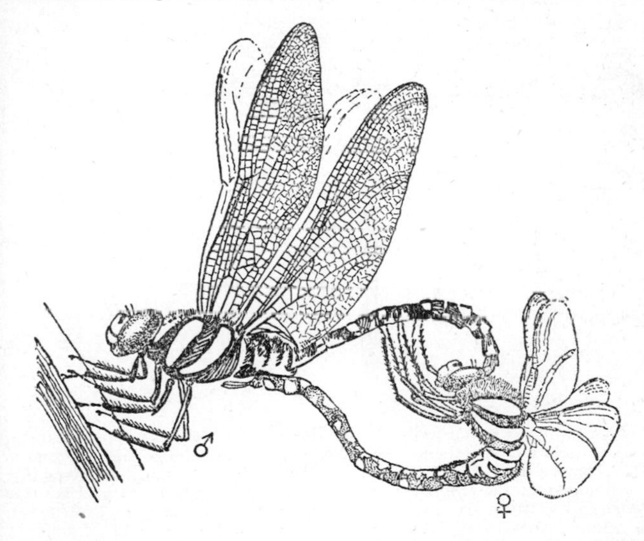

Our most widespread species, ***Aeshna juncea*** [reed A.], is here taken as an example of the family, and the sketches (see also p. 36) illustrate the differences in colour and hind wing shape between the sexes and the position when pairing.

One genus (*Anax*) has rounded wings in the males. They are all powerful fliers, hawking over the waters or neighbouring ground. The eggs are laid in water weeds or floating vegetation, or sometimes in peat. There is much variation in colour and in pattern between the species, the sexes, and also at different ages.

FAMILY *CORDULIIDAE* [Club-shaped]

Four British species, all 'large'

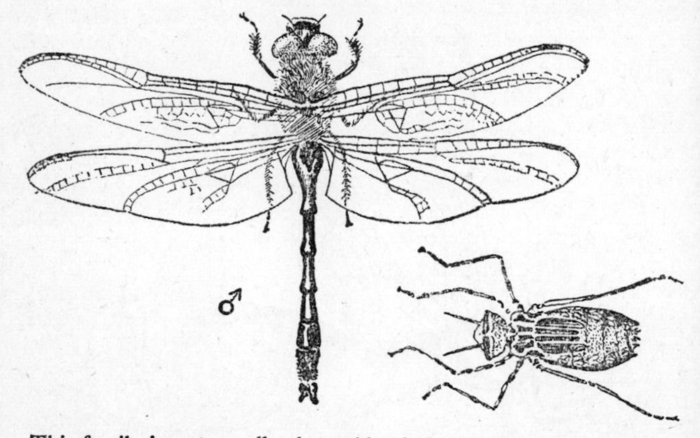

This family is structurally almost identical with the last and by some writers included with them. Their bodies are usually longer and narrower. The most marked difference is in colour, those of this family all showing a brilliant, metallic emerald colour on their heads and bodies. Like the Libellulidae, they are swift darters, and, like all the Dragonflies yet mentioned, they carry the wings out flat in repose.

The one here illustrated is ***Cordulia aenea*** [brazen Club (*p.* 36), which is the least rare of our four species.

FAMILY *LIBELLULIDAE* [Balanced (wings)]

Thirteen British species, all 'large'

These comprise most of our medium-sized Dragonflies and can be distinguished from the previous families by two characters. The **nymphs** have longer legs which stretch beyond their abdomens. A sketch of that

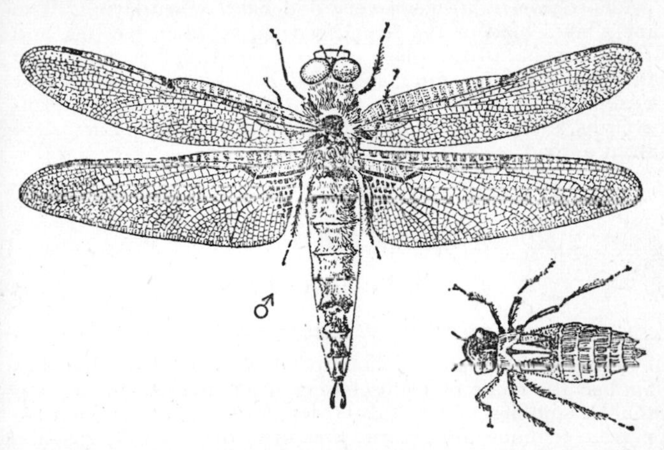

of ***Libellula quadrimaculata*** [four-marked Balance] (*p.* 37) is here given. It is the largest species.

The wing structure of the **adults** differs in that the triangles on the two pairs of wings are no longer the same. In the fore wings they point downwards, across the wing, towards the insect's tail: whereas those of the hind wings point along the wing, away from the body, as in the families already mentioned. Also, those of the hind wings are nearer to the body. There are other differences which need not be mentioned here, and each species has a peculiarity of veining which distinguishes it from the others. Males and females both have hind wings rounded.

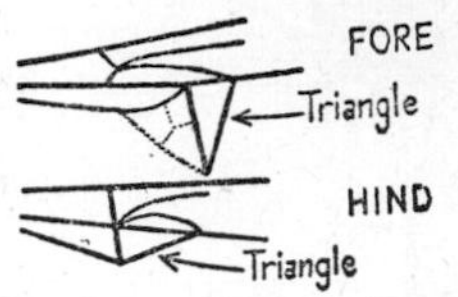

Several of our species, as that here illustrated, have blackish stains on the wing membranes and several have much bulkier bodies than the other Dragonflies. From their habits of hunting for flies around horses they have gained the popular name of 'horse-stingers' though they neither do, nor can, sting anything. They are chiefly dwellers in slow-running, or still, waters, laying their eggs in the water. One genus (*Sympetrum*) has a very odd habit when laying. The male takes hold of the female's neck, as when pairing, and takes her about from place to place, allowing her tail to dip into the water or mud and then helping to haul her out again. *L. quadrimaculata* is frequently found migrating in swarms, so that our native stock of these insects is replenished from abroad.

SUB-ORDER *ZYGOPTERA* [Yoke-wings]

DAMSEL-FLIES

Sixteen British species, all 'large'

These smaller Dragonflies, to which Miss Longfield has applied the name of Damsel-Flies to distinguish them from the Dragonflies of the sub-Order Anisoptera, are in comparison tenuous and delicate creatures, of slow butterfly-like flight, catching some of their insect prey on the wing, but more on the plants bordering the streams they frequent. They rest with the wings together over their backs, rarely spreading them out as do the Dragonflies.

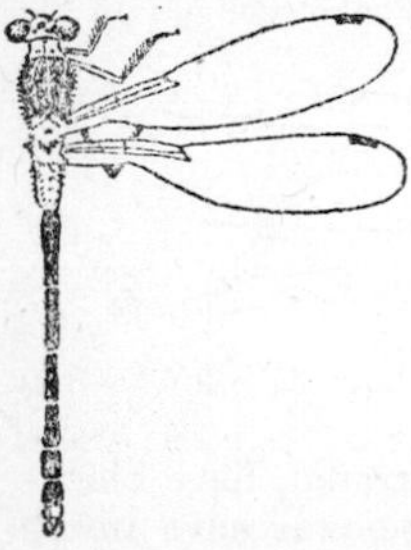

The main differences which distinguish them from the Anisoptera are as follows:

Their **nymphs** are all long slender-bodied creatures, with narrow, almost stick-like, abdomens, at the tail end of which the three gills are long and conspicuous.

The **adults** have the eyes wide apart; their bodies are all thin and tubular; and the hind wings are shaped like the fore.

Their general appearance is as here figured.

Note. All four wings have somewhat the look of the 'crosses' used in the game of lacrosse. In all except the *Agriidae* there is a distinct handle, the wing being narrow as it leaves the body. Attention is drawn to the 'ladders' formed by the veins crossing from the main vein, which forms the front edge of the wing (*costa*), to the two next veins parallel to it. The 'rungs' of these ladders, before the knot (*nodus*) half-way along the wing, are called *antenodal veins* and are alone drawn in the sketch on p. 262.

The Damsel-Flies are divided into four families.

FAMILY *AGRIIDAE* [Wildings]

Two British species, both 'large'

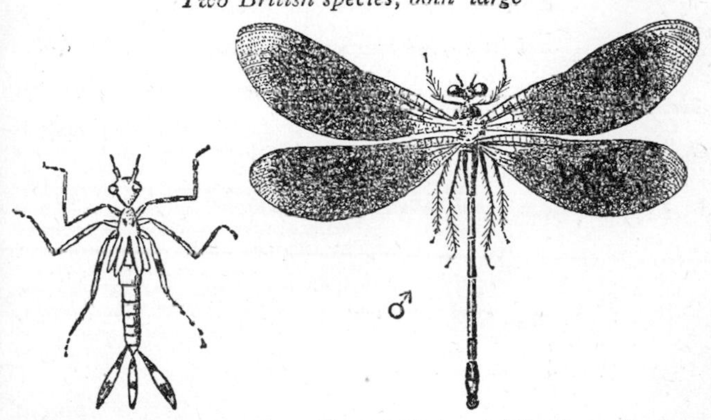

These are the largest of our Damsel-Flies and differ from all others in the following obvious characteristics:

The **nymphs** have legs as long as, or longer than, the bodies, only the tail gills projecting beyond them, and their antennae are relatively long, their first segment longer than the other six together.

The **adults** have numerous 'rungs' in the 'ladders' (referred to above) before the knots, and their wings are not markedly narrow at the handle of the crosses.

The sexes differ noticeably in colour. The males of both species have metallic blue bodies and, alone of our Damsel-Flies, have wings which are coloured over a large part of their surface with a deep rich brown which, at certain angles only, gives brilliant blue reflections. The females are mainly green-bodied and their wings transparent, with only a faint yellow or greenish stain.

When paired, the hold of the male ***Agrion virgo*** [damsel

Wilding] (*p. 37*) upon the scruff of his partner's neck is strengthened by her throwing back her head against her thorax.

They frequent rivers or streams (sometimes, but not usually, swift) or still waters and rarely leave the vegetation near them. Their flight is feeble and wavering. Their eggs are laid, one by one, in plants, either alive or dead, above or below the surface, and the larvae live among the weeds.

FAMILY *LESTIDAE* [Brigands]

Two British species, both 'large'

These two species, both of the genus *Lestes*, are smaller than the Agriidae, and differ from them as follows:

The **larvae** (also thin-bodied) are much smaller and the seven segments of their antennae are all short. Their masks have a hole in the centre shaped like the diamond of a playing card.

The **adults** have distinct handles to the crosses which are their wings (this is called being *petiolate*), and in the 'ladders' preceding the knots there are only two cross-bars or rungs. The stigmata on the wings are large, being equal in size to three of the neighbouring spaces and, scattered all over the wings, are a considerable number of pentagonal spaces. The wings are completely transparent and colourless.

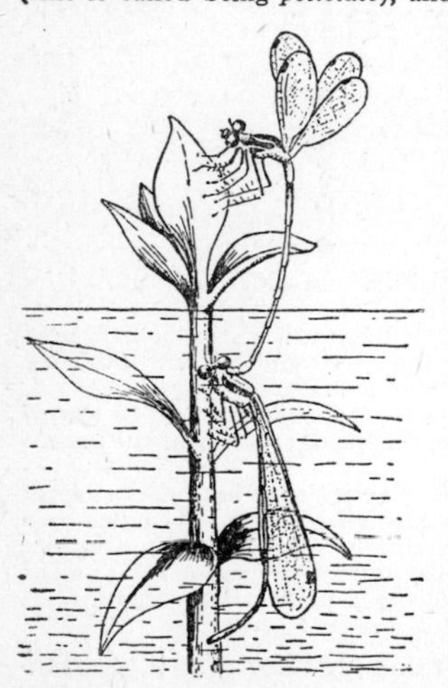

The eggs of ***Lestes sponsa*** [bride brigand] (*p. 38*) are laid well below the surface of the water (still, and sometimes brackish) in the stems of the weeds, and, in the laying of them, the male assists by taking hold of the female's neck, lowering her into the water, and, after the egg is laid, hoisting her again to the surface, when they fly on, in tandem, to the next weed chosen.

FAMILY *PLATYCNEMIDIDAE* [Flat-legs]

One British species, 'large'

Platycnemis pennipes [feather-foot Flat-leg] (*p. 38*) is a relatively small species differentiated as follows:

The **larva** is long-legged and its antennae (though composed of short segments only) are longer than those of any of our other families except

the Agriidae. There is no 'window' in the mask, which has one long and one short hook on each side.

The **adults** (alone of our dragonflies) have the shins of the hind pair of legs white, broad and flat, and feathered with projecting bristles on both sides. Thus the hind legs look like white feathers. Its wings are colourless and transparent, narrow handled (*petiolate*), with only two rungs before the knot (*antenodals*), and generally very sparsely veined and with few or no pentagonal spaces.

They are found in quick-running streams and fly low, often resting upon floating vegetation. The male helps with the egg-laying, as in the last family, but their habits differ in that the female does not go under water, but, usually, only puts in the end of her abdomen to lay the egg on the under side of leaves floating on the surface. Meanwhile the male, gripping her by the neck, as when pairing, hovers in the air above her.

FAMILY *COENAGRIIDAE* [Common-wildings]

Eleven British species, all 'large'

All the remaining British Damsel-Flies belong to this last family. They include our smallest and most delicate species.

CHARACTERS. **Larvae** slender and short-legged (hind legs not reaching to the end of their bodies), with short 7-segmented antennae. The masks are like those of *Platycnemis*.

The **adults** vary much in body colour, being red, green, blue, and black. None have any colour on the wings, which are transparent. The wings have definite 'handles' (are *petiolate*) and only two rungs before the knots. There are few pentagonal spaces in the veining, and such as there are are all at, or near, the outer and hinder edges of the wings.

Coenagrion puellum [maid Common-wilding] (*p. 38*) is figured.

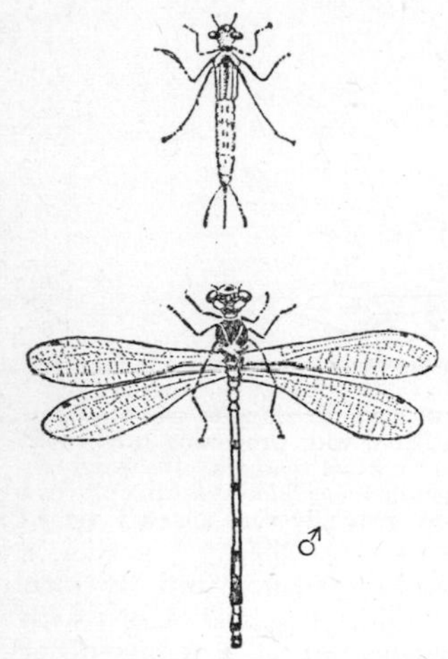

There are specific variations in manners and customs. Some choose swiftly-running waters, some still, and some are found in brackish water. Sometimes the two sexes are seen flying about in tandem. The eggs are laid in the fibres of the water plants and at very varying depths. In several species the mother goes right under water, while in others she merely dips her abdomen. In almost all, the male helps in the egg-laying and sometimes, where he has lost hold, he has been seen to return to tow the female out of the water when the eggs have been laid.

ORDER *EPHEMEROPTERA* [One-day wings]

FISHING FLIES

Forty-six British species, of which two are 'large'

CHARACTERS. Incomplete metamorphosis, there being no pupal stage. Between nymph and adult there is an intermediate form, the winged *sub-imago*, unique amongst insects. The **nymphs** have chewing-mouths, are aquatic, and vegetarian. The **adults** are short-lived and take no food. They have soft bodies, four wings with very numerous veins, which are held erect when at rest, and three long tails.

ANATOMY. Their **eggs** are remarkable for their great variety of form. They are often very numerous—as many as 4,000 having been counted from one mother—and are laid on or over fresh water, in bulk or individually. Several of them have filaments hanging from them by which they become attached to weeds or stones.

The **larvae** or nymphs have much the form of the adult insects without the wings and for a short time after hatching have no visible breathing apparatus, getting their oxygen from the water through the outer skin. After a few weeks they grow a number of external gills of a leaf-like form, usually seven in number, which grow along their backs, two from each of the abdominal segments. These gills provide a water-breathing system, and the differences in their form and in that of the main jaws (*mandibles*) enable the various species to be distinguished in the larval stage. Their general appearance is shown in the accompanying sketch. The mouth-parts are well developed and of the usual chewing type. They undergo a considerable number of moults, during the last few of which the wings are formed in cases. Their antennae are fairly long and in some species feathery, and some have three tails, the two side ones *cerci*, the middle one a tail-filament.

The nymphs come swimming up to the surface of the water when the adult flies are ready to emerge and the process of emergence is almost instantaneous, taking only a few seconds. The larval skin cracks at the back, and the winged adult draws itself out and instantly flies away. Although in this metamorphosis there is little external change of appearance, except for the addition of the wings, several important internal changes have occurred. Firstly, the gills are left behind in the sloughed skin and where they were are found the air-holes (*spiracles*) by which all other insects breathe the air. Secondly, the mouth-parts have disappeared, or at any rate become minute and useless. The adult does not eat during its short life. Thirdly, the gullet, which is large in the larva, has narrowed down to a small air-passage leading to the stomach, and the stomach itself has become an air sac, the purpose of which seems to be twofold, reducing, when inflated, the specific gravity of the fly's body and, in some way, stimulating the sexual organs. The following sketch gives an idea of the form of the adult Fishing Fly.

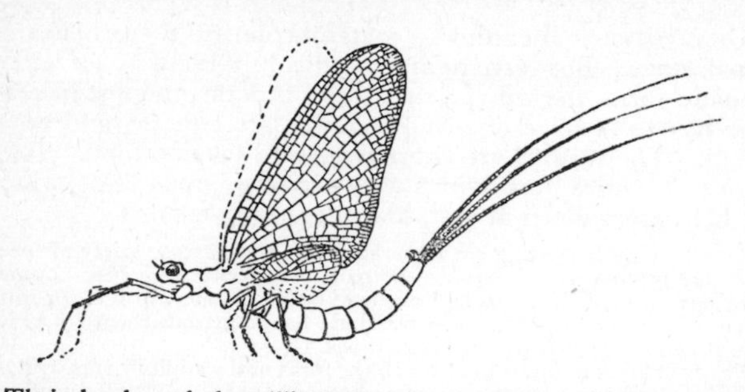

Their heads and threadlike antennae are small and they have two compound eyes and three simple ones. The middle segment of the thorax is far the largest and the fore wings, borne by it, are much larger than the hind wings. In some ('small') species the hind wings are absent. The veining consists of a large number of veins and cross-veins and round the edges of the wings is a fringe of short veins parallel to, and between, the longer ones. The veining distinguishes the various species. The fore legs are long, both other pairs very short. At the end of the abdomen are two very long tails (*cerci*) and sometimes a third appendage. The males have at the root of these tails also a pair of claspers, used to hold the females when pairing.

There is one very unusual thing connected with all the Ephemeroptera. The adults after emergence have yet another moult to undergo before being ready for pairing. When they first emerge they are known to fishermen as 'Duns', and to scientists as *sub-imagines*.

These sub-imagines are darker in colour and less active than the perfect insects, having a thin hairy skin enclosing the whole body and all appendages. This skin is moulted shortly after emergence, and the imago is then ready for its brief life of mating and egg-laying.

HABITS. The various species differ in habit as larvae. Some live in swift-running waters and some in sluggish streams or lakes. Some are active swimmers and others dig into the mud or cling to stones or vegetation in the water.

The Order is divided into eight families. We have in this country only two 'large' species[1] both of which belong to the genus *Ephemera* (Family *Ephemeridae*) and are both known as Mayflies. The commonest of these is ***Ephemera danica*** [Danish Ephemeral], known to fishermen as the Green Drake, the life of which will be described as typical of the whole Order. Sketches in colour of the larva and of both male and female Spinners and Duns of this species will be found on p. 39. Its larvae are found in swift-running streams and dig into the banks or mud. The larvae live for two or even three years before they float up to the surface ('rise') for the emergence of the sub-imago stage of the adults. The life of the adults is usually not strictly ephemeral (lasting only one day) and, in captivity at least, they will live for three or four days. Once the 'dun' skin is shed they begin their wedding-dance, rising a foot or so in the air and falling back to the previous level with outstretched wings and tails. When a mate has been found the male flies beneath her, takes hold of her with his long fore-legs and then, grasping her body from below at the 7th segment with a short pair of claspers which are situated (in the males only) just below the roots of the tails, passes his outer tails between the hind and fore wings of the female. Thus united, the pair float to the ground, where their union is completed. The instant they separate the females return to the water and drop their eggs on its surface. Then their short life as 'spinners' is over and, as 'spent gnats', they fall dead into the stream.

[1] The March Brown (*Ecdyonurus venosus*) and *Siphlonurus armatus* are sometimes 'large'.

ORDER *PLECOPTERA* [Folded wings]

STONE FLIES

Thirty-two British species, of which about twelve are 'large'

CHARACTERS. Incomplete metamorphosis, having no pupal stage. The larvae have chewing-mouths, are aquatic, and predacious. The adults are short-lived and take no food. They have soft bodies, four wings with numerous veins and usually two tails, of very varying length. The wings are laid lengthwise along the body when at rest, the fore wings flat above the hind, and the hind, which are the broader, folded lengthwise and laid below them. Their antennae are long.

The **eggs** are usually laid in a single mass (sometimes containing as many as 2,000 eggs) which separates in the water, and the separate eggs have threads which attach the eggs to plants or stones in the water.

The **larvae** bear a general likeness to those of the Ephemerids or Mayflies, but have no gills for water-breathing, as the Mayfly larvae have. They mostly appear to breathe wholly through the skin while in the water and therefore frequent swift-running streams, the water of which is highly aerated. Some of them, however, have some gill-threads along their sides and at the tail end.

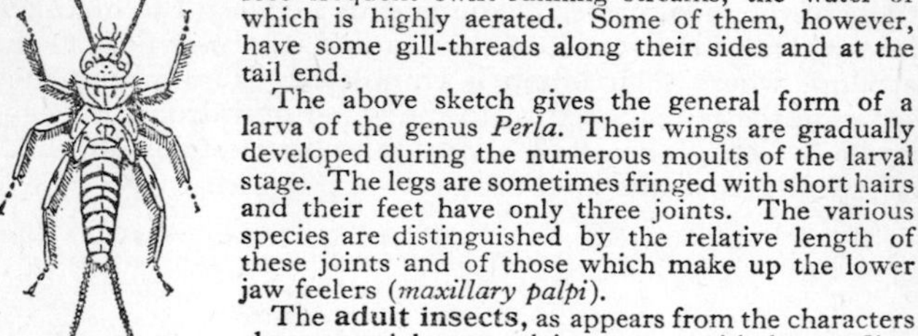

The above sketch gives the general form of a larva of the genus *Perla*. Their wings are gradually developed during the numerous moults of the larval stage. The legs are sometimes fringed with short hairs and their feet have only three joints. The various species are distinguished by the relative length of these joints and of those which make up the lower jaw feelers (*maxillary palpi*).

The **adult insects,** as appears from the characters above stated, have much in common with the mayflies, but the carriage of the wings prevents any possibility of their being mistaken. In flight, or when set out in a collection, they look much more like short-legged grasshoppers, though they have no such thickening of the fore wings as characterizes the Orthoptera. Their antennae are threadlike and long, being made up of, in some species, as many as eighty segments. The length and number of segments composing the tails differs much, and the small order has been split up into three different families on the strength of these differences and of differences in the lengths of the three segments of which the feet are composed.

The sketch of *Perla carlukiana* shows the form of these insects, extended and in repose. The wings are fairly large, and although the

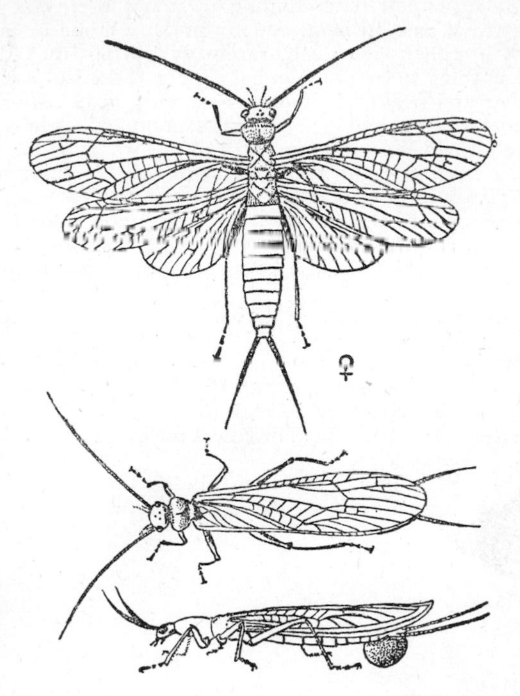

hind wings are usually somewhat the shorter, they are broader and have an extensive area at their backs, which is folded fanwise under the fore part of the wing when at rest. They have two compound eyes and three simple ones (*ocelli*) on the forehead between them. The three parts of the thorax are about equal in size and the legs are also of about equal length. There are ten segments in the hind body, from the last of which the tails spring.

Habits. The Stone Flies have been but little studied. They are chiefly known to anglers as useful bait for fish. They are at all stages sluggish. The larvae are poor swimmers and spend most of their time clinging to stones or weeds. The adults, which pair on land, usually under a stone or on the twigs of a stream-side bush, rarely fly. When they do fly there is nothing to recall the aerial dances of the Ephemerids. The short and heavy flights are made only in hot sunshine. The females carry their eggs, in a mass, under their tails until they are all laid, and then go back to the water and deposit the whole bundle in the water. On touching the stream, the bundle dissolves into its component parts and the eggs float down stream until their threads catch up upon some object. Most of our species are of a dirty brown colour and are seen on stones, though some are green and these are found on plants.

The name *Perla* [pearl] is derived from the brightness of their prominent eyes.

Perla carlukiana (*p. 40*) frequents running water. In it, particularly in the north, there are two forms of the male. In one of these the wings are normal, in the other so reduced as to be useless for flight. Such flightless males are, more rarely, found in other species.

The Plecoptera do not moult again after leaving the water. This is the case only among the Ephemeroptera.

ORDER *PSOCOPTERA* [Gnaw-Wings]

BOOKLICE

About sixty-eight British species, all small

The British species all belong to the sub-Order of *Psocida* [Gnawers], which is treated by some recent writers as an Order, under the name of *CORRODENTIA*.

They are all minute insects (the largest 5 mm. long) and many species are wingless. Those that have wings carry them roof-wise and look much like Aphids. But they have chewing mouths. They have no pupal stage, growing gradually, the last moult revealing the compound eyes and the fully developed wings of the winged species. They live upon animal and vegetable matter, and are found indoors among books or papers or, out of doors, under leaves or on tree-trunks. The outdoor species seem to feed on minute fungi, the indoor species upon paste or mould upon animal or vegetable refuse.

ORDER *HEMIPTERA* [Half-wings]

BUGS

1,411 British species, of which only about thirty are 'large'

Characters. With the exception of one family, the *Cicadidae*, none of our Large Bugs have anything like the usual three changes. In general, they pass from the state in which they leave the egg to the final adult stage without any great change. There are marked changes in colour and, of course, size, and there is in some families a gradual change of form as their various moults occur, and the wings are fully developed only at the last moult, but there are no distinct larval, pupal, and adult stages. Almost all have four wings of which the hinder pair are membranous and transparent, while the fore pair are thicker and more or less horny. In all the families in which there are 'large' species (the Cicadidae again alone excepted) the fore wings are divided into two distinct parts, one of which, that nearer the body, is thick and horny, while the rest of the wing is transparent and membranous like the hind wings. Hence the name of 'half-wings' given to the Order as a whole. The Bugs are all suckers of plant sap, or of the blood of other animals—mammals, birds, or other insects. For this purpose their mouths take the form of a piercing and tubular proboscis, which is usually bent under their heads and stretches in a straight line under their bodies. These probosces, or beaks (*rostra*) as they are called, are usually made of several segments and are bent downwards, at right angles to the body, when used for feeding. The actual parts of the mouth need not be considered here. The beak consists of a sheath containing four rods (*setae*) which pierce the skin or bark of the plant or animal from which food is to be sucked.

Anatomy. There is much variation in the shape and general appearance of the bugs. Some are elongated and almost stick-like, others flat and circular. Their heads carry the beak, already described, the antennae, the compound eyes, and usually two simple eyes. The antennae are of two different kinds, either freely projecting from the head like those of most insects, or lying hidden in grooves so as to be almost unseen. This latter type is that of the families which live in water.

The three segments of the thorax carry the legs, the feet of which have from one to four joints and are with or without claws, and the wings. The wings have already been described. It is sufficient to add that in those bugs the fore wings of which are made up of both horny and trans-

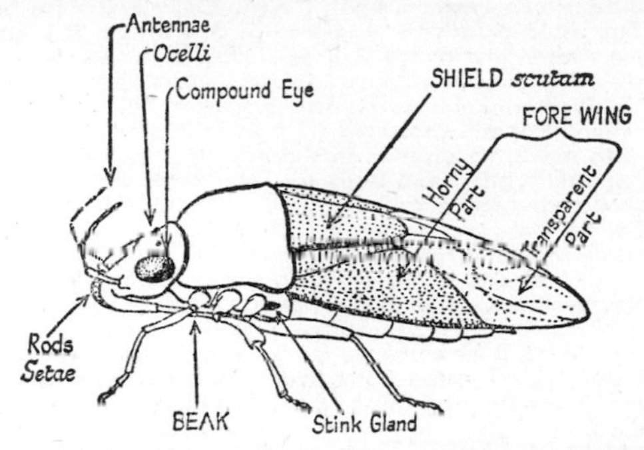

parent parts, the extent and shape of these different areas varies. The wings are usually carried flat on the back, with their tips crossed, though some extend straight backwards without crossing. Between the wings at the back is a triangular area called the shield (*scutum*) which varies greatly in size. The abdomen, the back of which is largely, sometimes wholly, covered, shows six segments on the under side, and on the under side also, close to the bases of the hind legs, are the stink-glands, the use of which is usually the only means of defence available to the bugs.

The above sketch shows the typical form of a land bug with the various parts mentioned indicated.

HABITS. As above stated, all bugs, whether living ashore or in water, and whether vegetable or animal feeders, live by suction, and this throughout their lives. It has been said that of all the Orders of insects which threaten us by competing with us and depleting the world's stock of vegetation, the bugs are the most menacing. This applies most strongly to the smaller species, and particularly to the Aphids, or Green Fly, which have an amazing power of reproduction. None of our 'large' bugs are serious pests and, in fact, nearly all the 'large' species are animal feeders and not plant-bugs.

Classification. The main division of the Order of Bugs is between those of which the fore wings are partly horny and partly transparent (the *Heteroptera* or Diverse-winged) and those in which both wings are equally transparent (the *Homoptera* or Like-winged). Confining our attention to the 'large' species as we do, there is only one single, very rare, and local, species of the Order which belongs to the Homoptera. This is a Cicada found in the New Forest which will be dealt with on p. 282. Attention can therefore be concentrated upon the sub-Order Heteroptera.

These are divided into the Land Bugs which have free and visible antennae—called *Gymnocerata* or Free Horns—of which there are about 450 British species, and the Water Bugs—*Cryptocerata* or Hidden Horns—of which there are about forty British species. These latter have the antennae concealed, and protected from injury from the water in which they live and move, by grooves in the head in which the antennae lie. Speaking generally, the Land Bugs are Plant Bugs, and the Water Bugs are carnivorous, but there are exceptions in both cases. The terms land bugs and water bugs are in the case of one family here mentioned (the *Hydrometridae* or Water Spiders) rather misleading. These creatures are endowed with long and unprotected antennae and are therefore classed as land bugs, yet the water is their element. It will be seen, however, that they skate over the surface, unwetted, and that therefore, so far as the need for protecting their antennae from water is concerned, they belong to the air and not the water. The true division is between those bugs which live *in* the water and those which do not.

Even the water bugs, like the water beetles (see pp. 158–161), are air breathers and carry a bubble of air attached to them, which they come to the surface to replenish when it is exhausted.

The following table shows the classification of the Order of *HEMIPTERA* or BUGS.

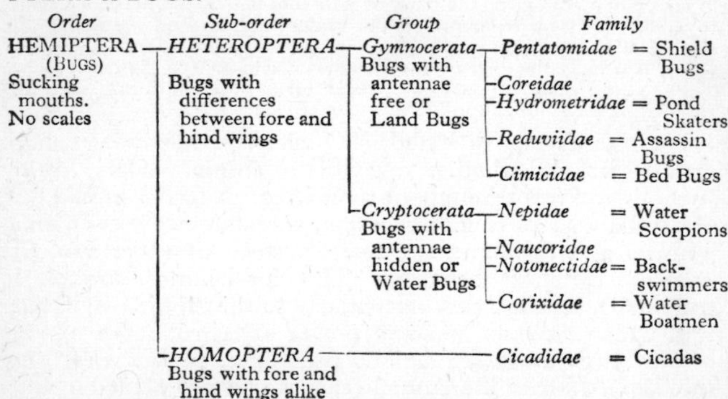

Order	*Sub-order*	*Group*	*Family*	
HEMIPTERA (Bugs) Sucking mouths. No scales	*HETEROPTERA* Bugs with differences between fore and hind wings	*Gymnocerata* Bugs with antennae free or Land Bugs	*Pentatomidae*	= Shield Bugs
			Coreidae	
			Hydrometridae	= Pond Skaters
			Reduviidae	= Assassin Bugs
			Cimicidae	= Bed Bugs
		Cryptocerata Bugs with antennae hidden or Water Bugs	*Nepidae*	= Water Scorpions
			Naucoridae	
			Notonectidae	= Back-swimmers
			Corixidae	= Water Boatmen
	HOMOPTERA Bugs with fore and hind wings alike		*Cicadidae*	= Cicadas

FAMILY *PENTATOMIDAE* [Five-sectioned]
SHIELD BUGS

Thirty British species, of which seven are 'large'

CHARACTERS. The shield, which forms the central section covering the back, is large, so that it reaches to the transparent part of the fore wings when folded, and sometimes covers the whole abdomen including the fore wings. The antennae, usually 5-jointed, spring from the under side of the head. The beak is 4-jointed.

All our species are plant-bugs. They have the power of emitting a stinking liquid for defence. Some display an instinct very unusual in the insect world: care for the young. The females of *Elasmucha grisea* have been found watching over their eggs and even over the young for some time after they have hatched, 'in a brooding attitude'. None of our species are serious pests to vegetation. ***Acanthosoma haemorrhoidale*** [blood-red Spine-body] (*p. 41*) is figured here.

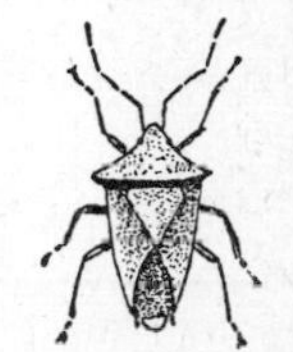

FAMILY *COREIDAE* [Bug-like]

Twenty-five British species, of which three are 'large'

CHARACTERS. Narrower in shape than the Pentatomidae and with shorter shields. Antennae with (usually) four joints and springing from the upper side of the head. The 'large' species are only just half an inch in length.

As an example, ***Coreus marginatus*** [rimmed Bug-like] (*p. 41*) will give an idea of their form, though there is considerable variety in the degree of slimness. They are almost all plant-bugs. They also emit nauseating smells.

FAMILY *HYDROMETRIDAE* [Water-measurers]
POND SKATERS

Comprising the two 'large' genera of *Gerris* and *Hydrometra* (= *Limnobates*). The former is now given separate family rank.

Twelve British species, of which four or five are 'large'

CHARACTERS. Living on, but not in, water. Covered, on the under surface, with a silvery down which keeps them from being wetted by the water. Many are wingless, and there are usually fully-winged, minute-winged, and wingless individuals of the same species. They have their (4-jointed) antennae free and exposed. They have no stink-glands. Their food consists of dead water-insects, or such as have fallen on the surface of the water.

Hydrometra (= *Limnobates*) ***stagnorum*** [pond Water-measurer] (*p. 41*), the Pond Skater, here illustrated, is the most elongated species. It crawls slowly over the film on the surface of stagnant water or upon the mud or weeds on the bank. Its eggs are laid on floating vegetation and, like those of the Chrysopidae (see p. 247), are raised from the plant upon a stalk. The other members of the family have not the long head of *Hydrometra* and their gait is different. They rest on the water upon the tips of the fore and hind legs and row themselves about with the feet of the mid-legs, often jumping over the surface. They are more active than *Hydrometra.*

FAMILIES *REDUVIIDAE* [Scrap-covered] and *NABIDAE*
ASSASSIN BUGS

Eighteen British species, of which one only is 'large'

Our only large species, ***Reduvius personatus*** [masked Scraps] (*p. 41*), has earned its name from the fact that the larvae cover themselves with dust or scraps of rubbish. The proboscis is short, consisting of only three segments, and is carried in a curve clear of the head and not laid along under it as are those of most of the bugs. They make a shrill sound by vibrating the proboscis against the thorax. The young larvae take to killing insects of various kinds. The adults are nocturnal, flying about inside houses and preying upon insects of many different kinds. They are useful in destroying *Cimex lectularius* (the Bed Bug). They can, and if handled do, use their probosces to stab man, and their bites are said to be very painful.

Among the thirteen other families of bugs with free antennae, all the members of which are 'small', is one, the *Cimicidae* (Bugs), which gains admission to this book because of the nuisance value of one of its members—***Cimex lectularius***, the Bed Bug (*p. 41*). These pests frequent dirty houses, laying their eggs behind wall-papers or in the cracks of wooden bedsteads, picture rails, or skirtings. They have no functional wings, these organs being reduced to small scales at the shoulders of their flat round bodies. They are nocturnal, feeding upon the unclothed parts of their human victims. Their stabs are not only painful, but, to many people, intensely irritating to the nerves, waking them, and distressing them to a remarkable degree. When killed they give out the usual characteristic bug smell. The eggs hatch in about eight days, and they are fully grown in about eighty. To free a house of bed bugs, once established, is not easy, but turpentine, paraffin, burning sulphur, and 'formol' are advised.

CRYPTOCERATA WATER BUGS

All carnivorous, sucking the blood of other insects which they seize by the help of their fore legs. The hinder two pairs are usually hairy and are used for swimming.

FAMILY *NEPIDAE* [Scorpions]

WATER SCORPIONS

Two British species, both 'large'

The two hinder pairs of legs are adapted for walking and swimming, the fore legs for gripping their prey, as the shin-joint (*tibia*) folds back into a groove along the thigh (*femur*) in the same way as the blade of a penknife folds into the handle. Antennae 3-jointed, feet (*tarsi*) single-jointed.

The two species differ in shape, the rarer, ***Ranatra linearis*** [linear Froggy] (*p. 41*), being very slender. Both species have a tube at the tail end which is used to bring air to their bodies.

Both are found in shallow stagnant water walking or swimming beneath the surface. They lay their eggs upon water plants, and the eggs are provided with thread-like filaments which come to the surface of the water and supply the eggs with air. These insects must be handled with care as they are capable of inflicting a painful wound with their probosces.

FAMILY *NAUCORIDAE* [Ship-bugs]

One British species, which is 'large'

CHARACTERS. Wings not folded roof-wise but merely crossed at the tips. Body oval, widest in the middle. No simple eyes, and no 'tail'.

It creeps about among water vegetation and comes to the surface to replenish its air-supply, which is kept between the wings and the back of its abdomen, which is somewhat hollowed to hold a bubble of air.

Our species, ***Ilyocoris cimicoides*** [buglike Mud-bug] (*p. 41*), is found in stagnant waters and swims freely.

FAMILY *NOTONECTIDAE* BACK-SWIMMERS

Four British species, all 'large'

Note. The members of this family are often called Water Boatmen, but they are here called Back-swimmers to distinguish them from the *Corixidae.*

CHARACTERS. Wings folded roof-wise over the back, which is convex. No simple eyes and no 'tails'. There are two joints in the feet and the hind feet have no claws.

They swim upside down in the water, using the hind legs for swimming, their wings forming a keel and giving a boat-like appearance to them. The two foremost pairs of legs are used for crawling. They swim rapidly and can leap clear of the water and fly without coming to shore. Their needle-like proboscis gives a painful wound. They attack fish and tadpoles as well as other insects and so should be kept out of aquaria. They come to the surface for air which, in their case, is retained in grooves along the sides of the abdomen by rows of hairs along both upper and under sides of the grooves. The females have an ovipositor with which the eggs are inserted into the stems of water plants.

Notonecta glauca [glaucous Back-swimmer] (*p. 41*), which is common in ponds or other stagnant waters, is here illustrated.

FAMILY *CORIXIDAE* [Buglike] WATER BOATMEN

Thirty-two British species, of which two are 'large'

CHARACTERS. Back of body flat. Proboscis has one joint only. Only the mid-legs have claws. The sides of the body are almost parallel.

Corixa punctata [pointed Bug] (*p. 41*) fastens its eggs to water plants with a sticky substance. It swims and flies well and lives in stagnant waters. The males make a sound by rubbing their fore legs against their beaks. Their heads rotate freely on a narrow neck. When resting, they hold on to weeds with the mid-legs. They are largely vegetarian.

SUB-ORDER *HOMOPTERA* [Uniform wings]

This sub-Order contains a very large number of, mainly, very small insects. Amongst them are the *Aphididae* (Green Fly), *Psyllidae* (Jumping Plant Lice), *Aleyrodidae* (White Flies), *Coccidae* (Scale-insects or Mealy-bugs), *Jassidae* (Leaf-hoppers), *Membracidae* (Tree-hoppers), and *Cercopidae* (Cuckoo-spits). All the above are 'small'.

Only one family in the whole sub-Order consists mainly of 'large' insects, namely the *Cicadidae* (Cicadas), and these are, in this country, represented by a single species which is

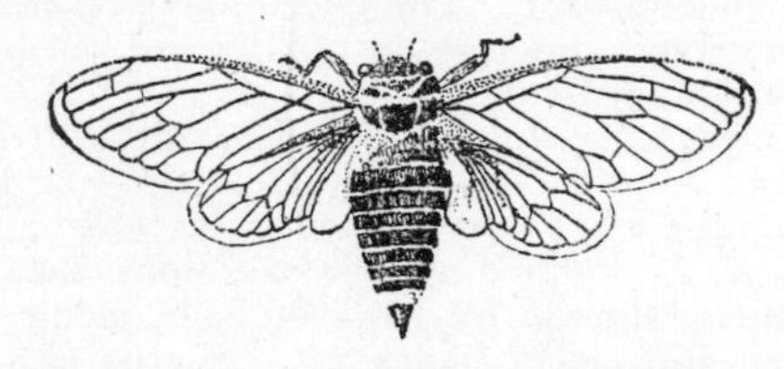

rarely found in the New Forest only. This single rarity, ***Cicadetta montana*** [mountain Little-cicada] (*p. 41*), is the most northern of all the members of its family. They are all plant-suckers, living, in the case of *Cicadetta* (in this country), probably on bracken and piercing the young shoots with their probosces to suck the sap. They are renowned for their cheerful creaking song which continues throughout the daylight hours. Only the males sing, or have the organ which enables them to do so. This is a membrane, or drum, situated at the base of the abdomen, not far from the base of the hind legs, and it is worked by the alternate tension and release of special muscles attached to it.

Their fore wings are transparent, as well as the hind, and there is no difference between one part of the fore wing and another. This is the distinctive character of this sub-Order of bugs. Although, like all other bugs, they have no true metamorphosis, there is a very distinct change in form between the larvae and the adults. The female lays her eggs in the bark of the dry twigs of the trees, and when they are hatched the larvae fall to the ground and burrow to the roots where they live, sucking the sap from the roots until, the wings being formed, they come to the surface, climb up the undergrowth, and undergo their final moult. Their life underground lasts for several years, in the case of the common Provençal Cicada four years, and in that of an American species as much as seventeen years.

The Greek poet Xenarchus is responsible for the ungallant opinion that 'The Cicadas are happy, for their wives are dumb'.

ORDER *ANOPLURA*

BITING AND SUCKING LICE

This Order consists wholly of very small insects which spend all their lives on warm-blooded animals (mammals including man, or birds). They are noticed here only because of those species of *Siphunculata* [Suckers] which prey upon man.

Pediculus humanus, the common Louse of man, is found in time of peace only on the bodies and clothes of people so unused to cleanliness that they do not object enough to the slight irritation, caused by the claws of these creatures as they wander over their bodies, to take steps to get rid of them. In war-time the conditions under which men are often obliged to live may make it impossible for the cleanest to escape these pests. Lice are responsible for the carrying of many diseases, including typhus, trench-fever, and relapsing fever.

Lice lay their eggs (or 'nits') on the hairs of the body or clothing and, at body temperatures, they hatch in about a week. The young are like the adults except in size, and throughout life the louse lives by sucking the body of its host. There are two races of this insect, one of which infests our heads and the other our bodies.

ORDER *THYSANOPTERA* [Fringe Wings]

THRIPS

183 *British species, all 'small'*

This is a group of minute insects, most of which are not more than 1 mm. in length and the (few) largest not more than 3 mm. One of these is shown on p. 7. They are distinguished by the form of the wings, which consist of a narrow bar fringed on one or both sides with hairs which provide a bearing surface in contact with the air. Each wing, therefore, resembles a single feather of a bird. They have no pupal stage, but grow gradually. Their mouths are built for piercing and sucking, like those of the bugs, and they mostly live on flowers or plant leaves and stems. Some are highly destructive. They are found among grasses or under loose bark. They rarely fly, but crawl, run, or hop.

ORDER *ORTHOPTERA* [Straight wings]

GRASSHOPPERS, CRICKETS, AND COCKROACHES

Thirty-eight British species, of which eighteen are 'large'

CHARACTERS. Biting or chewing mouths. Usually four wings of which the fore pair is leathery and serves as a wing-cover to the hind pair. The hind pair is large and transparent, folding, when at rest, under the fore. Many species are wingless or with short, useless wings and but few species make much use of the wings.

The abdomen has two appendages at the tail end (*cerci*). These are usually short and jointed. There is little or no metamorphosis: except for the increasing size and the gradual development of the wings and sexual organs, there is little difference between the young and the adults.

They are all tracheal breathers and nearly all terrestrial throughout life.

They may be conveniently divided into Runners and Jumpers, the latter including the *Acrididae*, *Tettigoniidae*, and *Gryllidae*, and the former the *Blattidae*.

FAMILIES *ACRIDIDAE* [Summit-jumpers] and *TETRIGIDAE*

SHORT-HORNED GRASSHOPPERS

Fourteen British species, of which thirteen are 'large'

CHARACTERS. Hind legs made for jumping. Antennae short. Song produced by fiddling with the leg upon the fore wing. Hearing by 'ears' on the 1st segment of the abdomen. Female ovipositors are short and used to dig a pit in soil or rotting wood. No marked metamorphosis. Three foot-joints. Vegetarians.

ANATOMY. Head large, with vertical or bent back face (*frons*) which is separated from the crown of the head (*vertex*) by a band, the form and markings of which serve for specific classification. Compound eyes and three simple eyes (*ocelli*), one between and two above the antennae, which are short and never have more than thirty segments.

Of the thorax, the 'hood' (*prothorax*) alone shows when the wings are closed, and usually has three keels, along its top and sides. In our 'small' species it is so long as to extend beyond the tail.

Hind legs long, and with powerful thighs, on the inner side of which is a row of minute studs which act as the bow to the fiddle-string on the fore wing which makes the chirping 'song'. They have three joints only

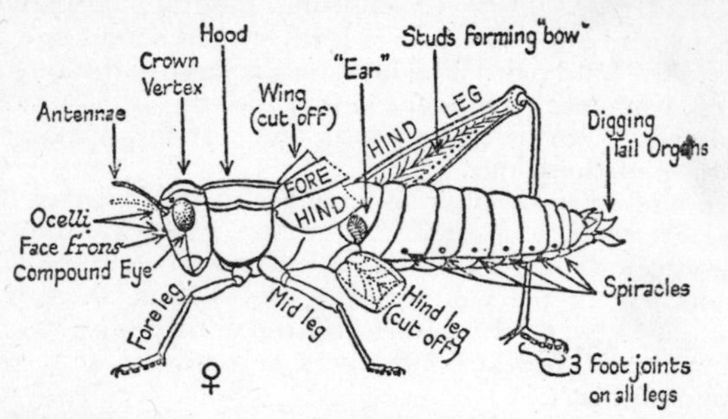

to all the feet, though, from below, the presence of three pads on the first of these joints make them look like five.

The fore wings are leathery, and they close as wing-covers (*tegmina*) over the hind wings. Their veining differs in different species. In the males, one vein on the outer side is raised and crested and forms the vibrating fiddle-string for the 'song'. In the females, the bow on the thighs is much smaller and they do not sing, or, if they do, their chirpings are above our range of hearing.

The hind wings are of equal length and broad, folding fan-wise under the fore, except in the later larval stages of the young, when the wings are twisted so that the hind wings cover the fore. Some species have short, and some no, wings.

Both sexes have 'ears', consisting of a membrane on each side of the 1st abdominal segment.

The genitals are at the tail end of the body. Those of the males end in an upturned plate which protects the organs, while those of the females have four short plates which take the place of an ovipositor, and are used to dig a hole for the eggs.

The species illustrated (opposite) is ***Chorthippus bicolor*** [2-coloured Grass-horse] (*p. 42*), one of our two commonest species. It varies much in colour, seeming to acquire the shade of its background.

LIFE HISTORY. The Short-horned Grasshoppers are almost wholly vegetarian, and, where their numbers are large, are fearfully destructive. The migrating locusts belong to this family, but none of them can, in any reasonable sense, be called British insects, for only scattered stragglers or, occasionally, small groups, ever reach these islands from the 'outbreak area' round the Black Sea. Our small species are

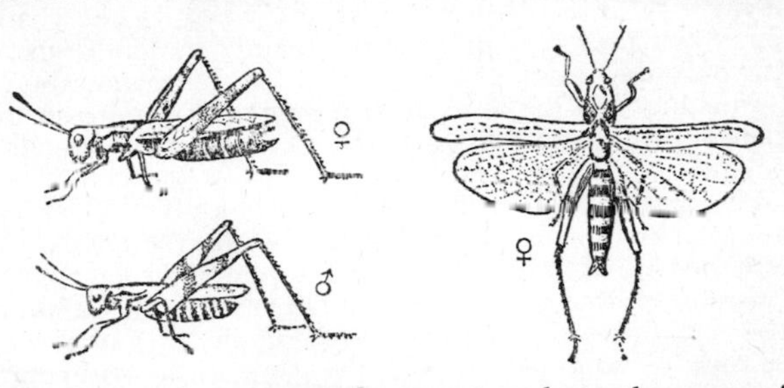

too few in numbers ever to be a pest, and merely serve, with their cheerful chirpings, to add to the pleasures of our too few summer days. The female, when about to lay her eggs, digs a hole in the ground with the help of the four short spades at her tail. This hole is the shape of her abdomen and goes down almost vertically, often into quite hard soil. In this hole she deposits her clutch of long and narrow eggs, and adds to them a quantity of whipped, mucous liquid which dries into a hard envelope surrounding the eggs. This process of laying takes some forty minutes and is repeated several times by the same mother. The eggs remain thus, underground, through the winter and hatch in the early spring. The hatching of the young has been described in the case of one foreign Acridian fairly closely related to species found here, as follows: When the young hatch out they are found to be provided with what is called a 'blister' (*ampulla*) at the back of the neck. The function of this blister, which is blown up with air and fluid from within, is that of the egg-tooth of the unborn chicken—to help the young creature to burst first the egg, then the envelope surrounding the eggs and, lastly, to force its way through the ground to the surface. These blisters are retained through the subsequent moults of the insects, and serve to help in such moults. This way of getting out of the egg is, however, not universal in the family.

The larvae gradually grow, through five to eight moults, developing and lengthening the wings, which are not available for flight until the final, adult, stage. They do not fly much, even when they can, progressing mainly by long hops. We hear only the 'singing' (*stridulation*) of the males, though it is probable that the females also sing with a note so highly pitched that it escapes our ears. The song is sung in full sunlight—a song of joy.

This family holds in the insect world a place which corresponds with that of the voles among the mammals. They form the base of the pyramid which supports the flesh-eaters—transmuting tough vegetable fibres into flesh which feeds other creatures. They bulk largely in the diet of the trout, the turkey, the domestic fowl, the game birds, and countless others, many of which, in turn, feed man.

Thus, though the gorge of civilized man may rise to prevent his imitating St. John the Baptist or the Caliph Omar (who burned the greatest library in the world and was greedy of grasshoppers), they still owe much of their food to these insects.

FAMILY *TETTIGONIIDAE* [Grasshoppers]

LONG-HORNED GRASSHOPPERS

Eleven British species, all of which are 'large'

CHARACTERS. In outward form generally resembling the Acrididae. Thus they have the hind legs made for jumping, a 'song' produced by fiddling, and no marked metamorphosis. But there are marked differences. Their antennae are long. The 'song' is produced by the friction against one another of the fore wings, of which the left wing always overlaps the right. The musical instrument will be described later. Hearing is by 'ears' which are situated below the knee-joints of the fore legs. The females have long sword- or sickle-shaped egg-laying organs (*ovipositors*) made up of six separate parts. They have four joints in the feet. They are either carnivorous or omnivorous.

ANATOMY. Their heads are usually less complex than those of the Acridians and have not the patterned band separating the face (*frons*) from the crown of the head (*vertex*). They

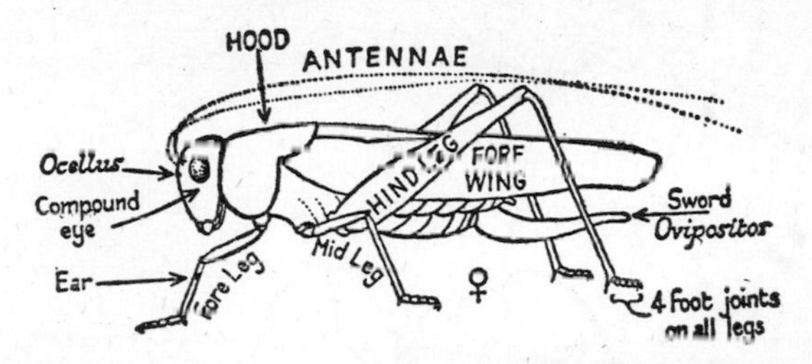

have compound eyes, but usually only one simple eye (*ocellus*) between the antennae which is often minute and ill-developed. The antennae are long, usually longer than the body, and have very many segments—sometimes as many as 400.

Of the thorax, the hood (*prothorax*) is usually simpler than that of the Acridians, being often without keels, or marked furrows. Although the legs are, in general appearance, like those of the last family, the hind legs have no studs or function in the chirping of these creatures. Also the fore legs have 'ears' which consist of transparent membranes situated on both sides of the shins (*tibiae*) just below the knees. These 'ears' are in some species on the surface, in others in a depression and covered by a movable lid.

The wings of the family differ greatly. Some species are wingless, in others the wings of the females are lacking while those of the males are mere vestiges, and in others again neither sex has more than short wings, incapable of flight. In the flying species, of which far the commonest is ***Tettigonia***

viridissima [greenest Grasshopper] (*p. 42*), the Great Green Grasshopper, here illustrated, there are differences in the length of the wings.

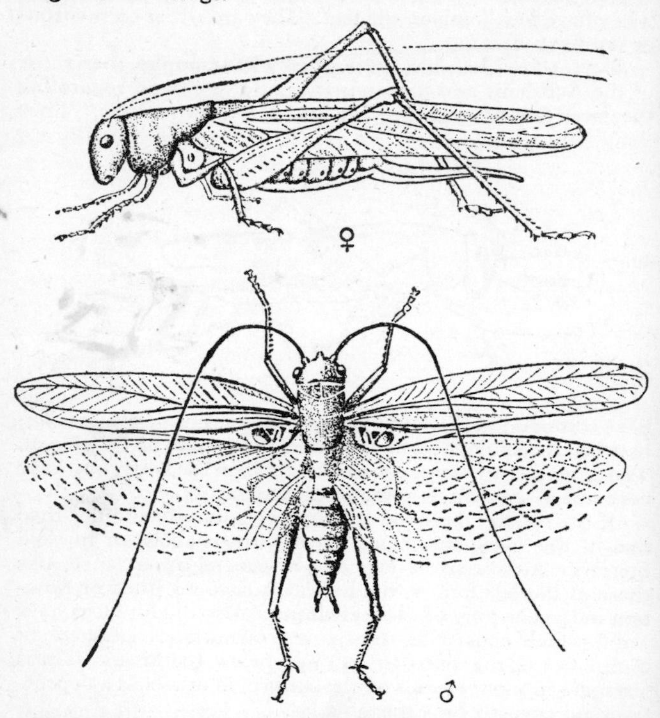

At the base of the fore wings lies the musical instrument with which the 'song' is produced. It is on the inner corner of the fore wings, which, as in the last family, are leathery in texture and, when at rest, wrap round the hind wings and the body. The left wing is always the overlapping wing. In the males there is a short file on its under side which rasps across the veins of the right wing. These encircle a transparent diaphragm (or 'mirror') which acts as a resonator for the sound made by the rasping. These organs differ much in different species, as do their 'voices', but their situation is the same in all winged species of the family.

There are no hearing organs in the abdomen, these being replaced by those in the fore legs above described. The genitals are situated at the end of the abdomens, and the method of pairing is quite unlike that of any other insect. It will be described later.

The long, sword-like, egg-laying organs of the females (*ovipositors*) are made up of six different blades of various lengths.

LIFE HISTORY. The eggs of the Tettigoniidae are not contained in any capsule of dried mucus as are those of the Acridians; they are placed, sometimes in the earth, sometimes in the bark of trees, with the ovipositor. The female bends her body and thrusts down her sword, to its full length, in the soil, where it remains for a quarter of an hour or so. The eggs will be found later, either singly or in comparatively small numbers, and quite unprotected. They are long, variously coloured, and, in the case of our Great Green Grasshopper, about sixty in number, when all the repeated plantings are finished. When the mother withdraws her 'sword', she loosens the earth with it and so conceals the place where the eggs have been sown. The laying having taken place towards the end of summer, the eggs will not hatch until the spring, and, to mature, they need moisture.

The young leave the egg in a pro-nymphal form, that is to say in a sheath which envelops the legs and the delicate antennae for the journey up through the soil to the surface. This movement is made by the alternate filling and emptying of a bulb at the back of the neck, similar to that of the Acridians, and, on reaching the surface, this bulb breaks the sheath and the insect emerges, complete in its adult form except for the development of the wings and of the sexual organs which appear in subsequent moults.

Unlike the peaceful Acridians, the Long-horned Grasshoppers are omnivorous, eating not only plants, of which they seem to eat chiefly the undeveloped buds, but also, largely, other insects, including the dead or wounded of their own species. These they hunt relentlessly, mainly by night. Active prey are killed by a bite above the neck, crushing the main nerve-centres.

Their 'song' is uttered by day and night, rather as a sign of contentment than as a call to their mates. The females are silent.

HABITS. The greater number of species are dwellers in trees, and, with us, they are near the northern limit of their distribution, few species, and those in small numbers, extending north of the Thames.

The pairing of this family is unlike that of any other insects except the Gryllidae. A full description is given by Fabre and may be summarized as follows. After a courtship, sometimes of some days' duration, in which the couple face each other and exchange caresses with their long antennae, the male throws himself on his back behind the female, with his head pointing in the opposite direction from hers, grips her body and sword with his legs, and then extrudes a gelatinous pouch containing the fertilizing sperms. This pouch is about half the size of the male's body and is described as being like a small raspberry of the size and colour of a mistletoe berry. It is pressed against the under side of the base of the sword, where it adheres, thanks to a clear transparent drop of adhesive gum, and forms, as it were, a basket hilt to the sword. This done, the male gets away, if possible before he is himself eaten by his mate. He lives on for a few days, still singing, but with decreasing energy, and then dies. If his mate comes across his corpse, she will eat it *in piam memoriam.*

The female carries the fertilizing pouch about with her until her eggs are matured, then, slowly and deliberately, eats it up, leaving the sword clean and without a hilt. To do this she may have to resort to some acrobatics: she may dig the sword into the ground and, standing upon a tripod composed of it and her stilt-like legs, curl herself into a question-mark. She then sows her seed and, with the first cold weather, dies.

FAMILY *GRYLLIDAE* [Crickets] CRICKETS

Three British species, of which two are 'large'

CHARACTERS. This family is in many ways very like the Long-horned Grasshoppers. They have the big-thighed, jumping, hind legs. The males 'sing' by friction of the fore wings, and both sexes have 'ears' in the shins of the forelegs. The main differences are that (1) they have only three joints in their feet, of which the 2nd is so small as to be barely seen; (2) the fore wings lie flat over the bodies, bending sharply at right angles so as to cover the sides; (3) their right wings lie over the left; (4) the male's musical instruments are relatively much larger and both files and mirror-drums are present on both wings; and (5) the 'ears' are larger on the outsides and smaller on the insides of the shins. Many, but none of ours, are wingless. The females have long egg-planting organs (*ovipositors*). They are usually heavier in build than any of the grasshoppers and their heads are large and rounded.

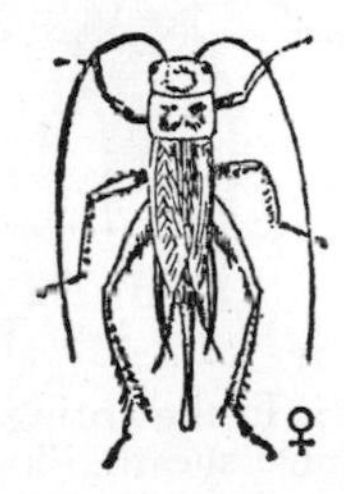

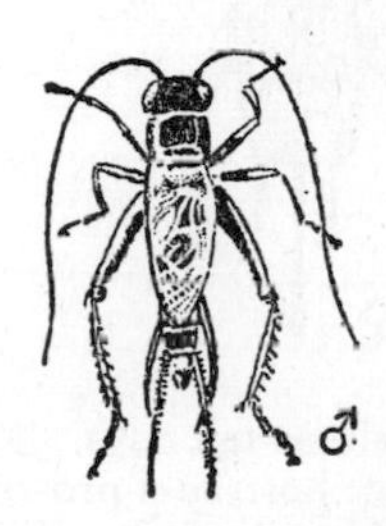

Our only common 'large' species is ***Gryllulus domesticus,*** the House Cricket, or the Cricket on the Hearth (*p. 43*). The hind wings are considerably longer than the fore and project, when folded, like a second pair of tails. Except in smouldering rubbish-heaps, they are nowhere found away from man's buildings—in bakeries or by the fires of our older houses—though in summer they go out into the open in the neighbourhood of their dwellings. Little is told of their diet except that they need water and nibble woollen clothes which are set out to dry by the fire.

The other 'large' species, unfortunately rare, is ***Gryllus campestris,*** the Field Cricket (*p. 43*). Of this fine singer we have a description and account by Fabre. It is larger than the

House Cricket and its hind wings are shorter, being covered by the leathery fore wings. The head is even larger and the antennae shorter. Its loud and cheerful chirping is heard through the daylight hours and carries to a distance of over 100 yards.

LIFE HISTORY. The eggs are laid, or rather planted, singly in the ground at a depth of about half an inch (those of the House Cricket in the crannies of buildings) and hatch very

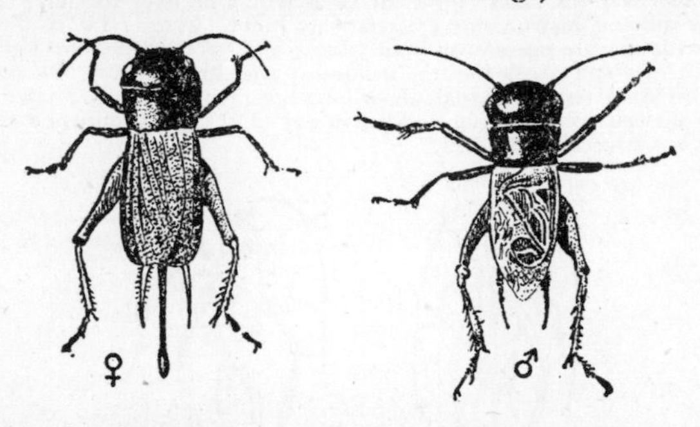

quickly, in about ten days. This is in the spring. Although the young are born in a pro-nymphal sheath, like that of the Long-horn Grasshoppers, this sheath is discarded with the egg-shell and the nymph (almost white in colour and wingless, but otherwise of full adult form) works its way to the surface without its protection. It gets its dark, almost black, colour within a day and sets off on its own. The Field Cricket is a vegetarian, living on grass, and in its life goes through a large number of moults, sometimes as many as twelve.

The Field Cricket is remarkable for digging itself a burrow, which is not a nest for its young or a trap for its victims, but a personal residence affording concealment from its enemies and, above all, shelter from the cold. This burrow is built by both sexes separately and not until the late autumn. It is carefully sited so as to have its entrance covered by a tuft of grass, which the cricket leaves uneaten; and here, coming out into the sun to sing if a male, or in any case to forage for its food, it remains through the winter and early spring. Then the males leave home, find the home of a female, and pair. The method of pairing is that of the Long-horned Grasshoppers, the male affixing to the base of the female's ovipositor a capsule containing the fertilizing germs as previously described. The continuance of the race being thus assured, the males go off and, apparently without returning to their lodgings, die. If they remain unmated, as in captivity, they live on, singing in monastic artistry, until the following winter.

FAMILY *GRYLLOTALPIDAE* MOLE-CRICKETS

One British species, 'large'

CHARACTERS. The females have no egg-planting organ. They live almost wholly underground, and their fore legs are, in appearance, astonishingly like those of the mole, from whom they get their name. There is only the one species, rarely found here.

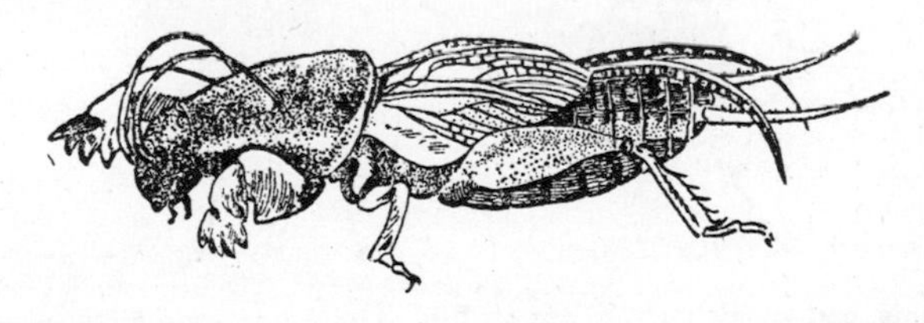

Gryllotalpa[2], the Mole-Cricket (*p. 43*), is carnivorous and so helpful to man, but, as its tunnellings cut ruthlessly through roots, it is not popular with gardeners. It lays all its eggs (some 200–300) in a single underground cavity, 'the size of a moderate snuff box' (Gilbert White, Letter 48), in which the mother lives with her eggs until they are hatched. It is strongly suspected that the mother eats many of her young when they do hatch, almost certainly the father does. The eggs hatch in mid-July and become adult in the following

May–June. They are rarely seen on the wing in the daytime and their flight is undulating. The wings are much longer than the wing-covers, as in the case of the House Cricket.

FAMILY *BLATTIDAE* COCKROACHES

Eight British species, of which four are 'large'

Note. The large species are importations from tropical countries. Some twenty other imported species have been recorded but are not established here.

CHARACTERS. Their heads are thrust forward and largely, often wholly, concealed from above by the upper plate of the 1st segment of the thorax, which forms a hood. The antennae are long and made up of very many segments. They have compound eyes and two small single eyes. The legs have well-developed hip-joints (*coxae*) and five foot-

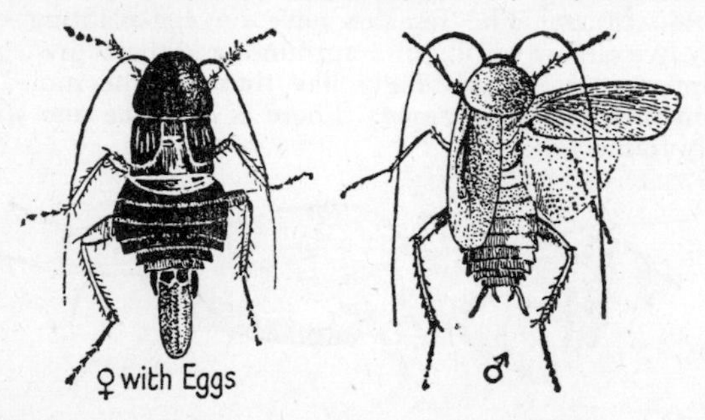

joints, and enable them to run swiftly. The wings are sometimes short and sometimes absent, often so in the females. When they exist, the fore wings are of a leathery consistency, so as to serve as covers (*tegmina*) to the hind wings when at rest. They are, however, used in flight. The hind wings are broad and fold as a fan, lengthwise, so as to be covered by the fore wings.

The main distinction between the cockroaches and the beetles (Coleoptera), with which they are confused in common speech with their name of 'Black Beetles', lies in the fact that they have no metamorphosis—the young emerging from the egg in most respects like their parents.

ANATOMY. Far the commonest of our species is ***Blatta orientalis*** (*p. 44*), the Common Cockroach, here illustrated. The head is completely covered by the hood. The female's wings are mere vestiges and are not used. Their bodies are very flat. Both sexes have two short, jointed, 'tails' (*cerci*) and the males, only, have also a pair of shorter, unjointed, projections (*styli*) at the tail end.

LIFE HISTORY. The eggs, sixteen in number (other species differ in this), are laid in a leathery egg-case or purse (called an *ootheca*) which is gradually extruded from the mother's body as it is filled with eggs. When it is full and closed up, it is carried about for some time by her and then deposited in a crevice and receives no further attention. The young are, of course, very small at birth, paler in colour, and at first wingless, but otherwise like the adults. They moult six times before attaining full growth, and they eat their skins after moulting.

The cockroaches do not bite or sting us, at least ours certainly do not, though travellers report that their toenails are eaten to the quick by Brazilian cockroaches while they sleep! The harm they do us is due to the fact that they destroy our food-supplies. This is partly by eating them: often a sack of flour has, on being opened at the end of a sea voyage, been found to be full to the brim with live cockroaches. Still more do they foul our food and our houses with their evil odour, traceable to stink-glands under the tail ends of their bodies. They will eat almost anything, animal or vegetable (even leather), and are especially fond of sweet or starchy foods. As they cannot climb a smooth surface, they are easily caught in a pie-dish with beer and sugar at the bottom of it. A hedgehog is said to do good work.

They are wholly nocturnal and run to their holes if a light is brought into the room in which they are foraging at night. By day they lie up under mats or in cracks or spaces behind skirting boards, or the like.

Our other large species is the Ship Cockroach, *Periplaneta americana* [American Vagabond], which is larger than the Common and has, in both sexes, wings longer than the body. The only native cockroaches are 'small' outdoor species.

ORDER *DERMAPTERA* [Skin Wings]

Nine British species, of which eight are 'large'

FAMILY *FORFICULIDAE* [Pincered] EARWIGS

Three British species, all of which are 'large'

CHARACTERS. Long shape. Broad head, with long, many-jointed antennae, biting mouths, compound eyes, and no single eyes. Wings, if present, as described below. Pincers at the tail end.

There is no metamorphosis, the young differing only in being more delicate, with undeveloped sex organs, and, in the winged species, the wings develop gradually through the series of moults.

ANATOMY. There is no waist between the thorax and abdomen, though there is great mobility at this point. The feet have three joints. The long abdomens have eleven segments, of which the 11th takes the form of a small block between the pincers, and, in the females, the 8th and 9th segments are very short. The pincers differ in shape in the sexes. Their use is not clear. They are weak and powerless to injure (us, at least) though they are used if the insect is held. They are apparently used in folding the wings, by those which have wings.

The two sexes of the Common Earwig, ***Forficula auricularia*** [ear Pincers] (*p. 44*), are here illustrated. It alone of our 'large' earwigs is a very numerous species and present everywhere in Britain. Most of the other species are rare, local, and some, at least, probably importations from abroad. One often flies and others are without wings.

The wings are most remarkable. The fore wings are short, beetle-like, wing-cases, thickened to a skin-like chitinous consistency, though not nearly so hard as those of the beetles. They do not, however, cover the whole of the flying (hind) wings when the latter are folded. The tips of the folded hind wings project beyond them, and the part which projects is also thickened so as to present the same appearance as the fore wings.

The hind wings, which are alone used in flying, are transparent and membranous and of extreme thinness except for the small part at the front of the wing and near the body behind which the rest of the wing is folded when not in use. So much so that black and white sketches do not give any idea of their delicacy. Except where they reflect the light they are hardly visible and their veining is hardly seen even when a white paper is placed behind them. The following sketches, with the above warning, give some idea of the remarkable way in which they are closed. The sketches are those of the right hind wing, in the successive stages of closing from the open position (A) to the completely closed state (F). It can be seen that when the wing is closed there are over forty thicknesses of wing under the covering fold.

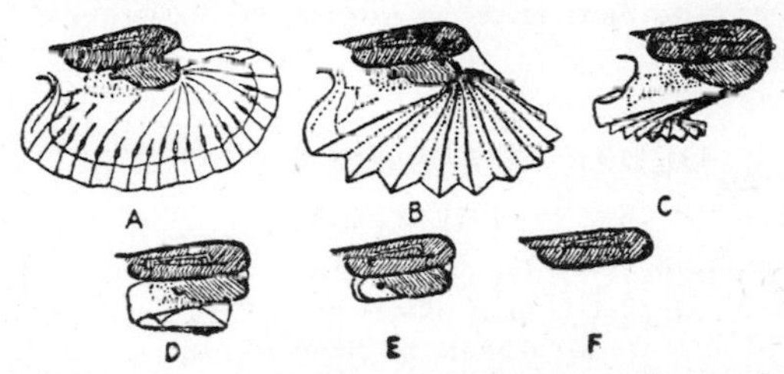

One of the oddest parts of this complex manœuvre is that the wings are so rarely used. Few people have ever seen an earwig fly, but they do so, as their remains are found in the droppings of bats.

Life History. The eggs are whitish and said to number about twenty-four. The insects seem to moult six times and are fully grown by midsummer. They survive the winter and the eggs are laid in the winter or early spring and there are records of a habit very unusual among insects. The earwig is a good mother. She stands guard over her eggs, and has even been found to collect them if, experimentally, dispersed and to resume her station over them. She dies, however, before the eggs are hatched.

Though ruthlessly pursued by gardeners, and capable of exciting much alarm and hostility in others, the earwig seems in fact to do little, if any, harm to us. It is more or less omnivorous, taking some animal food as well as nibbling blossoms, and when it is found in fruit it is often there to kill some previous destroyer of the fruit such as a caterpillar.

The story that it enters the human ear is so widely diffused—we have the German *Ohren-wurm* and the French *Perce-oreille* as well as the English name—that it is hard to believe that there is no foundation for it. Explanations based on 'ear-wing' disregard the rarity of any sight of the wings and do not account for the foreign names. The earwig will go into any small dark crevice during the day, being mainly nocturnal. Advantage is taken of this habit to catch them by supplying them with a straw-filled flowerpot. That is about all that is known of the ear story. At least let the earwig's virtue as a mother cancel an unproved accusation.

ORDER *COLLEMBOLA* [Glue-tips]

SPRING-TAILS

This wingless Order contains only 'small' insects. They mainly feed upon plants or excrements, and some of them are invaluable in cleansing sewage farms. The largest do not exceed 4 mm. in length.

ORDER *THYSANURA* [Fringe Tails]

BRISTLE-TAILS

Twenty-three British species, one 'large'

CHARACTERS. Completely wingless throughout life. Biting mouths, often sunk deep in the head. Long antennae with many joints. Head and fourteen segments, with little distinction between those of thorax and abdomen, the latter having some short, leg-like, appendages. The final (tail end) segment has two antennae-like appendages and is, itself, often prolonged in the form of a 3rd which lies between them. No metamorphosis.

In the Order many varieties of eye structure are to be found. Some have no eyes, others separate small eyes, and others a grouping of the small eyes, or some of them, into compound eyes.

Our only 'large' species is ***Petrobius maritimus*** [marine Stone-liver] (*p. 44*), here illustrated. It belongs to the family *Machilidae* which are distinguished by well-developed compound eyes, short projecting branches from the thighs of the two hinder pairs of legs, similar projections (*styli*) on almost all the abdominal segments, where there are also many blood-filled organs (*exsertile vesicles*) which the creature can push out or draw in. *Petrobius* is very tender and delicate, and covered with bronze-coloured scales. These and the thigh projections do not appear for some moults, of which there are in all at least six. It lives under stones along the sea shore or river mouths and can run and jump with considerable agility.

There are two other families in the Order, all consisting of 'small' insects amongst which is the 'Silver-Fish' (*Lepisma saccharina*) of our kitchens and the 'Firebrat' (*Lepismodes domesticus*) of the bakers' ovens.

CLASS ARACHNIDA

ORDERS: *ARANEAE* SPIDERS — *PHALANGIDEA* HARVESTMEN

CHELONETHIDA FALSE-SCORPIONS — *ACARINA* MITES

This Class of air-breathing, joint-legged creatures (Arthropods) has the head and chest (*thorax*) fused together into one block, called the head-chest (*cephalo-thorax*).

Sometimes (all except the Spiders) the abdomen is also fused into the same block. Sometimes (Spiders and Mites) there is no, sometimes (Harvestmen) little, and sometimes (False-scorpions) definite segmentation of the abdomen.

They have no antennae. They have one pair of hands (*palpi*), the bases of which (*maxillae*) help to serve the mouth, and they have jaws.

They all have four pairs of walking legs.

The jaws (*chelicerae*) are equipped with a claw or fang, which takes two different forms. In the Spiders it is like a folding penknife the blade of which folds back upon the handle. This blade, in the Spiders, is channelled and bears poison from the 'handle'. This form is called *sub-chelate*.

In the Harvestmen, False-scorpions, and most of the Mites, the claw closes against the member to which it is hinged as does a thumb against the hand. In this case the claw becomes a gripping and tearing hand for preparing the food and is said to be *chelate*. Other Mites have a different form of claw which will not be here described.

The hands (called either the *maxillary palpi* or the *pedipalpi*) begin with stout bases which work against each other at either side of the mouth and do the chewing, and are continued as leg-like limbs, ending with or without a claw or with a more complicated organ. This, in the male Spiders, is the operative sex organ, while in the False-scorpions it takes the form of a lobster-like claw resembling the chelate claws above described. These palpi in most cases seem to do the work both of hands and of the antennae of the Insects.

All Arachnids are air-breathers, either by air-passages (*tracheae*), similar to those of the Insects (see p. 55), or by openings leading into broader spaces (called 'lungs') of which the walls are pleated, like the bellows of a closed concertina, and which thus admit the air to a large surface in contact with the general blood-bath. These 'lungs' are found in the Spiders only.

The blood circulates as in the Insects (see p. 54) by the action of a single vessel along the back (the 'heart' or *aorta*) which pumps the blood towards the head, leaving it to make its own way back through the general blood-bath.

Sometimes the blood-vessel is continued, by branching channels, towards the organs of the head, mouth, and limbs.

Only one of these four Orders (the Spiders) contains any 'large' British species and is therefore here dealt with in detail. The others are referred to only so far as to give an idea of the creatures of which they consist.

In addition to the four Orders above mentioned there is an order (Linguatulids) represented by a parasite found, in its different stages, in hares and rabbits and in the nostrils of dogs (and sometimes men). This creature is classed with the Spiders, instead of the Worms, because it has four hooks towards the head end. It will not be further mentioned here.

ORDER *ARANEAE*

SPIDERS

557 *British species, of which about thirty are 'large'*

CHARACTERS. Arthropods having bodies clearly divided into two parts: the head-chest (*cephalo-thorax*) and the abdomen, connected only by a narrow waist. They show little or no signs of further segmentation, the segments being fused together. The head-chest bears six pairs of appendages, all articulated. These are (1) a pair of poison-claws, (2) a short pair of palpi springing from the mouth-parts (*maxillae*), and (3–6) four pairs of walking-legs. They have no marked metamorphosis after leaving the eggs—the young, throughout their numerous moults, being smaller, but otherwise very similar to the adults. They are all, throughout life, killers and eaters of other living creatures.

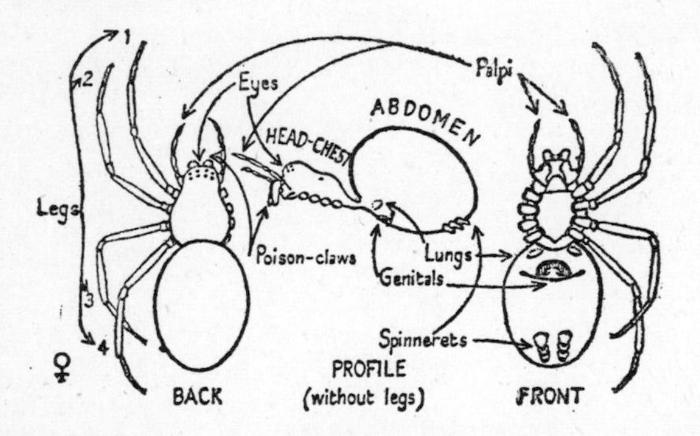

ANATOMY. The above sketches give a general idea of the form of a spider, as seen from above, in profile, and from below. It will be seen from these sketches that all the limbs come from the head-chest, and it will be well to deal with these first.

The foremost pair of limbs, present in all spiders, are the **poison-claws** (or *chelicerae*). These differ in shape in various species, but all consist of two parts, firstly, connected with the head-chest, the body of the claw and, hinged to the end of it, the fang, a sharply pointed hook which hinges back into a groove running along the edge of the body of the claw. The whole instrument may be likened to a single-bladed pocket-knife in which the blade is represented by the fang and the handle by the body of the claw. The knife opens only half-way: that is until the blade is at right angles to the handle. The blade is hollow and contains a channel connected with a poison-sac in the handle, from which, when a victim is pierced with the point of the blade, a drop of poison is forced into it along the fang. In the great majority of spiders these poison-claws are carried when at rest vertically downwards with the fangs on their inner sides, close to and opposite each other as in this sketch, which shows a head seen from the front. Thus when used the fangs open inwards towards each other and cross, piercing the victim from opposite sides. As will be noticed later, one family of our spiders have a different arrangement, the fangs being on the under sides of horizontally placed claws, held forwards when at rest, and so striking downwards and side by side. It is very usual for the edge of the handle of these knives to be equipped with a row of teeth, so that they can be used to grip firmly as well as to poison.

The next pair of limbs are the so-called **palpi.** These are leg-like appendages made up of five small sections and growing from the outer sides of the jaws (*maxillae*) which take the place of their hip-joints. These jaws work against each other sidewise, inside the lower lip (*labium*). Spiders having no antennae, these palpi do most of the work done by the antennae in the insects, smelling and feeling, in addition to acting as hands. They have also other functions which will be noted later.

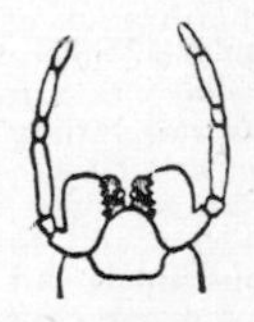

Behind the jaws and their palpi, and still growing from the head-chest, come the eight (four pairs of) **legs.** These vary much in length, but in structure they are all much alike and very similar to those of the insects. The diagram gives their general appearance and the names of their segments. They have either two or three claws at the ends. Note that, as compared with an insect's leg, they have an extra (knee) joint and the feet are divided into two (not five) segments. They are equipped with many spines and hairs (*setae*) for feeling and manipulating the silk. One family here treated (Dictynidae) has, on the *metatarsus*, a special comb for carding the silk which will be mentioned later (p. 322).

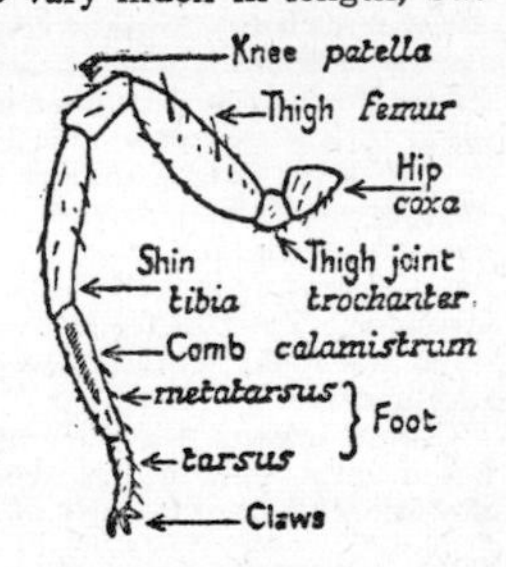

The only other organs visible on the head-chest are the **eyes.** These are eight (in some spiders six) in number and are situated on the summit of the head, just behind the poison-claws. They are simple eyes (*ocelli*) and vary greatly in size and in the pattern in which they are placed.

The abdomens of the spiders are without limbs and on their upper (*dorsal*) sides show nothing distinctive. They are mere seamless footballs (the ♀ Soccer and large, the ♂ Rugby and smaller). On the under side they show the various entrances for air to the lungs and air vessels (*tracheae*). The number of these is important in distinguishing the families. The vent is at the extreme tip of the abdomen and, just in front of, and below, it are the six **spinnerets.** These are short, leg-like appendages, each having, on its final segment, a great number of hair-like tubes from which come the minute threads of the silk material. They also differ in length, shape, and the pattern in which they are placed.

In the forward centre of the abdomen is, in both sexes, the opening to the **organs of generation.** These demand some explanation. The pairing of spiders is unusual.

Throughout plant or animal life, where two sexes collaborate to produce a new generation, it is necessary for the germs from the male to get access to the eggs of the female so as to fertilize them. The fishes leave the matter of fertilization, as it seems to us, largely to chance. The sperms of the male are released into the water near to the eggs deposited by the female and to their countless numbers alone is due the adequate fertilization of the eggs. The sperms are water-borne, just as the pollen of many plants is air-borne. Most of the amphibians (also breeding in water) take further precautions. Thus, the toad clings closely to the female throughout the long process of egg-laying. There is less danger of ova going unfertilized. The flowering plants are helped to get over the difficulty by insects, which are attracted to them by their colour, scent, and form. The great majority of the animal world—all the mammals and nearly all the insects—ensure access to the ova by means of direct contact between the breeding-organs of the two sexes. The spiders attain the same result in a unique way. The male transfers the sperms from the genital aperture on to a tiny web and then absorbs the sperms into complicated organs like fountain-pen fillers which develop (at the last moult when he becomes adult) in the last segment of his palpi. From these organs in his hands (palpi) he places it in the opening which leads to the ovaries of the female.

The adult female spiders have (in several families) a plate or lid (called an *epigyne*) which partially covers the aperture, and which her suitor's hand must open. Now, these two members, the (♀) plate and the (♂) hand, form, as it were, a lock and a key—mutually complementary and essential. They differ in every species. No bearer of the wrong key can open the lock. Unless the proffered hand is appropriate, the door will stay shut.

These organs are very small, but the specific differences are largely based upon them and as, when chemically treated so as to show up under the microscope, they are so eminently ludicrous in appearance, I cannot resist copying a few diagrams from T. H. Savory's ***Spiders and Allied Orders of the British Isles***, with the author's permission.

Of the internal anatomy of spiders we need not say much here. They breathe the air through openings (*stigmata* or *spiracles*) which admit it into what are known as 'lungs', or into long forked and sub-divided air channels (*tracheae*) similar to those of the insects. The 'lungs' are hollow spaces surrounded by numerous flattened tubes which allow a large area of the air to come into contact with the general blood-bath

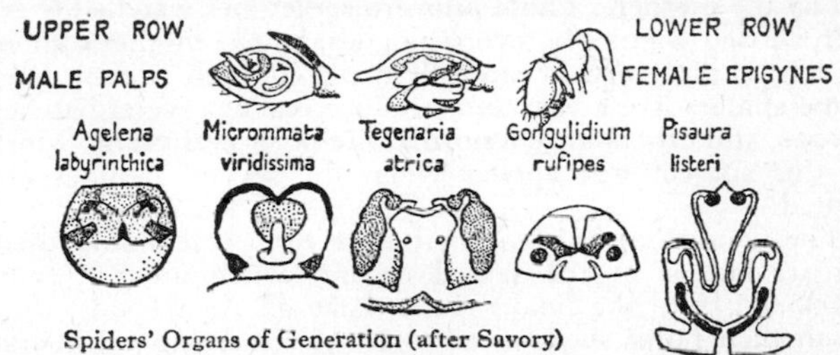

Spiders' Organs of Generation (after Savory)

which fills the inside of the animal. They show, on the outside, as pale areas on the under side near to the waist. They are either two or four in number, and, in the latter case, there are no other air passages.

The blood circulates, as in insects, by the operation of a single pumping-vessel called the heart (or *aorta*) which drives the blood, picked up from the general blood-bath, along its channel and delivers it back into the blood-bath at the other end. In spiders the heart is more highly developed than in insects, branching into separate vessels which go to the eyes and limbs on each side of the head-chest. The main nerve ganglia are in the head, below the eyes, and in the centre of the head-chest.

LIFE HISTORY. All spiders are beasts of prey, catching and eating such creatures (mainly insects) as they can. None of our spiders can do any injury to man, nor do they try to bite him. They all help in the fight against the flies and other insects, and the Scottish tradition that it is unlucky to kill a spider is eminently praiseworthy. Their hunting methods vary much. Some snare their prey with sticky webs, some by spreading a silken sheet under the threads of a balloon-barrage on which the fallen are killed; some by sheer speed rush out of their dens and capture them, and others hunt them in the open, rushing, or leaping, upon them. Others, again, run over the surface of water, or swim through its depths, to get their food. Speaking generally, those which hunt have learned so to place their bites that instant death follows, while those that entangle merely stupefy with a lesser venom indifferently placed.

The eggs are laid in a single mass, enveloped in a silken pill by the mother. These pills are sometimes watched over, even carried about wherever she goes, by the mother, others are left, in more or less carefully made cocoons, to their fate. Some spiders live a year and produce one or several batches of eggs, and others have a normal life of several years. More on this subject will appear when the several families are treated.

The young hatch from their eggs fully resembling their parents except in the sexual organs which are not fully developed until the final moult. Like all Arthropods, they moult their outer shells so as to grow, remaining naked and unprotected until the new skin has hardened. Until the first moult the young do not appear to be able to feed or hunt, or spin webs. How they are nourished during this time (for they are not inert, but active) is still doubtful. After their second moult they usually disperse (see p. 315) and begin life for themselves.

Some females kill or try to kill the males immediately after pairing, but this rule is not so general as is commonly supposed. The males are almost always smaller but often longer-legged and, when adult, can be recognized by the slimmer bodies and presence of the swollen 'hand' at the end of the palpi.

In addition to the eight families here treated because they contain 'large' species, there are twenty-six more families.

SUB-ORDER *ARANEOMORPHAE*

Having only two lungs and also two tracheal tubes which open at one single, or two separate, spiracles. Their poison-claws are pointed downwards, with the hooks turned towards each other so as to cross. They have usually six spinnerets, of which the two central ones are usually the smaller.

FAMILY *ARGYOPIDAE* [Bright eyes] = *EPEIRIDAE*

ORB-WEB SPIDERS

Thirty-five British species (excluding the nine Tetragnathidae) *of which five are 'large'*

CHARACTERS. They have usually rather short legs and round, globular abdomens. There is usually some narrowing of the head-chest which indicates the division into head and chest. Their spinnerets are grouped in a small cone. They have patterned covers to the (♀) genitals, and complex hands to the (♂) palpi. Their legs have, near the three claws, numerous spines which themselves are toothed along the edge to assist in manipulating the silk. They exude some oily substance which prevents their sticking to their own webs, though not always to those of other species of the same family. Some members of the closely allied family of *Tetragnathidae* do not spin orb-webs, but these are all 'small' and so do not concern us here.

For our purposes, therefore, the distinguishing characteristic of the family is that they are the builders of the true 'spider's webs', known as the 'orb-webs'. These are vertical or inclined nets, so thin as to be almost invisible, in which passing insects are entangled.

The web of each kind is different but the making of the web follows the same general lines:

The Main Cable. The spider stretches out her body, squeezes out some silk, and allows this to be wafted out by air currents (Fig. 1) until it attaches itself to a neighbouring twig or leaf. The thread is then pulled tight and the spider walks across and strengthens its bridge (Fig. 2).

The Framework. Upon this main cable she builds a frame which will finally surround the web. This frame is irregular, 3-, 4-, or 5-sided, roughly vertical, and in one single plane hanging below the main cable. Its shape varies and in no way matters. It is made by repeated journeyings and droppings starting at the two ends of the main cable and ending at the most convenient points which lie in the plane beneath it.

The Spokes. The first two spokes are made in the form of an upright thread crossing the middle of the frame. To make this the spider drops from the centre of the main cable to the lowest cross-bar of the frame, leaving behind her a vertical line (Fig. 3). Near the middle of this she pauses to amass a central lump of silk, drawn with her legs from the spinnerets and piled up upon itself before she goes on to the end of the line. This central lump forms the hub of the completed web.

When this diameter is placed, the spider completes the spokes by walking *the correct distance* along the frame from the end of each spoke to the place where the end of the next spoke should be, to make the angles between spokes equal. It should be noticed that to do this the distance to be travelled differs greatly between different spokes, and yet the evenness with which the spider spaces her spokes is quite astonishing. Having reached the place for a spoke-end, she touches down her thread and then (holding the thread away from all contacts until she gets there) walks back along the frame and along the last spoke laid until she gets to the hub, where she touches the thread down again on the central knob. Lastly, standing on the hub, she tightens the spoke thread and leaves any surplus length piled up on the hub-knot. Each spoke in turn is made, the strain on the centre being equalized by the spokes being added on opposite sides in turn. The process is illustrated in Fig. 4 and, when it is completed, the web has the appearance shown in Fig. 5. It will be noticed that, at this stage, the spokes are those of an irregularly shaped polygon, not of a wheel.

The Resting-place. When she has finished the spokes, the spider, slowly revolving upon the hub-knot, spins a thread from spoke to spoke, spiralling outwards from the hub and, later, leaving the hub, walks round and round it, fastening, as she goes, the thread to each successive spoke, until she has made a platform a couple of inches or so in diameter. This

FIG. 1

FIG. 2

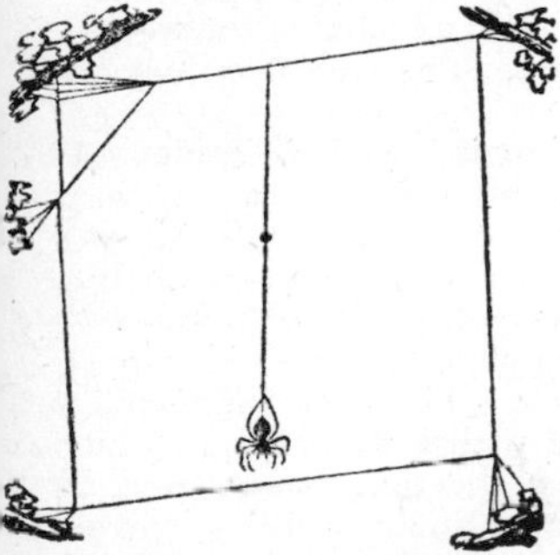

FIG. 3

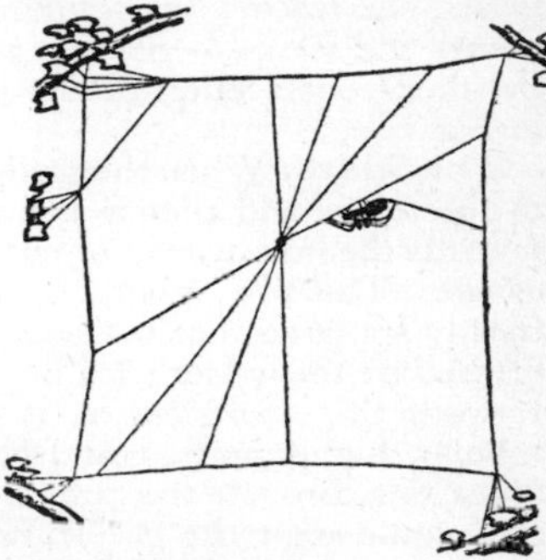

FIG. 4

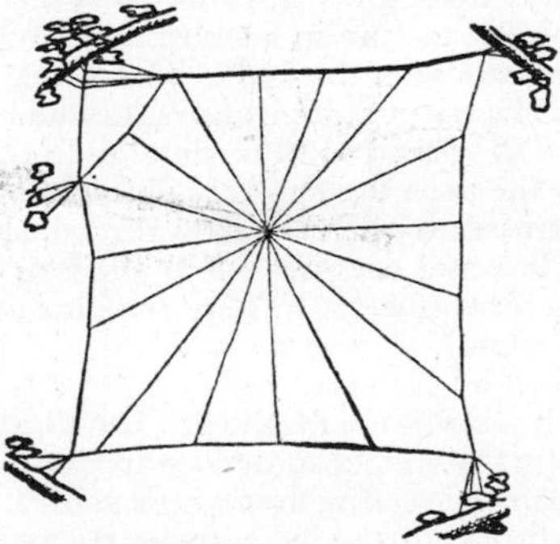

FIG. 5

platform will remain as it is, to form an area on which the spider can rest while hunting.

The Spiral Scaffolding. After completing the resting-place, she hastily goes on with this same spiral in a continuous thread passing from spoke to spoke and so encircling the hub at a swiftly increasing distance until, after at most four or five twists, she reaches the frame. This structure is purely temporary and serves to give her access to all parts of the web for the final construction of the snare. The web now looks as in Fig. 6.

The Snare. When the scaffolding is placed, the spider goes to the frame and thence begins, this time working inwards towards the hub instead of out, to spin a totally different kind of silk. The silk hitherto spun is adhesive only when it is freshly spun, so that it sticks to anything on to which it is pressed by the spider's leg or with which it comes in contact. It loses this stickiness as it dries. The new snare-silk is tubular, highly porous, and filled with a sticky liquid which oozes out through the tube when the tube is stretched, in tiny equidistant drops. It remains sticky until destroyed. Further, the thread is extremely elastic. No insect which has once touched it can escape except such as have the strength to smash their way through. This snare-silk the spider begins, slowly and carefully, to spin in a continuous spiral—this time working inwards towards the hub. The thread passes from spoke to spoke, always in straight lines, gradually nearing the centre, each line so spaced as to be parallel to the line outside it. As she goes she uses the spiral scaffolding to walk on and each time she crosses it with the new thread, she tears down the scaffolding line and eats it. When she gets to the resting area, the web is built (fig. 7). There remains only to cut out the central hub-knot, if she is a *Meta*, or draw meshed threads across it if an *Aranea*.

When the web is built, the method of **hunting** is as follows. The spider habitually sits, head downwards and each leg upon a spoke-thread, in the resting area at the centre. Some kinds, when frightened, shake the web furiously by jerking their legs. This vibrates the whole web so that the spider becomes

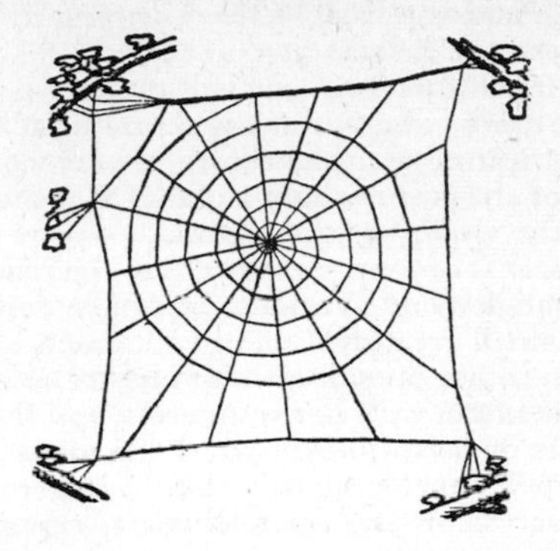

FIG. 6

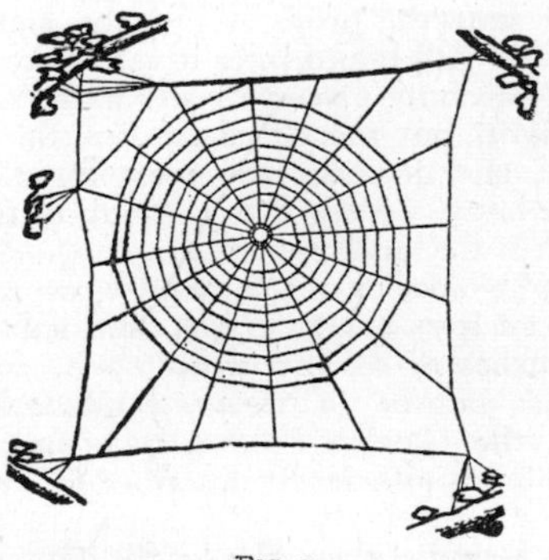

FIG. 7

almost invisible and is probably also alarming to some of her enemies. Should she be still further scared, she drops to the ground by a thread, up which she will return when the alarm is over. At all times, whether at the centre or at the end of a thread communicating with the centre, it is by vibrations, and not by sight (for she is very short-sighted) that she detects the presence and the vitality of the victim.

When an insect is caught, she hastens to the place and there perfects its entanglement. Various ways of so doing are used. In the case of small creatures, safe to approach, she may take and chew them in her jaws at once or else thrust forward her body, touch the insect with her spinnerets, and then, with the short third pair of legs, quickly whirl the victim round and round, completely enveloping it in silk. A larger prey, or one which, lying across several snare-threads, cannot be easily rolled, is similarly enveloped by the spider crawling round it, in and out of the web, and, in the case of the most dangerous, stinging, creatures, the same result is attained by pulling a mass of thread from the spinnerets and throwing it—from a safe distance—over the prey. When the victim is safely secured, she closes with it and bites it with her poison fangs. This bite is not carefully placed in any particular spot, nor does it kill outright, but merely causes inertia and, after it has so operated, she detaches the inert bundle and, on a thread from her body, carries it to the hub of the net, or to her nest, to suck it dry and chew it up.

Of our five 'large' species of this family, two frequent dark and damp sites such as caves, crypts, and ruins, while the others live in bushes or shrubs in the open. Far the commonest and best known is ***Aranea diadema*** [diadem Spider] (*p. 45*), the Garden Spider, here figured, and the habits of the family are sufficiently described by a brief account of its life.

The **eggs**, in a single mass of a bright orange colour, are laid in a cocoon situated close to the mother's web, towards the end of autumn, and remain there until early spring when the small spiders hatch out. The young, until after their second moult, in May, remain huddled together in a golden mass. They then awake from their torpor and swarm out of the cocoon, adding to it as they do so a nebulous cloud of threads which envelops it. They are moved by an impulse to climb to the highest available point. This they do partly by walking up the bushes or trees and partly by climbing their own or their brothers' silk threads. When they reach the

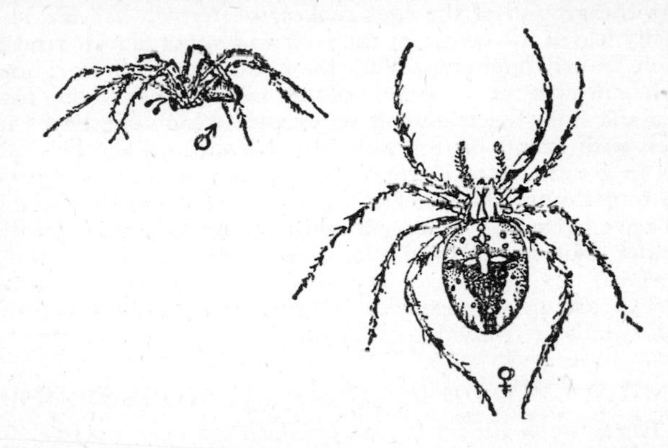

summit, each spiderling prepares for the great adventure of flight. Long threads float out into the breeze. So long are these that at last they carry into the air the tiny spider itself. Many will fall close to the starting-point, yet more will become a prey to birds or accident, but many will travel long miles before floating to earth to colonize new hedges.

Once the dispersal flight is ended and a landing safely made, the young spiders are ready to face the problem of every hungry hunter. By instinct they know all the rules for making an orb-web and make it, each for him or her self, spinning, entangling, rolling, poisoning, and eating—themselves minute—creatures smaller than they.

When fully grown, the male seems to cease to spin for himself and seeks out a female who will answer favourably to his signals and accept his proffered hand. There is no evidence of the immediate end of the marriage in the death of the male, buried by his wife in her ample paunch. On the contrary, the couple are seen living, for some time at least, peaceably together on her web. Whether in the end his fate is tragic or not, life for both of them is short, for death will come with the first real cold of the winter.

As the growth of the eggs makes the female heavier, she usually leaves the centre of the web and spins herself a nest, which she will later amplify for the use of her cocoon. There she lies in wait for her prey, holding in the claws of one fore leg a silk line (the telegraph wire) with which she keeps in touch with events on the web. In the autumn she lays her eggs in a rather loosely spun cocoon, as the young must be able to get out without help, for when they do so the mother will have been long dead. She protects the cocoon from the weather by some form of roof, and at the outset of winter she dies.

Webs are never repaired. During the summer months fresh spirals are provided every night.

FAMILY *LYCOSIDAE* WOLF SPIDERS

Thirty-seven British species, of which one only is 'large'

CHARACTERS. These are distinguished from other families by the eye pattern, the eyes being arranged in three rows instead of the usual two.

They are hunters, chasing their prey, either on land or on the surface of water, without spinning any snare. Most are purely errant species, but some of them have some kind of permanent dwelling such as an excavation of their own making in sand or soil. These dens are often silk-lined and in some cases equipped with a small ring of loose materials fastened together round the entrance so as to make a circular parapet wall. From the den they rush or leap out at great speed to seize any insect which ventures within range. They often spin a thread as they emerge to steady them on vertical surfaces and make it easier to get back home when loaded with their catch.

Our large ***Tarentula fabrilis*** [working Tarentula] (*p.* 45), found only in Dorset, is recognizable by the black under side to the abdomen, and much of our knowledge of the genus comes from Fabre's studies of a more southern member (*T. narbonensis*).

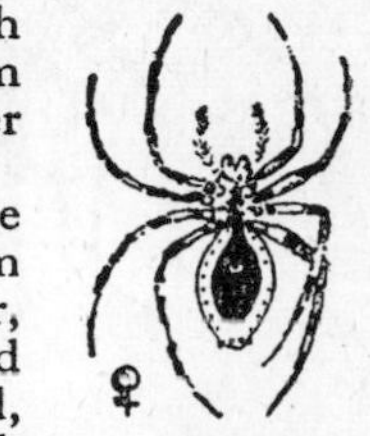

They lay the eggs in a cocoon, which, like the Pisauridae, they carry about with them until the young hatch out. Then, however, a different habit appears—the young brood instantly climb on to the mother's back, and, huddled there in a swarm, remain for a week or two until they moult for the second time, when they leave her in search of food. Like the young of most other families they disperse on warm sunny days by means of parachutes. Climbing to the highest available point, on wall or plant, they squeeze out a little silk which is drawn out from the spinnerets by air currents until it is long enough to lift the spider itself. The young adventurer may travel many miles by this means.

Gossamer on the grass, especially noticeable on fine days in autumn, is mainly caused by myriads of small spiders (chiefly Linyphiidae) walking about and trailing a thread before embarking on a 'flight'. When the morning dew clothes the gossamer threads, men will wonder and their spaniels snort and paw their faces.

FAMILY *PISAURIDAE*

Two British species, both 'large'

Characters. Structurally, they are closely allied to the Agelenidae (differing mainly in the eye pattern), but they are different in their habits, being both purely errant hunters, spinning no web as a snare.

The commoner species, ***Pisaura listeri*** (*p.* 46), is a wood, hedgerow, and grass spider, common and omnipresent. The female lays her eggs in a spherical cocoon which she carries about with her wherever she goes under her body, gripped by her claws and palpi, until the young are about to hatch out. She then fastens the cocoon to a low plant and spins a close web round it, which she, later, surrounds with a large enfolding web which encloses the young when hatched. Over this nursery web she keeps constant watch, and in it the young remain for some weeks before dispersing. Of the courtship of this species it is recorded that the male makes a gift of a fly to the female.

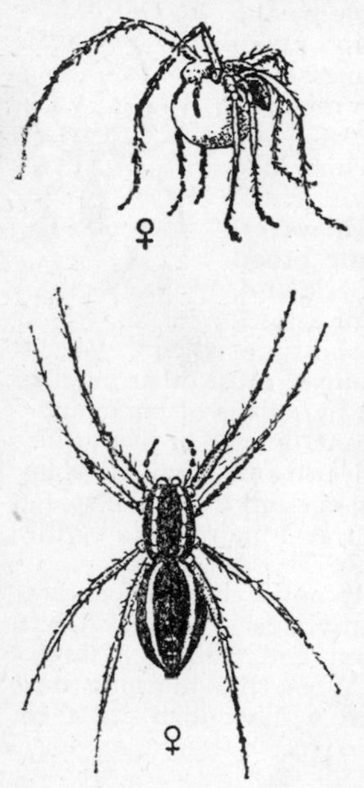

Our other species, ***Dolomedes fimbriatus*** [fringed Cunning one] (*p. 45*), is rarer and semi-aquatic. It hunts on the surface of fresh water, and can run down plants beneath the surface when danger threatens. It remains ashore or afloat on a leaf, whence it has gained the name of the Raft Spider, and always retains hold of weeds or some other solid object even when under water.

FAMILY *AGELENIDAE* [Restless ones]

Twenty-three British species, of which six are 'large'

CHARACTERS. This family contains most of our commonest house spiders which spin the horizontal cobwebs destroyed by the housemaid's broom. Structurally they are recognizable by the great length of one pair of the spinnerets, which stick out behind the body as if they were a pair of tails.

Of the three large species, two live mainly in our sheds or houses. The largest are *Tegenaria parietina* and ***T. atrica*** [wall-frequenting Roof-dweller and hairless R.], and they

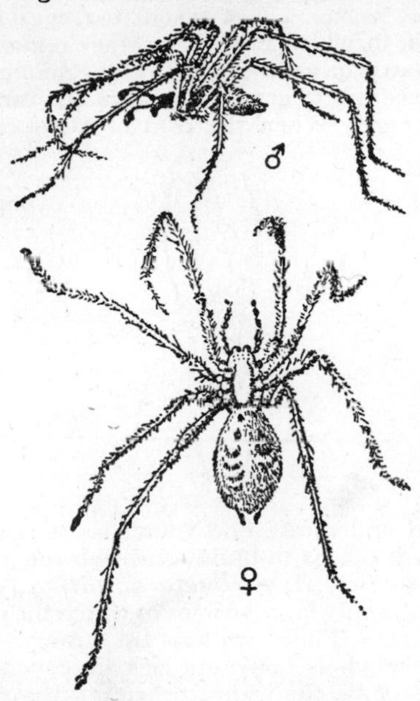

look quite formidable as they run across the floor. *T. atrica* (*p. 45*) is here sketched.

The cobwebs of this family have no sticky threads to ensnare their victims, as is the case with those of the Argyopidae. They are horizontal sheets of threads more and more closely woven as they approach the centre (or corner) where they lead to an open tunnel pointing downwards, in which the spider lies in wait.

One member of the family which is never a house-dweller,

and seems, in this country, to resort largely to gorse-bushes, is ***Agelena labyrinthica*** [maze Restless one] (*p. 46*).

When about to lay, the female deserts her web and, at some distance, makes a nest where the eggs are laid in a cocoon of silk, in which nest the mother remains on guard, continuing to strengthen the nest until the young are hatched. At this time she has to get such food as she can without the help of her maze. When the cold of October comes, she

ceases to feed and dies. The young leave the nest in the spring and each begins to build a cobweb for itself.

One large species, ***Argyroneta aquatica*** [water Silver-swimmer], is the only large species in which the male is larger than the female. These spiders are brown, without any pattern, and the whole body and legs are covered with close hairs which exclude the water, providing the creature with a coat of air the reflections from the surface of which, when under water, give it a silvery brightness. Though an air-breather, like all other spiders, it lives wholly beneath the surface of still fresh water, in ponds or sluggish streams, and its method of so doing depends upon its mastery of the principle of the diving-bell.

The diving-bell is made as follows. The spider spins for itself under water a web, at first flat, but soon buoyed up with air into the shape of an inverted thimble, open on the under side. The hairs covering the body and legs enable it, by protruding its abdomen above the surface of the water, to collect the bubble of air above mentioned. When building its bell it uses the hinder legs to enclose a larger bubble than that which is used for mere breathing when swimming, and this it brings down and releases under the silken web. It then goes up again and gets another bubble and repeats this process until the web takes on its thimble shape and is filled with air.

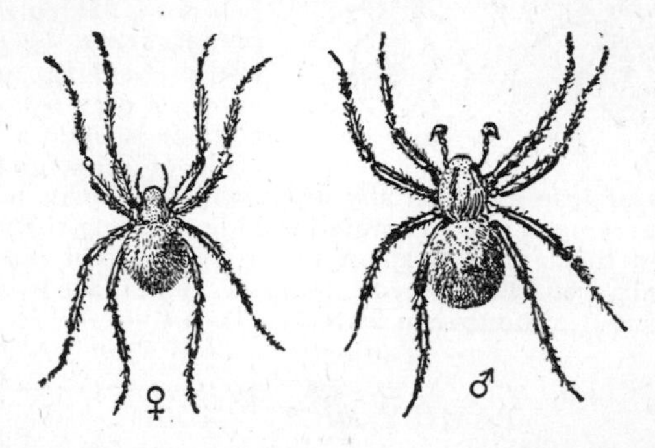

Then the diving-bell is ready to serve as a home and in it the spider spends the rest of its life, normally coming out only to hunt for its prey. An illustration of the Water Spider's bell will be found on p. 47. Food is obtained, without any form of snare, by hunting—swimming swiftly after and seizing all forms of small aquatic life, and particularly such insects as alight on the surface, seizing them from below and pulling them under, to be eaten in the water or in the diving-bell.

At the time of pairing, the male builds himself a bell close to that of the female and, after spinning a passage from the one to the other, tears an entrance into that of the female and thus combines households.

The eggs, when laid, are fastened by the mother to the inner wall of her bell and hatch there. Shortly after hatching, the young come out and proceed to make bells for themselves.

FAMILY *SPARASSIDAE* [Manglers]

Only one British species, which is 'large'

CHARACTERS. Only two claws on the feet.

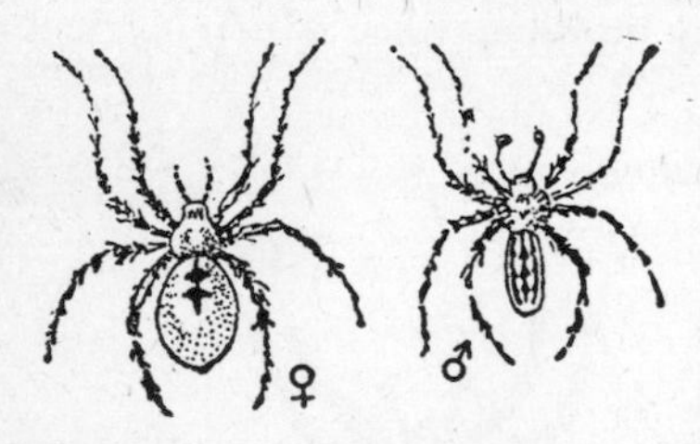

This spider is a wandering woodland species which employs no lure or snare to entrap its victims. Its name is ***Micrommata viridissima*** [greenest Little-eyes] (*p. 46*). It hunts its prey by waiting motionless upon a leaf or blade of grass and then darting or leaping upon any insect which happens to come near, carrying it when captured to hiding among the foliage.

When the female is about to lay, she spins a cocoon of white silk around her green eggs inside a tent made by fastening together a number of leaves.

FAMILY *DICTYNIDAE*

Sixteen British species, of which two only are 'large'

CHARACTERS. Alone of the families here treated, these spiders have a shin-comb on the hind legs and a silk-grid for carding the silk (see p. 305). The use of these tools gives to their webs a peculiar texture and a bluish colour.

They are common dwellers in our cellars, sheds, and palings. They make an irregular, rough, more or less round, patch of silken cobweb which spreads out from the hole or crevice in which the spider lives concealed. This web serves as a net for entangling insects, and the victims are taken into the den to be eaten there. ***Ciniflo similis*** [similar Hair-curler] (*p. 46*) is here sketched.

SUB-ORDER *MYGALOMORPHAE* (Shrew-spiders)

Only one British FAMILY, *ATYPIDAE* [Abnormals]

Only one British species

CHARACTERS. The sub-Order, which contains all the very large tropical spiders, is distinguished by having four lungs and no *tracheae*. The poison-claws are pointed forwards and strike downwards, without crossing.

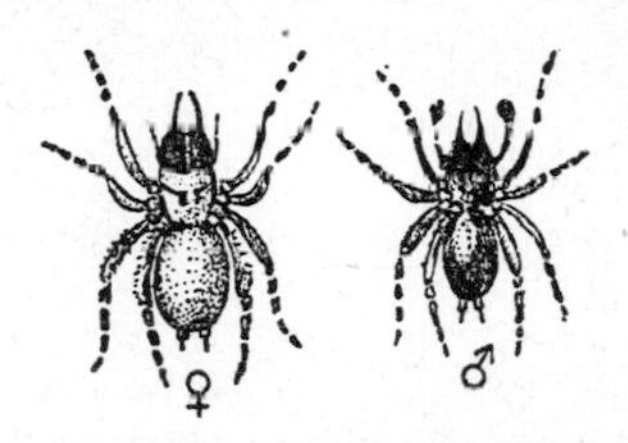

Atypus affinis [similar Abnormal] (*p. 46*), the English Purse Spider, has six spinnerets, of which two show from above. It is rather a rare spider, though common locally. It is found in southern England, Wales, and in Ireland, often at the edge of a bank covered with heather, where it excavates a burrow inside which it lives. The burrow is lined with a tube made of silk and earth. This lining is extended in a closed stocking-like 'purse' which projects some three inches beyond the mouth of the burrow and forms the spider's snare. The instant any insect alights upon the purse, the spider rushes out and strikes it, through the web from within, tears a hole in the purse, and drags it in to be eaten in the burrow. The hole is then mended.

Both sexes live this claustral life while unmated, but, in the autumn, the adult males come out of their burrows and each seeks the purse of a female, on which he taps with eager hand (*palp*) his proposal. If the answer is favourable (a jerk signifies refusal and a hasty flight of the suitor—immobility, acceptance and his admission) he breaks into the purse and the pair live happily for some time in the same den. This harmony ends when his faithful wife kills and eats him.

The eggs are laid the following summer in a silken cocoon placed at the bottom of the burrow on a cushion of silk and plant fibres and hatch there in the autumn. The young spiders remain in the burrow until the spring, when they disperse and each builds its own. They do not become adults until four years old and may live to the age (very unusual among spiders) of eight years.

ORDER *PHALANGIDEA* [Porters]

HARVESTMEN

About twenty British species

All species are 'small' in body although their legs are long

This Order differs from the Araneae, Spiders, in having no waist. The whole body—head-chest and abdomen—forms a

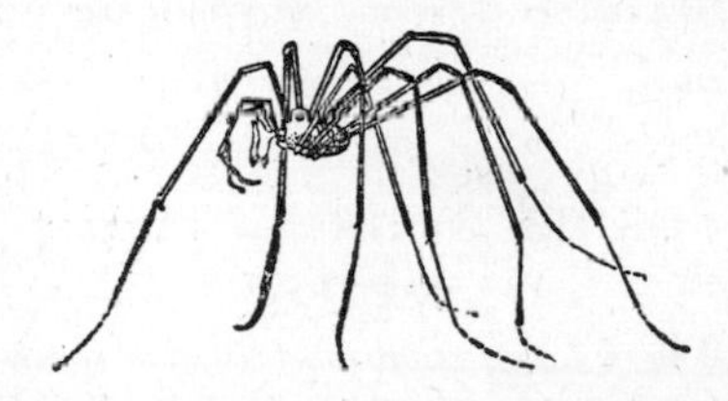

single, undivided, and usually globular, block. Though undivided, their bodies show more of the original segmentation than do the spiders, being marked across by grooves or rows of tubercles. They have only two eyes, mounted on a short periscope in front of the body. They breathe by *tracheae* and have no 'lungs'. They are usually very long-legged. One is here illustrated as an example. They are omnivorous and wholly nocturnal, lying up by day under shelter. Their fore claws are *chelate* and tear, but do not poison, and they neither spin nor build. Little is known of their way of living, though it is possible that some have two generations a year and that others survive for several years. They lay underground.

ORDER *CHELONETHIDA* [Clawed ones]

FALSE SCORPIONS

Twenty-four British species, distributed among three families

All species are 'small' (1 to 3 mm.)

They have no waists, and no 'tails' or prolonged abdomens. The abdominal part of the bodies is segmented. Their large claws are on the palpi and they have smaller poison-claws on their *chelicerae*. They live in moss or under stones and run backwards. They spin silk from the smaller claws and carry their eggs in cocoons. They are carnivorous and completely harmless to man. Their general appearance is as here illustrated.

ORDER *ACARINA* [Atoms]

MITES

A very large number of British species

All species 'small', mostly microscopic

The great majority are parasites on man, animals, and plants. Some live independent lives and others again use animals, especially insects, as a means of locomotion.

Among them are included Cheese mites, Sugar mites, Itch mites, Hair-follicle mites, Ticks, Plant-gall mites, 'Harvesters', and Ants'-nest mites.

One example is here given, one of the largest of these creatures, the Common Sheep Tick, ***Ixodes ricinus*** [castor-oil-bean Sticky]. It has a form of metamorphosis, passing through three stages after leaving the egg: (1) a 6-legged larva, (2) 8-legged nymph without sexual organs, and (3) adult. It lies in wait on the grass and clings on to the hairs of sheep, dogs, or other animals, or on to the clothing of man, and, then, plunging its head into the skin, sucks blood until (full) it drops off on to the grass again. This is repeated at each stage. In the third, they pair on the host's body, and the fertilized ♀ drops off, when full fed, to lay her eggs. To remove ticks from the skin, first touch with benzine or petrol or the head will remain and cause a sore.

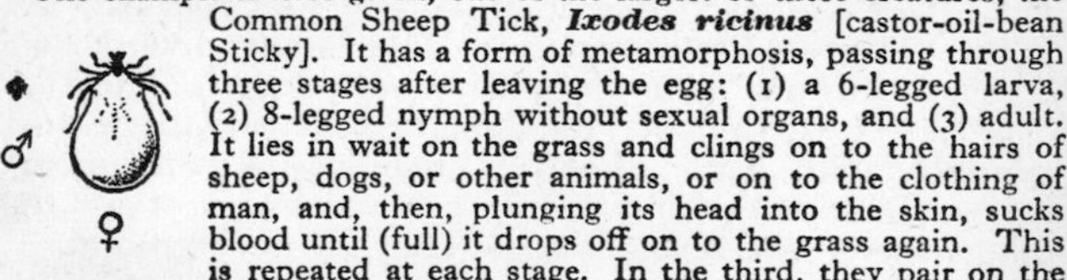

Various mites of this order are responsible for the itch and facial 'blackheads' in man, Isle of Wight disease in bees, 'witches' brooms' on birch-trees, the purple blotches on the leaves of sycamore, 'big-bud' in black currants, and 'leaf blister' in pear-trees.

CLASS *MYRIAPODA* [10,000 feet]

104 *British species*

ORDERS: *CHILOPODA* CENTIPEDES — *DIPLOPODA* MILLEPEDES

These creatures breathe the air through spiracles and *tracheae*. In one small family, foreign, the spiracles open into 'lungs' like those of the spiders, but in all others the breathing is like that of the insects.

Their bodies are divided into (1) heads and (2) numerous segments all much alike, without clear distinction between chest (*thorax*) and abdomen. All, or almost all, these segments bear one or two pairs of legs in the adults.

The head has a single pair of antennae and, behind them, a group of single, small, eyes (*ocelli*), except in certain blind species which have none. None of our species has the compound eyes so common among the insects. In the head are also the mouth-parts: an upper lip (*labrum*), a pair of upper jaws (*mandibles*) and two pairs of lower jaws (*maxillae*) attached to a lower lip (*labium*).

All our Myriapods are dwellers in darkness and live under stones or in moss. Some are cave-dwellers and are blind.

ORDER *CHILOPODA* (1,000 feet)

CENTIPEDES

The British examples of this Order are all carnivorous, and therefore innocuous to man and even helpful destroyers of destructive insects.

Structurally they differ from the other Myriapoda in having only one pair of legs in each segment of their bodies. They have also longer antennae, and the first pair of legs are devoted to the killing of their prey, being armed with poison claws (*forcipulae*). There are also minor differences in the mouth-parts, those of this Order having both pairs of lower jaws attached to the lower lip. Their breathing spiracles are ranged along the sides.

FAMILY *GEOPHILIDAE* [Earth-lovers]

The British species are all 'large'

These are the longest and most powerful of our centipedes. They have from 31 to as many as 173 segments, and are usually reddish-brown in colour. Their bodies are flat. Their antennae are composed of fourteen segments, and the final pair of legs are joined together at the hip-joints.

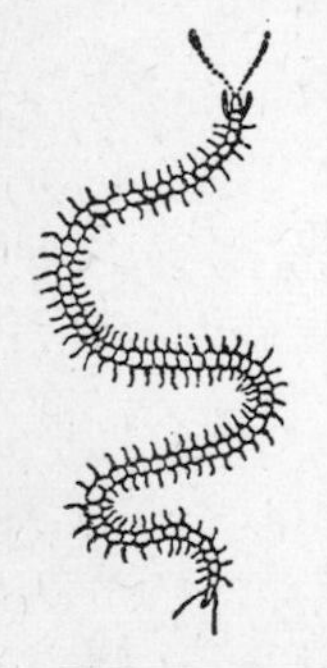

Each leg consists of seven joints. The example here illustrated, ***Geophilus linearis*** [linear Earth-lover] (*p. 48*), is widely distributed. It lives by day in moss or decomposed vegetation and, at night, comes out to hunt insect larvae and worms, slugs and smaller centipedes. It is blind. Several species of this family are phosphorescent and give off quite a bright light if touched. The young are born with all the adult legs.

FAMILY *LITHOBIIDAE* [Stone-dwellers]

The British species are all 'large'

These centipedes are characterized by the fact that their segments are alternately small and large. They have fifteen pairs of legs, one on each segment and have two groups of four eyes each on either side of the head. Their antennae have from twenty to fifty segments.

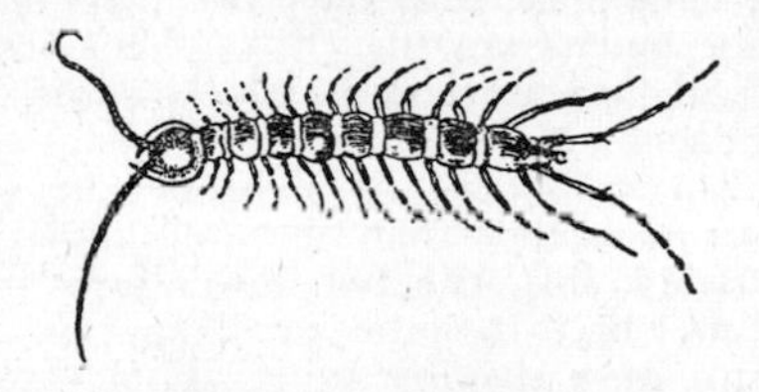

The species here figured, ***Lithobius tricuspis*** [3-pointed Stone-dweller] (*p. 48*), gives a general idea of their shape. They are longer-legged than the Geophilidae. Their lives are similar and they are useful to the gardener. Their young are born with seven pairs of legs only.

ORDER *DIPLOPODA* [Double-legs]
MILLEPEDES

These creatures are wholly vegetarians and some are harmful to man. Their bodies are very differently shaped, but the greater number are tubular, rather than flat.

Unlike the Chilopods, they have two pairs of legs to each segment of the body from the 5th segment onwards to the last. Their antennae are comparatively short, made up of seven or eight segments, and, frequently, bent at an angle.

The mouth-parts consist of an upper lip (*labrum*) and below it a pair of toothed mandibles, equipped for chewing vegetation. Below this, the two lower jaws (*maxillae*) are united in a 'lower lip'. In some 'small' species, this lower lip takes the form of a sucking tube. Their breathing-holes (*stigmata*) open between the legs, in the central line under the body in each segment.

Like the Chilopods, they are to be found under stones, moss, leaves, or other decaying materials.

Their young leave the eggs (which are laid in a mass under ground, sometimes watched by the mother) with only three pairs of legs on the first three segments.

Some are very small, but we have five families which have 'large' species.

FAMILY *JULIDAE* [Downy]

These are long and tubular and roll in a spiral when alarmed. They have more than thirty segments. Their heads are fairly large, with eyes in front and the antennae at

the sides. They have stink-glands all along their bodies on both sides.

Sometimes they are to be found inside fruit, or, again, in the stems of plants into which they have bored. The species here figured, ***Julus albipes*** [white-footed Downy] (*p. 48*), is usually found near houses, in rubbish heaps or cow-pats, or under stones. The species differ much in colour.

FAMILY *CRASPEDOSOMIDAE* [Fringe-bodies]

Generally similar to the Julidae, but with a narrowing of the body between each section and the next. They are mostly

smaller than the Julidae, and the species vary in the number of their eyes and in the form of the front pair of legs. These legs, in this family and in the last, are adapted to serve as pairing organs in the males. ***Chordeuma sylvestre*** [wood Eel] (*p. 48*) is here figured.

FAMILY *POLYDESMIDAE* [Many-belted]

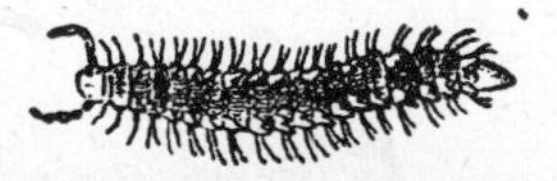

Bodies rough to the touch. Usually blind. ***Polydesmus complanatus*** [flat Many-belts] (*p. 48*) is shown here.

FAMILY *GLOMERIDAE* [Rolling into a ball]

Wood-louse-shaped. When alarmed rolls into a ball as does a hedgehog. The males have nineteen pairs of legs, the females seventeen. The last male pair is a pairing organ and takes the form of pincers.

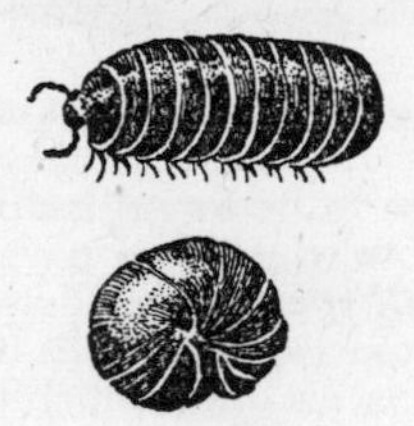

In appearance they are quite unlike any other Myriapods but very like a woodlouse, although they are more shiny.

Glomeris marginata [edged Roll-ball] (*p. 48*) appears here.

CLASS *CRUSTACEA*

CRUSTACEANS

This Class is almost wholly marine, though some of its members are fresh-water creatures. It includes the Lobsters, Crabs, Prawns, and Shrimps, with which we are not here concerned. Only one family (the *Oniscidae*) are land animals and would usually be regarded as 'insects'. These are the Woodlice and are divided into numerous species, of which only a few are 'large'.

Our commonest species is ***Oniscus asellus*** [little ass Little Ass] (*p. 48*) and is here figured. They are to be found under stones or tree bark and appear to be omnivorous. They are to be distinguished from the Glomeridae by having only seven pairs of legs. Structurally they are very different, as they breathe through air-holes in the hinder pair of legs. They roll themselves up into a ball, as does a hedgehog, if alarmed.

BIBLIOGRAPHY

THE following select list of books is designed to help the reader who wishes to study in greater detail the subjects dealt with in this book. For fuller information, Smart's *Bibliography of Key Works for the British Fauna and Flora* (Adlard, Dorking, 1942) is indispensable, as is the pamphlet *The Amateur's Library* reprinted from *The Amateur Entomologist*, vol. 8, no. 41 (1944).

There are various important series of publications which can be found in most good scientific libraries, among them may be mentioned the Ray Society series, the *Scientific Publications* of the Freshwater Biological Association of the British Empire (Wray Castle, Ambleside, Westmorland, referred to below as F.B.A.B.E.), and the publications of the British Museum (Natural History) (B.M.). A new series of volumes is now in preparation by the Royal Entomological Society of London. The forester, the farmer, the gardener, and the fisherman will find the numerous pamphlets issued by the Forestry Commission and the Ministry of Agriculture and Fisheries invaluable, readily available, and remarkably cheap.

GENERAL

Between 1879 and 1907 the great French naturalist, Jean Henri Fabre, to whose memory this book is dedicated, produced his ten volumes of *Souvenirs Entomologiques*, which are not only classics of descriptive biology, but are the best introduction for the general reader to the marvels of insect behaviour. The material in these books has been arranged and admirably translated into English in a series of volumes most of which were published between 1911 and 1925. For general accounts of insect behaviour there are *Social Life in the Insect World* (1912) and *Wonders of Instinct* (1918). *The Life of the Fly* (1913), *Hunting Wasps* (1916), and *Mason Wasps* (1919) are among the best of the books on separate groups.

For a popular account of many of the more striking discoveries in entomology made during the present century, Malcolm Burr's *The Insect Legion* (1939) is good. Shipley's *Minor Horrors of War* (1915) is a little classic on the subject of lice, bugs, fleas, ticks, mites, mosquitoes, flies, and other direct enemies of man. Balfour-Browne's *Insects* (Home Univ. Library, 1927) is a good general introduction.

The student may be recommended to the following: Imms's *Social Behaviour in the Insects* (1931); G. H. Carpenter's *Biology of Insects* (1928); Imms's *Outlines of Entomology* (1942) and his standard *General Textbook of Entomology* (4th ed., 1938); Wigglesworth's short *Insect Physiology* (1934) and his monumental *Principles of Insect Physiology* (1939); Eltringham's *Senses of Insects* (1933); G. D. H. Carpenter and E. B. Ford's *Mimicry* (1933); and Miall's excellent *Natural History of Aquatic Insects* (1895).

For scientific accounts of various economic pests there are Chrystal's *Insects of the British Woodlands* (1937), Massee's *Pests of Fruits and Hops* (1943), Hayhurst's *Insect Pests in Stored Products*, including clothing (1942), Fox Wilson's *Pests of Ornamental Garden-plants* (1937, Min. Agric. Fisheries), Miles's *Insect Pests of Glasshouse Crops* (1935), the Department of Scientific and Industrial Research's *Beetles injurious to Timber and Furniture* (1940).

The angler will find aquatic insects taken as food by fish discussed in M. E. Mosely's *Dry-fly Fisherman's Entomology* (1921), C. A. N. Wauton's *Troutfisher's Entomology* (1930), and W. G. Bainbridge's *The Fly-fisher's Guide to Aquatic Flies and their Imitations* (1936).

HYMENOPTERA

Maeterlinck's *Life of the Bees* (1901) and of the *Ants* (1930) are popular classics, in addition to Fabre's books already mentioned above. Step's *Bees, Wasps, Ants and Allied Insects of the British Isles* (1932) is the best short general account. Sladen's *Humble Bee* (1912), Donisthorpe's *British Ants* (2nd ed., 1927), Connold's *Plant Galls of Great Britain* (1909), and Swanton's *British Plant Galls* (for the gall-making species) are standard works. For identification of species Saunders's *Hymenoptera Aculeata of the British Islands* (1896) is still indispensable.

For Bee-keeping there are W. Herrod Hempsall's *Bee-keeping New and Old*, 2 vols. (1930–7); the same author's *Bee-keeper's Guide to the Management of Bees in Movable Comb Hives* (1943, 6th ed.); B. Gamble's *Bee Keeping* (National Federation of Young Farmers' Clubs, Booklet no. 2, 1939) and E. W. Teale's finely illustrated *The Golden Throng* (London, 1942). *The Hymenopterist's Handbook*, edited by B. A. Cooper (*Amateur Entomologist*, vol. 7, 1945), contains many hints on collecting and rearing.

DIPTERA: There is nothing available between Fabre's *Life of the Fly* and such specialist monographs as *British Blood-sucking Flies* by Edwards, Oldroyd, and Smart (B.M. 1939) and *British Mosquitoes* by Marshall (B.M. 1938). Of the immense work on *British Flies* planned by Verrall, only two volumes appeared (vol. viii on Syrphidae in 1901, vol. v on Stratiomyidae and succeeding families in 1909).

SIPHONAPTERA: The standard monograph on British Fleas is Rothschild's *Synopsis of the British Siphonaptera*, which appeared in 1915 in the *Entomologist's Monthly Magazine* (vol. 51) and has been reprinted separately.

COLEOPTERA: Joy's *British Beetles: Their Homes and Habits* (1933) is a good general introduction. The same author's *Practical Handbook of British Beetles* (2 vols., 1932) is the standard monograph, but gives little beyond keys. W. W. Fowler's *Coleoptera of the British Islands* (6 vols., 1887–1913) contains descriptions and much additional biological information. See also Balfour-Browne's *British Water Beetles* (Ray Society, 1940).

LEPIDOPTERA: Books on this popular and much-collected Order, especially on Butterflies, are legion. Eltringham's *Butterfly Lore* (1923) is a valuable book. General accounts of our butterflies, with a description of the species, and plates in colour, are to be found in Sandars's *Butterfly Book for the*

Pocket (1939), South's *Butterflies of the British Isles* (new edition, 1941), Frohawk's *British Butterflies* (1934), and Ford's *Butterflies* (The New Naturalist, 1945). Stokoe's *Observer's Book of British Butterflies* is a useful 'vest-pocket' guide.

South's *Moths of the British Isles* (2 vols., new edition 1939) is good, but deals only with the 'big' moths, the Macrolepidoptera. P. M. B. Allan's *A Moth-Hunter's Gossip* (London, 1937) and *Talking of Moths* (Newtown, 1943) are very entertaining.

For the identification of caterpillars there is O. S. Wilson's fine but rare *Larvae of the British Lepidoptera* (1877), and the magnificent Ray Society volumes, *Larvae of British Butterflies and Moths* (1886–99). Stokoe's *Caterpillars of the British Butterflies* (1944) is easier to come by. A. G. Scorer's *Entomologist's Log-book* (1913) gives useful summaries of life-histories and lists of species associated with particular food plants. Newman and Leeds's *Textbook of British Butterflies and Moths* also gives useful calendars, &c. Valuable for the collector is Tutt's *Practical Hints for the Field Lepidopterist*, 3 vols. (1901–5).

There is only one book that deals with the whole Order, Meyrick's *Revised Handbook of British Lepidoptera* (1928).

TRICHOPTERA: See Mosely's *British Caddis Flies* (1939).

MECOPTERA: The only detailed account of this order is in vol. i, part 1 of the *Transactions of the Society for British Entomology* in a paper on the *Feeding Habits of the British Mecoptera* by Hobby and Killington (1934).

NEUROPTERA: Killington's *British Neuroptera* (Ray Society, 2 vols., 1936–7) is standard. See also Kimmins's *Keys to the British Species of Aquatic Megaloptera and Neuroptera* (F.B.A.B.E., no. 8 [1943]).

ODONATA: Lucas's *British Dragonflies* (1900) has fine coloured plates. Miss Longfield's *Dragonflies of the British Isles* (1937) is much more up to date.

EPHEMEROPTERA and PLECOPTERA: Keys to the British species have been made by Kimmins (*Ephemeroptera*, F.B.A.B.E., no. 7, 1942) and by Hynes (*Plecoptera*, ibid., no. 2, 1940).

PSOCOPTERA: The best account so far available is A. Badonnel's *Psocoptères* in the famous *Faune de France* series (no. 42, 1943).

HEMIPTERA: E. Saunders's *Hemiptera-Heteroptera of the British Islands* (1892) and J. Edwards's *Hemiptera-Homoptera* (1896) are still standard. See also E. A. Butler's *Biology of the British Hemiptera-Heteroptera* (1923) and Theobald's monumental *Plant Lice of Great Britain* (3 vols. 1926–9) and, for specific identification of aquatic species, the *Keys to the British Water Bugs* by Macan (F.B.A.B.E., no. 1, 1939 and no. 4, 1941).

ANOPLURA: P. A. Buxton on the *Louse* (1939) is the standard work. For specific identifications, E. Séguy's *Insectes Ectoparasites*, Faune de France (no. 43, 1944), is useful.

ORTHOPTERA and DERMAPTERA: See Lucas's *British Orthoptera* (Ray Society, 1920) and Burr's *British Grasshoppers and their Allies* (1936).

SPIDERS: Savory's *Spiders and Allied Orders of the British Isles* is a useful introductory book. Bristowe's *Comity of British Spiders* (Ray Society, 2 vols., 1939–41) is indispensable.

PERIODICAL PUBLICATIONS

The Royal Entomological Society of London issues *Transactions* and *Proceedings*; The Society for British Entomology *Transactions* and a *Journal*; The South London Entomological and Natural History Society an annual *Proceedings and Transactions*; The Amateur Entomological Society a regular *Bulletin* and an annual *Journal*. Independent publications are the *Entomologist* (Lepidoptera and Odonata chiefly), *Entomologist's Monthly Magazine* (emphasis on orders other than Lepidoptera, especially Coleoptera, Diptera, and Hymenoptera), and the *Entomologist's Record* (mainly Lepidoptera, also Coleoptera and Diptera).

Much information concerning the entomology of the north of England is contained in the *Naturalist*.

INDEX

The names of Species illustrated in colour are in Clarendon type, **English** or ***Latin***. Names of Orders are in capitals, ENGLISH or *LATIN*. Names of Families or Genera are only indexed where they differ from the species chosen to represent them: thus, *Cephidae*, represented here by *Janus femoratus*, is indexed, but *Apidae*, represented by *Apis mellifera*, is not.

Page references printed in Clarendon type are to the coloured illustrations on pp. **13–48**.

SET IN
GREAT BRITAIN
AT THE
UNIVERSITY PRESS
OXFORD
PRINTED BY
RICHARD CLAY AND
COMPANY, LTD.
BUNGAY
SUFFOLK